D1251377

OUTWARD BOUND
SURVIVAL HANDBOOK

OUTWARD BOUND
SURVIVAL HANDBOOK

Editor Bob Barton

WARD LOCK

A WARD LOCK BOOK
First published in the UK 1997
by Ward Lock
Wellington House
125 Strand
LONDON
WC2R 0BB

A Cassell Imprint

Copyright © Text Ward Lock 1997

This book includes material previously published in the 'Outward Bound' series.

All rights reserved. No part of this publication may be reproduced in any material form (including photocopying or storing it in any medium by electronic means and whether or not transiently or incidentally to some other use of this publication) without the written permission of the copyright owner, except in accordance with the provisions of the Copyright, Designs and Patents Act 1988 or under the terms of a licence issued by the Copyright Licensing Agency, 90 Tottenham Court Road, London W1P 9HE. Applications for the copyright owner's written permission to reproduce any part of this publications should be addressed to the publisher.

Distributed in the United States
by Sterling Publishing Co., Inc.
387 Park Avenue South, New York, NY 10016-8810

A British Library Cataloguing in Publication Data block for this book may be obtained from the British Library

ISBN   0-7063-7574-2

Designed and typeset by Ben Cracknell Studios
Printed and bound in Finland by Werner Söderström Oy

Contents

About Outward Bound® **7**

Introduction **9**

PART I: BASIC SURVIVAL

Introduction 14

1 Planning **16**

2 Clothing and Equipment **54**

3 Navigation **102**

4 Avoiding Danger **130**

PART II: COPING WITH ACCIDENTS AND EMERGENCIES

Introduction 171

5 The Approach to Medical Problems **175**

6 The BIG 3 Body Systems **208**

7 Bones, Joints and Soft Tissue   231

8 Toxins and Allergies   275

9 Environmental Medicine   281

10 Common Medical Problems   305

11 Rescue   317

Appendix I: Personal First Aid Kit   343

Appendix II: Water Purification   344

Glossary of Medical Terms   345

Index   353

About Outward Bound®

The Outward Bound Trust provides high-quality courses in a range of exciting outdoor activities. Our fully qualified instructors maintain the highest standards of tuition, and our safety record is second to none. Everyone who takes an Outward Bound course enjoys a rewarding and memorable experience, the benefits of which will last a lifetime.

Outward Bound courses have been available in Britain since 1941. The original courses were the outcome of a meeting between Kurt Hahn, the educator, with Lawrence Holt, the owner of a shipping line. The marriage of the worlds of education and business is a vital feature of the Outward Bound movement. The courses are both a valuable adjunct to formal education and an important part of career development.

From its beginnings in Britain the Outward Bound movement has spread throughout the world, with 38 centres in 23 countries.

A typical course in the UK lasts from one to three weeks and may be based at one of our five national centres or take the form of an expeditionary journey by foot or by sailing boat in a wilderness setting. We run courses for all age groups, from 14 to 70!

The Outward Bound Trust also designs programmes to help companies through periods of change. This may involve developing leadership skills for your managers or assisting in building cohesive teams. The courses balance challenging outdoor tasks with reflection and review. They are specially designed so participants can translate what they gain back to their working environment.

After an Outward Bound experience, people discover many positive attributes about themselves. They become more confident;

they learn to share; to lead and to follow; to understand their own strengths and to work together as a group. By safeguarding each other, they form bonds of trust. They discover that many problems can be solved only with the co-operation of all members of a group.

To find out more about Outward Bound courses or to request a brochure, please contact us at:

Outward Bound Trust,
PO Box 1219,
Windsor,
Berkshire,
SL4 LXR.

Tel (01753) 731005

Michael Hobbs
Outward Bound Trust

Introduction

Many people today seek enjoyment and release from the pressures of modern life by exchanging the intensity of the office or factory for an intensity of quite a different kind – high on a mountain, perhaps, or at sea out of sight of land. The urge to voyage into uncertain territory is an ancient one and the depth of satisfaction the adventurous traveller feels today must spring from the experiences of a hundred generations of our ancestors: the Neolithic hunter finding new sources of food by passing through an unexplored forest; the Inuit in a skin boat dwarfed by icebergs; the early crossers of great oceans. We are by no means all Shackletons or Shiptons or Slocums, but because adventure is *relative* to the prior experience and capability of the participant, we can enjoy an intensity of challenge and satisfaction on our own journeys close to that which drove these great travellers.

Educationalists have developed a three-layer model to map the experience of an individual who moves further and further from their own 'comfort zone' and which can thus be used to describe the level of adventure of an enterprise:

- *Trivial* experience may be enjoyable and relaxing but the outcome is never really in doubt.

- *Adventure* has a significant degree of uncertainty of outcome and a noticeable level of challenge. Those involved must employ skill and judgement close to the limit of their abilities to achieve a favourable outcome. High levels of satisfaction and considerable opportunities for personal growth are both likely.

- *Misadventure* occurs when the level of challenge seriously exceeds the capabilities of a participant. Physical or psychological damage is then likely.

Walking in a park would be a trivial experience for an able-bodied person. An experienced coastal sailor undertaking a short offshore passage for the first time would be involved in adventure, but if their first voyage out of sight of land were an Atlantic crossing, then misadventure is a likely outcome. The most intensely productive and memorable experiences for an individual are likely to be those within adventure yet close to its boundary with misadventure, but if your expectations prove to be unreasonably rosy then you may, against your wishes, slide over the edge into misadventure. In planning a journey in wild country, you should therefore decide with what level of uncertainty of outcome and risk you want to engage and where you want to position yourself on this spectrum of adventure.

This book aims to give you the knowledge to ask the right questions and make informed decisions about your adventures, but also to deal with the consequences of misadventure or of sheer bad luck. Thus, Part I – Basic Survival – concerns itself with the defensive skills of planning and preparation, while Part II – Coping with Accidents and Emergencies – deals with the worst-case scenario where something that might have gone wrong has gone wrong, and helps you to avoid turning a difficulty into a disaster.

In this connection, one of the most difficult yet valuable things you can acquire is an understanding of how in one context a small problem is no more than that, yet in another can open the door to disaster. Typically, a disaster is preceded by a chaining together of circumstance, an escalation where inconvenience shifts to become danger and danger to become catastrophe. For instance, in the evening following a successful ascent in the Highlands, a group celebrates enthusiastically and their departure for the hill next day is late and in mild disarray. They have been unable to get a weather forecast and there is some consternation when, high on a remote mountain, the week's gentle weather deteriorates into vicious squally showers. A few minutes later it is realized that in the chaos of the morning Angus, a big cheerful man, has come without his waterproof clothing. He reassures the group that he is quite warm enough – 'A bit of rain never hurt anyone' – but 40 minutes later he is starting to shiver violently and it is decided that they need to get off the hill, and fast. They are now too far along their journey to retrace their route comfortably, yet not far enough along to be able to continue safely. The morning's hasty plans did not consider an escape route and the group has no leader. There is some argument about the correct course of action and the minutes tick away. Jim, a successful businessman, is the strongest personality, and although not the most experienced walker he claims a prior knowledge of the ground falling away to the south of them. Relieved that someone seems to have made a decision, everyone follows, fighting their way down into the teeth of the gale.

Unfortunately, in the hostile weather no-one has been monitoring progress on the map, and when visibility is lost in an advancing wall of cloud, their position is uncertain. The southward descent leads them not to escape, but into ever-steepening ground. Everyone seems mesmerized by disbelief, and nobody is capable of questioning the chosen course of action.

Finally, at the top of some steep, broken rocks a consensus emerges and the majority of the group refuses to continue with what they see as a dangerous descent rapidly exceeding their capabilities. Jim feels the burden of his earlier decision and insists that they continue down to get help: 'I did a bit of climbing in the Army 25 years ago, and I'm sure the rocks are very short.'

The entreaties of the others that 'We must stick together' are ignored, and he makes slow progress down the black, greasy rocks. He is almost out of sight in the swirling mist when the onlookers see him stiffen and, with a short exclamation, slip and fall. For a long fraction of a second they can hear, but not see him until, despite the wind and the clatter of a few rocks, there is only the awful, uncanny silence that follows a person falling.

This is a story, of course, but not an atypical one. You can make your own guess at the likely outcome of events, but what is much more difficult to decide is where the party went wrong and where the chain of events leading to disaster started. Were they victims of their success of the previous day or of the excess of the previous night? Would a single leader have helped the situation? Were they unlucky? Were they incompetent? What could they have done differently? What would *you* have done differently?

The decision-making process is usually enhanced if a single person has responsibility for it. Such a leader will often consult and discuss plans of action with the party, but the final decision lies with that individual. The more flexible and more practised the judgemental skills of the leader are, the more likely it is that the party will have a successful and enjoyable day without crossing the line into misadventure.

We go to the hills or out to sea to escape the confinement and regulation of the day-to-day. Using the outdoors in a straitjacket of safety dos and don'ts will spoil the day and, paradoxically, may not enhance your safety very much, since it is the alert, flexible and experienced leader who will recognize the significance of the unusual event and act accordingly, while the slave of an over-ambitious route card persists doggedly with an unviable plan.

This ideal of the wise and flexible practitioner is difficult to attain and is reached only by the hard road of experience, of miles under the feet and storms weathered. Rules and guidelines, training courses and the counsel of more experienced practitioners all speed the learning process and help you to make the most of the unfolding variety of your own mountain experience, but they are no substitute for time spent on the hill or the water. A few minutes spent reflecting on the decision-making process at the end of each day out, or quizzing more experienced leaders on *why* they make certain decisions, will develop your instincts and make it that much easier for you to make the right decisions when the chips are down.

Having a sixth sense as to when the factors influencing a situation – like those described above – have ganged up to push it into misadventure, or, even better, an ability to guess what these factors might be while the enterprise is still at the planning stage, is perhaps the best guarantee of safe and successful adventures – in the final analysis, of survival – for you and your companions.

We hope that you have exciting and challenging adventures, and that the defensive skills of Part I of this book help you to avoid ever needing to apply the reactive skills of Part II. Good luck!

PART I

BASIC SURVIVAL

Introduction

Safety and survival are rarely based solely on a reaction to events and adverse circumstances. Proper planning, the choice of appropriate equipment and an awareness in advance of some of the main hazards that might be encountered should all be part of your defensive arrangements. In addition, you need to have an appropriate set of skills to address the challenges ahead, and enough understanding to know what those skills might be.

In this section we start with planning, looking at some of the steps to follow and the questions to ask at this crucial stage. There are a number of important differences of detail between land- and water-based activities, so these are treated separately.

Any regular traveller in the outdoors will at some time have been in the position of carrying the wrong equipment for the prevailing conditions: you will have a painful bivouac close to the top of Kilimanjaro on a night of hard frost if you are wearing only lightweight clothing aimed at equatorial conditions – the mountain does lie close to the equator, but the summit is at an altitude of almost 6000m (19 500ft). Chapter 2 on clothing and equipment is aimed at helping you to avoid similar pitfalls.

Of all the skills you will need, navigation is the most fundamental, and it is difficult to imagine any realistic planning or successful journeying taking place without the appropriate ability in map reading and navigation. Probably the single most common initial cause of accidents in wild country is faulty navigation: in itself, being lost does not necessarily have serious consequences, but it is often the trigger that panics the inexperienced walker into the descent of a dangerously steep mountainside or the novice helmsman into a tide race that overwhelms the vessel.

Fortunately, there is a great deal of transferability of navigation skills between different activities, so if you can take a magnetic bearing and read a contour pattern on a topographic map you will not have too much difficulty in learning to read a marine chart and plot a course – the details differ, but the principles are the same. Chapter 3 on navigation covers the basics.

Finally, Chapter 4 on avoiding danger looks at some of the more important hazards you may encounter, and particularly those that can be addressed and prevented at the stage of planning and preparation: if you know about the dangers of snowblindness, then it is a simple matter to take dark glasses; if you anticipate stonefall, then although a helmet will not eliminate the risk it will certainly improve your chances.

1

Planning

The defensive skills for safe operation in a challenging environment have to be deployed long before you set foot in the great outdoors. If you make the wrong choice of terrain for a walk and find yourself in the middle of a military firing range, launch your dinghy in a six-knot tide or overlook a 6m (20ft) waterfall in the middle of an otherwise moderate canoe journey, then no amount of good technique or prompt emergency response is likely to salvage your day.

Good planning and accurate research can identify some of the problems you will have to deal with or avoid, and they can also help you get the most out of your journey by, for example, spotting that a slight detour will open out a stunning view or that a short wait at anchor will allow you to sail effortlessly with the tide instead of battling stubbornly against it. Maps, charts and guidebooks make fascinating reading in themselves and the more of their contents you are able to absorb – even at a subconscious level – the more likely you are to avoid elementary and often dangerous errors.

'Time spent in reconnaissance is seldom wasted' is a useful maxim of military origin, but a complementary perspective is given by a second: 'The best of plans rarely survive first contact with the enemy'. Planning is extremely valuable and often great fun, but try not to lose sight of the fact that some uncertainty of outcome is vital to retain the spark of adventure in an enterprise and, in any case, is probably unavoidable.

You should therefore try to use your planning to achieve the level of adventure that you want, rather than to prepare every last detail to a degree that reduces your journey to little more than a sterile timetable.

On land

There are a number of basics to be considered when planning a trip into the outdoors. These include the obvious one of actually where to go, which will be affected not only by personal preference but also by the transport available to the area and the costs involved. Other factors to be considered early on include the season and weather, and the time you have available for the trip. You can then begin to plan your route in more detail.

When to go

As far as choosing the time of year goes, it is easier to plan for the season and be prepared for whatever the weather brings. It may be that you have other criteria than the weather for choosing a particular season: any right-minded person avoids Skye in Scotland during the summer because of the unbearable midges, for example. It may be that you want to avoid crowds, in which case the English Lake District, America's Grand Canyon or Chamonix in France at the height of the tourist season are not the places to visit. If you are committed to an expedition in the summer, when of course the weather is usually at its best, a bit of research will repay you with 'unexplored' areas.

Do not always assume that the off-season means bad weather. If you are willing to take a chance, autumn and spring can provide some wonderful walking days – as can winter, of course, if you are prepared and equipped for harsher conditions. The biggest constraint is usually that the days are shorter, considerably so as you move further north, so the margin for error becomes smaller and smaller.

Weather

Forecasts

Weather forecasts are usually available for everywhere except the most remote regions and it is essential that you know how to interpret them.

First, obtain a forecast that is as up to date as possible. Newspaper forecasts are of little use as they are already many hours out of date by the time they reach you. For example, if you want a forecast for Saturday, the Friday paper will be using information from Thursday – it will be nearly two days old by the time you get out on your walk. However, a good paper will show a synoptic chart (Fig 1.1). By following these charts over a few days you will be able to see how the weather is developing, which will give you a good indication for the days ahead.

A better forecast for everyday use is one that is updated regularly, especially if it specifically covers the area you want to visit. The forecasts on local television and radio are good because they are up to date, but usually the best option is a 'weatherline' telephone service, if available. These are often operated by national parks and similar authorities or outdoor organizations; they are not only up to date but also very specific for the weather in the area of interest. Many now offer a 'faxback' service, which provides a useful written forecast with the option of a synoptic chart.

Synoptic charts   When reading synoptic charts you are looking for two features and, more importantly, the way in which they are moving. The first feature is any area of low pressure, marked in Fig 1.1 as areas (a) and (b). These can usually be relied upon to bring bad weather, because of the associated fronts which travel around them (marked in the figure as (c), which is a warm front, and (d), a cold front). Sometimes these fronts can move together and form an occluded front (e).

Lows and fronts mean wet weather, but that information is useless unless you know which direction they are moving in. This is usually mentioned on the chart, as is what is happening to the pressure systems (f). It is best if you can watch the charts over a few days to gather a picture of how the weather is developing, which is often according to a set pattern. In the UK, for example, it almost invariably comes in from

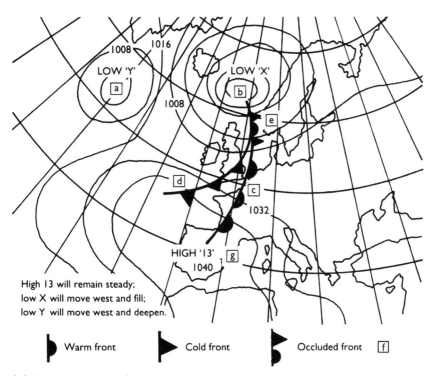

Warm front   Cold front   Occluded front   [f]

1.1 A typical synoptic chart.

the west because of the UK's position in relation to the air streams which move the weather around the globe.

The alternative to low pressure is, of course, high pressure (g). High-pressure systems bring good weather, although in winter it will be very cold. They can block lows from moving in and, when over land, they tend to 'hang around', which means that they often bring very settled weather.

It can be seen from Fig 1.2 (overleaf) how the leading warm front brings a long period of drizzle or light rain, while the following cold front will bring short but often heavy showers. Note that the high cirrus clouds, which are a good indicator of an approaching front, may be 15–20 hours ahead of the rain.

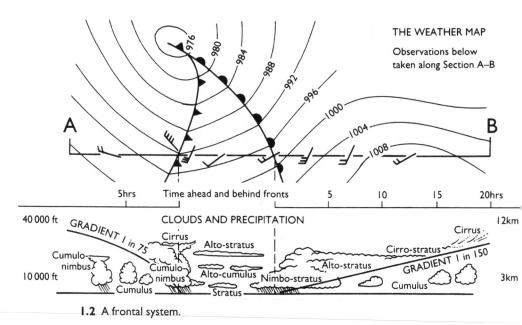

1.2 A frontal system.

Mountain weather

Mountainous areas can have profound effects on the behaviour of the weather. For example, it will usually be much wetter on the windward side of the mountains – indeed, it is possible for one side of a mountain range to be wet while the other is a known dry area. More immediate effects are that the temperature will decrease as you climb higher: allow for a drop of 1°C (1.8°F) for every 150m (490ft) that you climb.

Wind is also affected, often dramatically, by the mountains. Ridges and high plateaux will always accelerate the speed of the wind as it 'squeezes' over the top. There will also be a noticeable increase in the speed of the wind where it is pushed into small gaps, such as along high passes. This funnelling effect will often be enough to turn a gentle wind into a gale strong enough to make walking difficult.

On the coast, you will generally find that steeply rising coastlines facing onshore air streams are very wet places.

Other considerations

Some of what follows might seem more appropriate for planning an intrepid expedition to the far-flung corners of the earth than for a weekend walking trip, but the theory for both is the same – only the quantity really varies. It is often the short, simple trips that go wrong because people tend to forget things like matches or the tent pegs. Planning a trip is something that becomes easier with experience but it will soon become as much a part of the trip as the walking itself.

Equipment

Firstly, decide what equipment and clothing you are going to take, and how much can you carry comfortably. A useful tip when you get back is to empty out all your equipment: if something was not used, ask yourself why, and if you cannot think of a decent reason do not take it again. Travel light.

If you are going abroad, take clothes that respect the local culture. Many villages in Nepal, for example, do not take kindly to skimpy western clothes being worn.

Decide how many tents you are going to need to take and whether they are suitable. Do you have enough spare pegs and other necessary accessories?

Buy and pack your stove, fuel and food. Is it possible to carry all your food, or are you going to be able to replenish your supplies? It is unlikely that you will want to carry more than three or four days' food. Is the food suitable for the conditions on this particular trip? (Dehydrated food, for example, might be a problem in an area where water is hard to come by.) If you are travelling by air at any stage, remember that it is illegal to carry fuel, so ensure that your chosen fuel is going to be available where you are going. Do not forget the matches – and spares!

Detailed information on clothing and equipment is given in Chapter 2.

Route planning

You can now start thinking about planning your route in detail. Are you sure you know all the potential hazards on your route? For example, are all the rivers crossable, and can you still get past them if a spate follows torrential rain?

It is also important to take into consideration a number of factors which might not occur to you initially such as access, interest, timing and fitness.

Access

In many countries of the world it is still possible to tramp through glorious wild areas without any problems of access. In other places, organized groups will find access relatively easy to secure. It seems a pity that after such freedom from other peoples we often have to be so circumspect in our own country.

The Ramblers Association, a national organization formed to protect the interests of walkers, was formed in 1935. In 1949 the National Parks and Access to the Countryside Act appeared from the impetus of the post-war spirit of reconstruction, but it was not until 1965 that the Pennine Way was opened. It was described as Britain's first long-distance footpath by some who forgot that the Ridgeway was in use about 10 000 years ago, the Roman High Street along the Lakeland fells nearly 2000 years since, and, much more recent, the Corrieyairack Pass and other military roads across the Central Highlands in Jacobite times.

Some wild areas in Britain are restricted because they lie within Ministry of Defence training areas. They are shown on the maps as danger areas and are well marked by warning notices. If live ammunition is not used on the ranges, they are sometimes open to the public at weekends and holiday times: contact the relevant Range Liaison Officer.

While considering access, mention should be made of insurance. It would be remiss to go to wild areas in the Alps, say, without rescue cover, because you (or your estate) could be charged thousands of pounds for recovery by mountain rescue teams or helicopters. Up to now – and long may it remain so – all rescue and recovery services have been absolutely free to all in Britain. Recently in Scotland, fired by publicity over the high fatality rate of walkers and climbers in the Highlands during recent winters, there have been proposals to compel mountaineers to insure themselves against the cost of rescue operations. Most outdoor people, and the volunteer rescuers themselves, have condemned the suggestion, since they rescue not for profit but for humanitarian reasons.

Planning an interesting route

Try to plan a route that has some intrinsic interest rather than being just a journey from A to B. Good use of your map will often point to a number of features, both natural and otherwise. Contour lines show not only the slope of hills but also peaks which might stand out and provide good viewpoints. Map symbols can provide a wealth of information on constructed features that might make a good diversion or objective.

   Use guidebooks and local organizations when researching your route. Another good idea is to discover the meaning of some of the local names on your map. For example, 'Hafotty', which is often seen on Welsh maps, is the local word for summer farms used by shepherds in days gone by. Knowledge of this kind means that the ruined buildings which you pass become alive with local history.

Time

Always allow more time than you expect to need (see page 26). For a start, it is always better to finish early than to finish late and miss the last bus home. Secondly, extra time gives you more leisure to enjoy the walk and the sights around you – a rushed walk can become little more than a blur of footpaths and stiles.

Fitness

Never overestimate your own fitness and ability. Walking for, say, three days or more does not compare with day walks, and your planning needs to allow for the fact that any long walk becomes very tiring.

Until you have gained some experience and knowledge of your own ability, it would be sensible to plan a route that passes stopping points for public transport, or to plot a circular route that can be curtailed by heading directly for the finish when you become worn out or run out of time.

Route cards

You will need to let somebody know exactly where you are going, including planned alternatives. This information, in the form of a route card, should be left with a responsible person who knows what to do if your return is overdue. Route cards not only aid a potential rescue team but also help you to make decisions about, and be able to follow, emergency and bad-weather routes, details of which should be on the cards.

The route card is not intended to be a substitute for taking a map on to the hills, but it can be used in a situation where you are cold, the wind and the rain are blowing down, and it would be a nightmare to get out your map and compass and start working out bearings to the next point. Having them already worked out back in the comfort of your base is a great asset. You will, of course, still need to have your map out so that you can keep an eye on your check features as you pass them.

A typical route card is shown in Fig 1.3. Note that the day is divided into legs, with the end of each one written down as a grid reference and description. Each leg should be short enough so that it can be done on a single bearing, without losing track of where you are. The exception would be if you were following a major footpath or track, where it would be a nonsense to treat each bend

ROUTE PLAN

ate:_____Members of party:_____

Weather forecast: _____

arting point reference: _____Description:_____Time:_____

(grid rence)	Description (of target)	Direction	Distance	Time (for distance)	Height gain	Time (for height)	Total time	Description (of route and terrain)	Possible alternative route	Escape route

nishing point reference: _____   Estimated pick up time:_____

escription: _____   Estimated phone in time: _____

1.3 A typical route card.

in the path as a separate leg. In this case, just give a general direction of the path and note any major check features.

Completing a route card before each walking trip requires you to work out the times for each leg and the overall day (see page 26). In this way you will avoid any unpleasant surprises such as finding yourself still walking at midnight. When working out your timings, for every hour or so add 5 minutes to allow time for the inevitable stops, and also allow time for lunch.

An alternative route might be a low-level one (if your original route was at a high level) so that you could substitute it in the event of bad weather. Escape routes should be quick, safe ways off the route that you can take in the event of a crisis. (It is a good idea to note the locations of the nearest public telephones here.) Wind direction is all important: it is all very well to get blown up a mountain with the wind on your tail, but consider that if you do not attain the summit for any reason you may be faced with a long descent into the wind. You should therefore plan your route with knowledge of the forecast wind direction and strength. Also remember that lee slopes for escape routes may be the most prone to windslab avalanches in full winter conditions.

Whenever you go out walking, you should prepare at least two route cards. Take one with you and leave the other one with a responsible person who will know whom to give it to if you fail to return by the stated time.

Satellite navigation (Satnav)
Modern technology has brought satellite navigation (Global Positioning System, or GPS) within the reach of many travellers. Programming the coordinates of important positions on your route as 'waypoints' achieves a similar purpose to the route card, but with the considerable advantage of being able to tell you whether or not you are there! Satnav is a tremendously powerful tool, but it is a complement to conventional navigation, *not* a substitute. Remember that when your batteries go flat at a crucial point in the journey!

How far, how fast?
Maps can tell you two things you really need to know before you launch yourself into the outdoors: can I get there from here, and how long will it take?

Direct routes

If a path leads to your destination, then all you need to know is the time required.

Calculating distance

First, calculate the horizontal distance. A ruler makes it easy to measure the straight-line distance, but tracks never run straight. In fact, they are notorious for taking many more kilometres or miles to reach a destination than the straight-line distance would indicate.

To calculate distance along a path, use a bit of string or soft wire. Place one end on your starting point, then trace the path with the string, following it as it twists and turns. Use your thumbnail to mark the point where the string crosses your destination, then bring it down to the scale at the bottom of the map and read off the distance. It is a good idea to add a pessimism factor of 10 per cent to account for the curves you shortcut and the switchbacks the map-maker neglected to show.

As an alternative measuring tool, use the edge of your compass. One edge on many models is marked in inches and another in centimetres. Use short, straight distances to approximate curves. As a third option, buy a map-measuring device. The most common ones have a wheel which you roll along the map surface. A pointer indicates kilometres or miles for several different map scales.

Measuring distances by any method is easiest on a flat surface, such as your kitchen table the evening before a day walk, or your tent floor before you strike camp.

Calculating height change

After determining the mileage, you will need to calculate the height change. First, determine your starting altitude. Find the index contour closest to your starting point, yet still below it, and trace along it until you find a place where the map gives its altitude. Then count the number of intermediate contours between the index contour and your starting point. Multiply the number of intermediate contours by the vertical interval (given at the bottom of the map) and add that number to the altitude of the index contour. For example, let us say the closest index contour below your starting point on a road is 300m. The contour interval is 10m, and the road is three contours above the 300m index contour, so you are at 330m.

Determine the altitude of your destination in the same way. Subtract the lower from the higher, and you have your height gain or loss.

In some cases, you may find that the map doesn't give an altitude for the first index contour below your starting point. In that case, find the nearest one which does have an altitude indicated and calculate the altitude of the index contour you need. If every fifth contour is an index contour, as is usual, then the height difference between index contours equals five times the vertical interval. For example, if the contour interval is 10m and every fifth contour is an index contour, the height difference between index contours is 50m.

If the path runs up and down more than once, be sure to add up all the individual segments of height gain.

Other factors
You now have the most important information for estimating travel time – distance and height gain. But there are other variables as well: your fitness, your load, the roughness of the ground, the depth of snow (if any), your mode of transport (foot, cycle or skis), and whether you are out for the exercise or to admire wildlife. On foot, 3kmph (2mph) is a reasonable pace on a level track with a moderate load. For every 600m (2000ft) of height gain, add an hour to the time you calculated for the distance alone. This will give you a very rough estimate – then go out and walk some tracks. Write down your times over different kinds of terrain, and make sure you add in rest stops. You will soon learn what is reasonable

for you. The same process can be repeated to calibrate your pace for travel by ski or bicycle.

Cross-country routes

If no path leads to your destination, getting there may be problematic. Your map can give you important clues to the easiest route, but only an actual visit or a phone call to a knowledgeable local will tell you if your planned route is feasible – those green areas, for example, may be open woods allowing pleasant strolling, but they may also be nearly impenetrable plantations of conifers. The most important information the map gives to those planning a cross-country journey is probably the average slope of the steepest part of the route.

Calculating slopes

Find your route's steepest part by locating the place where the contours are closest together. Then measure that horizontal distance. Next, measure the vertical rise over that same horizontal distance.

If the vertical rise is the same as the horizontal distance, you are looking at a 45-degree slope that is likely to be very tough walking. In fact, it probably involves stiff scrambling, and it may confront you with some real cliffs. If the vertical rise is greater than the horizontal distance, you are most likely to be confronting mountaineering territory where you would be advised to have a rope, some hardware and well-honed climbing skills.

When the rise is only half the horizontal distance, you are looking at a slope of 27 degrees – steep walking, but that is all. You can probably find your way around any small crags that may be hiding in between the contour lines.

Like all generalizations, these have exceptions. The average angle of the slope climbing out of a ravine may be quite moderate, but the steepest angle is often vertical. Short but impassable cliffs can run for miles without a navigable break.

An example of a 45-degree slope is the East Face of the Devil's Point (1004m/3290ft) not far from Corrour Bothy near the River Dee, Cairngorms. In 400m (1300ft) of horizontal distance the slope rises from 600m to 1000m (2000ft to 3280ft) – a 400m (1300ft) vertical rise – and so is exactly 45 degrees. Any who have crossed the Lairig Ghru and seen this face in profile behind the bothy would not consider it a mere walking route, because it is a slabby face rather than a jagged one. It looks really evil. It all depends on the rock, but this one is definitely a rock climb.

A slope of about 30 degrees forms the top part of the north-east ridge of the Angel's Peak nearby. It rises from 950m to 1258m (3117ft to 4127ft) in 500m (1640ft) of horizontal distance – not to be undertaken lightly, but a reasonable scramble in dry summer weather. Once again, local experience is the real key.

Calculating times

How long will a cross-country route take you? If you are bashing through deep heather, or through bracken among boulders, or scrambling amid cliff bands, the time required is anyone's guess. It could take two hours to travel 1km (½ mile). On the other hand, if you are strolling along a smooth, level ridge above the tree line, the same distance might take you only 15 minutes. Travelling on skis on deep, untracked snow can be even slower than travelling cross-country in the summer, because of the extra effort of making a track. In the summer, if you are fit, carrying only a daypack and moving hard, you may be able to gain 600m (2000ft) in an hour, at least for a while. In most cases, you are likely to do less. If your route combines track- and ridge-walking, you will usually save time if you stick to the track until you are at the pass between two peaks, and then follow the line of the ridge to gain your desired summit. Leaving the track when you first catch sight of the peak you want to climb and heading diagonally up a steep slope usually takes longer. As with path-walking, you have to spend some time in the country to learn how map features translate into terrain, and what your personal capabilities are.

It is as well to read a glossary of place names, usually available from the map-makers, to understand terms describing mountain features of the country you are operating in. A pass or col (French) might be 'lairig' or 'bealach' in Highland Gaelic; 'nant' or 'bwlch' in Eryri (Snowdonia); 'hause' or 'nick' in England. A similar saddle in Yorkshire might be described by dalesmen as 't' gap beyond top o' t' fell, like'.

Rock climbing

The world at large seems to hold the view that anyone taking up rock climbing is completely mad or at the very least has a total disregard for normal standards of safety and propriety. The truth is that rock climbing is nowhere near as dangerous as it appears to be. Modern equipment and protection techniques are so well developed that most of the attendant risk is very much in the control of the individual climber.

It is, of course, impossible to eliminate risk totally. A boulder that has remained in place for millions of years might detach itself and fall on top of you, or you might be struck by lightning. Neither of these events is one over which you have much control – they are 'acts of God' or described as 'objective danger'. In the normal course of things, however, by proper planning and the use of climbers' guidebooks an experienced climber can choose a climb that presents just the right degree of difficulty and of insecurity.

The degree of difficulty and the degree of risk that a climb might offer are very separate matters. Some extremely hard climbs are so well protected that one would have to make a strenuous effort to sustain an injury by falling. By contrast, some easy climbs, particularly classics or those on roadside crags, are polished to such a glassy finish by the passage of hundreds of thousands of hands and feet that they can present to the uninitiated both insecurity and a lack of proper protection.

The point to emphasize is that the experienced climber can control the level of risk to a very high degree and can make the proper decisions. It is the relative novice who may get into difficulties, either because their ambition exceeds their capability or because their ropework and protection technique are inadequate. Starting to climb with a more experienced friend can be the ideal way to get to grips with rock climbing. However, you are dependent on the judgement and expertise of that individual. Most climbers are sound and sensible in their approach to safety, but some are not.

Locations

Choosing the right crag and the right climb for your abilities and experience is vital. The nature of a climb depends on where the crag is situated. The rocks high on Everest are made of limestone (from the shells of marine animals) but the high mountain environment and constant weathering by frost have produced crags very different from, for instance, the limestone sea cliffs of the Pembrokeshire coast. Some of the very finest cliffs are situated in high mountain areas but, since all large mountains breed their own weather, there may be only a few days each year when the weather and conditions are suitable for an ascent. On Ben Nevis, for example, it is possible to spend several separate weeks in the year waiting for conditions to be right for tackling some of the best rock climbs in Scotland, only to be restricted to a couple of days' activity or less. The rest of the time it is either raining, or the lichen-encrusted rocks stay so damp that they have all the frictional properties of wet liver. However, Scotland may well be an extreme case!

Sea cliffs have become highly developed in Britain, particularly on the quartzite of Anglesey and a variety of rocks around the coastline of Devon and Cornwall. Similar climbs have been developed in

Brittany and on the tremendous limestone sea cliffs in France and southern Spain.

Some notable climbing areas are found in river gorges, perhaps the most famous examples being the awesome Gorge du Verdon in southern France and parts of the Grand Canyon in Arizona. Climbs on sea cliffs and in deep gorges often have to be approached from above by abseil, and this provides a considerable incentive to make a successful ascent once you have pulled down your abseil ropes.

The most popular areas for climbing will offer a variety of different crags – some small, some big, some with easy climbs, some fiercely intimidating, some near the road, some remote. A relatively inexperienced climber will find many advantages in such an area: the climbs will be well known, loose rock is unlikely to be a major problem and other parties will be around to assist with locating the correct line. If a crag looks promising, the next thing to check is that there are a variety of climbs available at (or slightly below) your own standard. The best source of such information is the climber's guidebook.

Guidebooks

In your early climbing days, the foremost thing is to find the route and to have an understanding of its standard. However, most climbers also develop an interest in the history and growth of the sport and its pioneering personalities.

When climbers make the first ascent of a climb they normally record a description, indicate its provisional grade and choose a name for the climb. Some first ascents will be the result of months of careful training and planning, so the first ascendants put a great deal of effort into coming up with a suitable name. Names can be descriptive, such as Black Slab or Overhanging Wall; they can refer to the pioneers (Kelly's Overhang, Helfenstein's Struggle) or to the effect of the climb on the climber (The Rasp, Kneewrecker Chimney). They might allude to the intimidating power of the climb (Il Duce,

Carnivore) or be inspirational (The Ascent of Man, A Dream of White Horses – a climb poised above the breaking sea).

The writer of the guidebook collects all the climbs for a particular area together, checks out the descriptions and endeavours to achieve some consistency in the grading of these climbs before publishing them. The book will usually contain details of access, maps, and diagrams or photographs of the crag with route lines marked. On larger crags, it is worth taking some time to look at the latter before you get too close to the crag, when foreshortening can make it difficult to work out what goes where. Below are examples of two descriptions, one for a single-pitch hard climb at Stanage (a gritstone edge in Derbyshire) and the other for a classic climb in the English Lake District. Each has the accolade of three stars, thereby denoting a climb of the highest quality.

*** **360 Ulysses** 20m [65ft] E6 6b (1983)

> The rounded arête right of Goliath's Groove achieved classic status even before it was finally led! An audacious route requiring 'clean' technique and a great deal of psyche. A route for those who would rather be sorry than safe!

> (British Mountaineering Council, 1989)

What this climb lacks in height, it makes up for in impact. Finding the climb is straightforward using the clear diagram. Climbing it will not be. The climb is number 360 for Stanage Edge, a very extensive crag, and it is 20m (65ft) in height. The grade is E6 6b, which is pretty fierce (see page 37) and 1983 is when it was first ascended. At the back of the British Mountaineering Council's 1989 guide is more information on first ascents, where you can find out who first did the climb and various snippets of historical background. If you are climbing at this standard it will be clear to you that this is a climb on which you either climb well and successfully or you get hurt – the protection is poor.

*** **Tophet Wall** 75m [245ft] HS 1923

A true classic, winding its way through some very impressive rock architecture. It is one of the best climbs of its grade in the Lake District. Start right of an overhanging crack in the centre of the wall.

1. 20m [65ft]. Climb the wall just right of the crack, until a step left can be made into the crack, which is followed to a ledge. An ascending traverse right leads to a ledge at the foot of the wall. (The original route joins the climb at this point along easy grass ledges from the right.)

2. 17m [55ft]. The wall above is climbed to a broken ledge and corner on the left. Climb the crack in the corner followed by the right wall, to a slab that leads to a corner.

3. 15m [50ft]. Semi-hand traverse 10 metres [33ft] right in a sensational position, to a corner. Climb the rib on the right to a ledge.

4. 23m [75ft]. Ascend the small pinnacle on the right, then step left into the crack which is followed to a rock ledge. Easy climbing leads to the top of the ridge.

(Fell and Rock Climbing Club, 1988)

This climb is about one hour's walk from the road and one needs first to find the cliff! A clear diagram helps you to find the start of this middle-grade classic. Athletic beginners are quite likely to do a 'Hard Severe' very early in their climbing career, perhaps even on their first day, but the traverse on Pitch 3 of the climb may not be well protected for the second climber.

A great asset to the international climber is the increasing use of 'topos' or topographical diagrams which show the line of the climb with a minimum of narrative description (Fig 1.4).

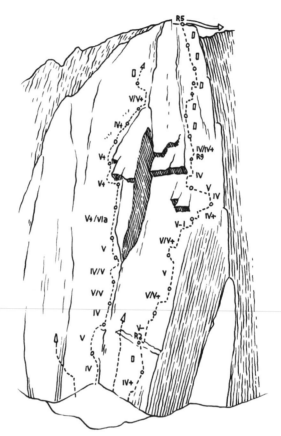

1.4 A 'topo' with Alpine grades marked.

Grades

Many of the difficulties you might encounter when climbing are subjective, so no grading system can be precise. Different areas have developed different grading systems, and they all seem to work well if you use one particular system regularly and become familiar with its quirks.

Perhaps the most logical system is the Australian one, which is entirely open-ended and which starts from 1 and uses increasing numbers for increasing difficulty, so that a Grade 17 is a little harder than a Grade 16 and an awful lot easier than a Grade 23, and so on.

The British system combines an adjectival grade for the overall difficulty with a so-called technical grade for harder climbs. Thus, Tophet Wall, Hard Severe, would be regarded as a middle-grade climb, for the full sequence of grades is as follows: Easy, Moderate, Difficult, Very Difficult, Severe, Hard Severe, Very Severe, Hard Very Severe, Extremely Severe. Most beginners would quickly manage a climb of Very Difficult standard in good conditions, but climbs of Severe and harder begin to make greater demands on technique.

When this adjectival system was developed, Extremely Severe climbs were the preserve of a very small number of the best climbers. Standards of performance have escalated so much that climbing Extremely Severe climbs is almost commonplace and the grade has had to be made open-ended by using E1, E2, E3 and so on. We are currently at E9 or E10, but watch this space!

On the harder climbs, a technical grade is used and you can only get to know this through familiarity and by comparison. Technical grades ascend as follows: 4a, 4b, 4c, 5a, 5b, 5c, 6a, 6b, 6c and so on. Roughly speaking, Very Severe climbs will be 4b, 4c or 5a; Hard Very Severe will be 4c, 5a or 5b; E1 will be 5a, 5b, 5c, and so on. The degree of overlap is related to the degree of protection, thus a climb graded VS 5a will be technically difficult but well protected and 'safe', whereas a climb that is graded E1 5a will be of a similar technical difficulty but will be a much more serious undertaking, possibly with loose rock and poor protection in an intimidating situation. The combination of the grade and the guidebook description helps the climber to avoid some of the most unsuitable climbs, but the system, of course, is not absolutely foolproof.

In the USA, different levels of scrambling or unroped climbing are graded. Roped climbing is called 'fifth class' and the grades are 5.1, 5.2, 5.3 etc. A grade of 5.7 would be roughly equivalent to British VS 4c and 5.9 to E1 5b. The upper grades are subdivided (in the same way as British E grades) into 5.10a, 5.10b, 5.10c and so on.

Finally, the 'Graded List' is a useful and entertaining adjunct to a grading system – it includes all the climbs of a particular grade and is arranged in what consensus agrees is their hierarchy of difficulty.

Never forget that the grading of climbs is an imperfect science and that in adverse conditions, or if you are having a bad day, even climbs of a very lowly grade can present what seem to be ferocious difficulties.

Also, it will take you a while to become accustomed to the style of climbing and the level of grading on a new crag, so it is wise to start at a grade well within your abilities. Many Very Severe climbers have had the depressing experience of going to a new crag (usually Northumberland sandstone!) and failing to ascend anything above Very Difficult standard until the esoteric techniques necessary are mastered.

On water

Sailing

When planning a sailing trip, one of the most important things is to stay flexible. Having checked the weather and tidal information (see pages 40–4) it is always worth reconsidering your plan and deciding on something appropriate to the conditions. Be prepared not to go if the weather is not to your liking. As you become more experienced you will get a feel for the wind conditions in which you and your boat are happy, those in which you are glad to have the club safety boat on patrol, and those where you would rather not be on the water at all.

If you are not sure, then ask the advice of someone experienced, take them with you if you can and make sure that help will be at hand if you needed it. In these sorts of circumstances you will gradually expand your experience and develop the ability to sail in more testing conditions – an essential skill of the intermediate and developing sailor.

Choosing the conditions

Any coastal trip will require good planning even if you are simply going to take a short trip locally. You should plan for the forecast weather, but make sure you have thought out alternatives if the weather does not turn out as expected – your idea of a beautiful day's sail in gentle winds and sunshine might turn into a nightmare if the wind increases by a point or two on the Beaufort scale, while at the other extreme the wind might die altogether and leave you to row home.

The main point is not to assume that the conditions will remain constant and that you will be able to cover the same distance in the afternoon as you did in the morning.

If wind is the only factor that you need to take into consideration, then it is often sensible to head upwind on the outward journey so that you can return with the wind behind you. However, bear the wind forecast in mind and consider whether you expect the wind direction to change. You should also consider the tidal stream direction for the duration of your passage – depending on the relative strength of wind and tide, it is often advisable to be able to head downtide on your return journey. This is, of course, much more predictable than the wind, which can confound even the best-laid plans.

For your first session at least it is best not to go out in much more than a force 2 on the Beaufort scale. We have all derived learning from various epic adventures and misadventures, but there is not a lot of point in starting that way! It can quickly turn from being a bit of fun into an unnerving or frightening experience when things get a bit out of control, and it is essential to appreciate that you are participating in a sport that is usually very safe but can turn dangerous when things go wrong. In a force 2 or less your inevitable early mistakes are unlikely to do damage to you or your boat, and you would always be able to row or paddle around if you needed to.

Checking the weather

The first thing, then, is to check the weather forecasts in the days leading up to your chosen weekend or day off. There are a huge number of sources of weather information nowadays and they provide the relevant details to varying degrees. Whether it is going to be sunny or not is usually given as the most important, closely followed by the air temperature. Unfortunately, brief forecasts such as 'sunny with a high of 17' are pretty useless as far as sailing is concerned. You need something a bit more comprehensive which includes the wind speed as well. This is given either in knots or as a value on the Beaufort scale. The table opposite shows a comparison between these and a description of how to judge the wind strength.

It is important that you learn to read the signs of wind strength both ashore and afloat, as you cannot just assume that as the forecast indicated a certain wind strength then that is what it is blowing. The actual wind state can vary wildly from the forecast due to local variations, changing conditions, and even inaccurate forecasting! To be fair, it must be said that while satellite observations and computer analysis have greatly improved the methods of recording and processing weather information, the art of prediction is still subject to such a large number of variables that we cannot yet rely on the forecasts to be perfect. The best answer is to develop an understanding of what happens during certain weather fronts and systems and keep a good awareness of the weather changing around you, relating it back to the best information you got from the forecasters. This will give you more confidence when the weather is not as forecast and can help you to work out what else you might expect. It might be that the timing of changes is different or that the track of a depression is not as the forecasters expected: if you know whether the front has passed yet or whether you expect the wind to go on changing in strength or direction, then you are in a better position to make best use of it and avoid conditions you do not want to be out in.

		WIND STRENGTH CHART:		
Beaufort force	Description	At sea	On land	Wind speed in knots
0	Calm	Mirror-like.	Smoke rises vertically.	<1
1	Light air	Ripples like scales.	Wind direction shown by smoke but not by wind vanes.	1 to 3
2	Light breeze	Small wavelets. Crests appear glassy and do not break.	Wind felt on face, leaves rustle.	4 to 6
3	Gentle breeze	Large wavelets, crests begin to break.	Leaves and small twigs in constant motion. Wind extends light flags.	7 to 10
4	Moderate breeze	Small waves becoming longer, fairly frequent white horses.	Raises dust and loose paper; small branches are moved.	11 to 16
5	Fresh breeze	Moderate waves, many white horses, chance of some spray.	Small trees in leaf begin to sway. Crested wavelets form on inland waters.	17 to 21
6	Strong breeze	Large waves begin to form; white foam crests are more extensive everywhere. Probably some spray.	Large branches in motion; umbrellas used with difficulty.	22 to 27
7	Near gale	Sea heaps up and white foam from breaking crests begins to be blown in streaks along the direction of the wind.	Whole trees in motion; inconvenience when walking against the wind.	28 to 33
8	Gale	Moderately high waves of greater length; edges of crests begin to break into spindrift. Foam is blown in well-marked streaks along the direction of the wind.	Breaks twigs off trees; generally impedes progress.	34 to 40
9	Severe gale	High waves. Crests of waves begin to topple, tumble and roll over. Spray may affect visibility.	Slight structural damage occurs (chimney pots and slates removed).	41 to 47
10	Storm	Very high waves with long overhanging crests. Whole surface takes on a white appearance. Visibility affected.	Seldom experienced inland; trees uprooted; considerable structural damage occurs.	48 to 55

Canals

These may be accessible to people who cannot get to other bodies of water. The inland waterway system in England and Wales is fairly extensive. There may be the occasional sofa or car to bump into, but canals are usually more sheltered places as far as the weather is concerned, although they do carry other water-borne forms of transport such as canal barges and power boats. Pollution is potentially a problem and the disease leptospirosis, or Weil's Disease, carried by the urine of rats, is known to be widespread on some canals.

British Waterways

British Waterways is the navigational authority for over 3200km (2000 miles) of canals and river navigations in England, Scotland and Wales – about 640km (400 miles) of British canal is navigable by canoe.

In order to use these waterways, a licence is required from British Waterways. The waterways are navigable by means of locks and weirs, and the payment of the licence fee helps contribute towards the cost of running and maintaining them. Licences for British Waterways and a few other waterways are free to BCU members, but can be obtained from the various waterways authorities for non-members.

Canoeists' code of conduct

This code of conduct (see opposite) is designed to promote good relations between water users and to maintain access, so please do abide by it.

A kayak at sea

'The sea is a hard teacher. She gives the examination first and the lesson afterwards.' Never lose your respect for the sea. It is a very powerful and changeable force of nature, but can be irresistible to the kayaker because it offers so much diversity and unpredictability

Canoeists' code of conduct:

- Ask and obtain permission before you use restricted areas.
- Thank people afterwards!
- Park in sensible places, even if it means paying for a car park. Do not block narrow areas and keep off grass verges.
- Be discreet when getting changed – for other people's sakes.
- Pick up litter, close gates, stay on paths, do not damage crops or land.
- Obey National Trust regulations, local by-laws and regulations for camping and caravanning.
- Keep away from banks from which people are fishing.
- Please keep the peace.

of mood, from a raging, capricious beast during storms to a vision of tranquil beauty in sunsets.

The canoe is quiet, does not pollute and leaves no trace. Seals, sea otters, dolphins, puffins, fulmars and other wildlife become curious or watch, unthreatened, as you drift quietly by at a distance. You can explore cliffs, caves, islands and marshes that no other vessels can see at such close quarters. The same trip is never identical, conditions change, you can paddle in waves and exciting tidal races, or you can choose smooth and calm, mirror-like seas; and, last but not least, it does not have to be raining to find enough water.

The sea can be a hostile place for a beginner to learn, unless it is the calmest of weather and water. Make sure that for your first journeys you are with someone who is an experienced sea kayaker and will teach you good seamanship.

All the information on tides and weather in the sailing section on pages 40–4 is relevant to the kayaker at sea, but because the only motive power of a kayak is *you*, the paddler, it is doubly important to avoid adverse tides and unfavourable conditions of wind and weather. A kayaker will quickly tire in conditions of adverse wind or tide, and if these are of any strength you can be carried miles in the wrong direction. Because of this, it is vital to take into account all the variables and to err emphatically on the side of caution. A pleasant sunny day on shore can blind the novice to dangerous conditions of wind, wave and tide only a few hundred metres from the coast.

Your first trips at sea should all be made in good weather with only very light winds and calm conditions. The sea should have no swell or breaking waves and little or no tidal influence. Ideally, the coastline will permit easy landings at any point. A good paddler in good conditions will be able to paddle at normal walking pace (4.8kmph/3mph), so a beginner would travel more slowly. Do short distances first to develop your stamina and judgement.

Canoeing magazines are a good source of information on potential areas for kayaking at sea, but as you learn what are the right questions to ask then Ordnance Survey maps, charts and pilot books (but take care – these are written for larger vessels) will become an engrossing and absorbing source of information.

Access to the sea

Generally, access to the sea poses few problems, but in some areas it is restricted or controlled. Some sections of coast, and many islands, are coastal reserves and have bird sanctuaries or other wildlife. Canoeists need to give a wide berth to these protected areas during nesting and nursing seasons. During the breeding season, noise and activity nearby alarms the adults, causing them to desert, or permanently abandon, their young. If you are in doubt, keep well away from the cliffs.

Surfing beaches

Some of the more popular surfing beaches are divided into sectors for different uses, such as swimmers, surfboards, canoes and so on, and it is important to abide by the posted regulations for everyone's safety. These beaches are sometimes patrolled by lifeguards, but the same regulations should be practised anywhere where there is a variety of different activities requiring the use of the same water.

There are often conflicts between the various water users occupying the same area, so basic wave etiquette and protocol need to be observed. For example, the first person to ride the wave has the right of way or, if two people choose the same wave, the person closest to the shoulder of the wave has right of way. It is sound practice to keep surfboards and kayaks in different areas if at all possible. A swimmer is extremely vulnerable to injury from a rapidly moving kayak or surfboard.

Firing ranges
Active firing ranges exist along some sections of the coast, and may or may not be marked on the maps. However, the ranges usually display a signal when they are firing, such as a series of red flags, and sometimes these flags are left up all the time. The coastguard is a good source for information on the days and times that firing ranges are active.

Harbours
Depending on where you are, harbours can be busy places for shipping and are usually managed by a Harbour Authority. Shipping has the right of way in restricted waters (under which harbours are classified) and canoeists should keep well clear. Remember that a canoe is a very small craft, unable to be identified as a canoe on a radar and more than likely unable to be distinguished from the blips or clutter, called interference, which are usually associated with waves. Ferries in particular move in and out of harbour walls incredibly quickly and without much warning, and these walls are also great places for fishermen, so beware of their lines and hooks.

The coastguard

Her Majesty's Coastguard is responsible for the co-ordination of maritime search and rescue off the coast of the UK. All distress radio calls on VHF channel 16 and the relevant 999 telephone calls are channelled into one of 21 district headquarters that operate 24 hours a day.

Lifeboats and search and rescue (SAR) helicopters carry out the majority of the responses to incidents on the sea. The coastguard cannot cope with every single paddler, sailor, windsurfer, power-boat user, sea angler and yachtsman who telephones them or calls them on the radio to say that they are going out for the day.

Information the coastguard should have:

- Number in group and where they are from.

- Canoe types and colours.

- The group's intentions, with estimated times of departure (ETD) and arrival (ETA). Give emergency routes or alternatives. Will there be rescue practice or not? This is useful to know so that if a member of the public reports in that canoeists have capsized, then the coastguard can refer to their log and take appropriate action. This is the same for any night-time paddling.

- What equipment is being carried? Radio, distress flares – if so, what kind – distress beacon, buoyancy aids? Is protective clothing being worn, such as wetsuits or drysuits? What is the level of experience in the group? Are food and drink being carried? Do they have navigation equipment such as a compass, charts or maps? Are they equipped with any other emergency equipment? And so on.

- Is there a vehicle being used or left anywhere? Include the registration number.

However, they would like to hear from those people who operate as groups, or who are undertaking an extended journey, or who may be going into remote or dangerous places.

If you contact the coastguard to let them know your plans, you must also have someone ashore to raise the alarm to the coastguard if a problem is suspected with your safety. The coastguard *do not* follow up your safe arrival! They do, however, log the information they receive and from this can make a quick and effective response if needed. The person ashore should have all the details of your party and intentions, and should be the one responsible for raising the alarm if they become concerned for your party's safety. The burden of responsibility that this person takes on is huge, and should not be undertaken lightly.

It is also important to inform the coastguard of your safe return. They are friendly people who can give you information such as the latest weather forecasts, hazards in the area, tidal information, local conditions and advice but, not surprisingly, their professional involvement with large vessels does not always help them to understand the potential of smaller craft.

2

Clothing and Equipment

You need clothing and equipment to be warm, dry, comfortable and safe, and you also require an efficient means of carrying your equipment and supplies. Whatever you carry, whether on your body, on your back or in your boat, ensure firstly that it works, secondly that it is light and finally that you really do need it. Every ounce counts when *you* are carrying everything.

There is a bewildering choice available and it is easy to buy the wrong gear when taking up a sport. It is always worth listening to the opinions of experienced performers on the equipment that they use, and there is much to be said for building up a relationship with a reputable retailer rather than always buying from a different supplier. Good advice will save you a great deal of money and help you to meet the outdoors equipped with the right gear.

It is well worth trying to be objective about what you need. You could classify items into categories.

Equipment categories:

- Essential for your safety, eg rock-climbing harness, lifejacket.
- Aids your safety but not essential, eg fleece jacket, sighting compass.
- Distinctly improves your comfort or enjoyment, eg gaiters, wetsuit boots for canoeing.
- Luxury, eg map measurer, camp stool.

Don't stint on what you spend on items in the first category, but equally don't pay for more than you need: the best gear available is probably designed for the top of Everest or an Atlantic storm and is unnecessary if you are in the Peak District.

On land

Basic clothing

Unless you are heading for a hot climate, your clothing requirements can be based around staying warm, dry and comfortable.

The layer system

It has long been accepted that the way to keep warm and dry outdoors is to adopt a layer system that keeps the elements at bay, whisks the sweat away from your skin to keep you dry and traps air to keep you warm. Layers can also be removed or added in order to cope with varying conditions. The system is divided into a base layer, a warmth layer and a foul-weather layer.

Base layer

This is the layer worn next to your skin. It is normally made up from polypropylene/nylon mixtures that will 'wick' moisture away from your skin. These clothes are vital, as sweat next to your body will cool quickly and make you very cold when you stop. The top layer is usually a thin, long-sleeved top with or without a roll neck; a bottom layer of long johns is useful in winter. Some people wear the long johns as trousers, with shorts over them.

Warmth layer

The top half of this layer usually consists of a shirt of some sort under a fleece or pile jacket or pullover. The main advice when choosing a fleece from the overwhelming selection on the market is that if it is really cheap you should be asking yourself why.

For the bottom half of this layer, avoid wearing denim jeans: they provide no warmth when wet and the thick seams will rub skin raw. Polycotton or fleece trousers are ideal. Salopettes will prevent your shirt riding up under a rucksack and are very warm and cosy to wear, but if you ever need to get them off in a hurry under several other layers you will curse the day you bought them!

55

Foul-weather layer

This is where things suddenly start to get very expensive. What you are looking for is a layer that will do two rather incompatible things: keep out the cold, the wind and the rain *and* let your perspiration escape. All waterproof garments manage the first requirement to a greater or lesser extent but the second requirement, known as breathability, is a different matter.

Traditional waterproofs are made with a totally waterproof material, usually nylon coated with polyurethane (PU), which works well at keeping you dry from the outside. However, as soon as you start to exercise you will perspire, and this type of garment can leave you very wet from the inside. This problem is overcome by using a wide range of sophisticated technologies to produce garments which 'breathe': in other words, outside moisture is kept out while perspiration is allowed to escape. Some of the main trade names to look for are Gore-tex, Sympatex, Cyclone, Hydro Dry and Triple Point. These all work in different ways and have slightly different properties. When you come to make the decision about buying waterproofs, perhaps the biggest help is to listen to the experience of friends and do a lot of asking around.

Double-P system

There is a recent innovation in outdoor clothing which many people are using in preference to the layer system. This is the Double-P system of clothing where the double Ps stand for Pertex and fibre Pile. In this system fewer layers are worn, the theory being that the fibre pile will stay warm against the skin even when wet. These clothes, of which 'Buffalo' is the most popular make, need to fit much more tightly than conventional outfits.

Making a choice

Choosing your basic clothing can be daunting in terms of both the range of products available and their prices. Always keep in mind what you want the garment to do and be honest with yourself. As already mentioned, there is little point in buying a very expensive top-of-the-range mountain jacket if all you intend to do is walk on local trails; likewise, a cheap jacket from the local corner shop could be a major hazard if you were to wear it in the mountains in winter. Do not be fooled by superficial gimmicks, but go for the essential features. Do your trousers really need eight pockets? Is the map pocket on the jacket large enough? Is the hood large enough? How long will the garment last? On this last point, be aware that many breathable fabrics have a short useful life, sometimes three years or less if you buy an inappropriate one.

When you try clothes on, move around in them to ensure that they give a good fit. In particular, stretch your arms above your head and bring your knees up high to see if there are any tight areas. With top layers, bear in mind that you might want to put several other layers beneath them. Ensure that all zips are substantial and, if needed, will open in either direction. Waterproof trousers should have long zips, enabling them to be put on while wearing boots.

Hot climates

Care needs to be taken when choosing your clothing even if you are fortunate enough to be walking in a hot country. Under no circumstances should you walk in the sun without a hat on, as you are inviting at best a pounding headache and at worst a very unpleasant dose of heat stroke. A wide-brimmed hat is desirable; a baseball cap is better than nothing.

Shorts and vests or T-shirts are very comfortable, but it is best to avoid sunburn by wearing trousers and long-sleeved shirts in lightweight cotton or a modern synthetic equivalent. You never see the local population of desert countries anything less than fully covered.

The danger in hot climates is in being too casual: you still need to be prepared for everything that the local weather might throw at you. Nights can be very cold in hot regions and you might also be subjected to violent thunderstorms.

Boots

There is now a wide and diverse range of boots on the market but essentially they can be split into several categories.

Shoes and lightweight boots

Shoes designed for walking might be adequate for simple trail walking, but they do not give any ankle support and should not be used on anything more rugged. Lightweight boots are a step up from shoes and give a minimal amount of ankle support, but they tend to be made of fabric and are not waterproof – they are not recommend for off-trail walking.

General walking boots

Medium-weight, general-purpose boots are made from water-proofed leather or fabric. They should be substantial enough to

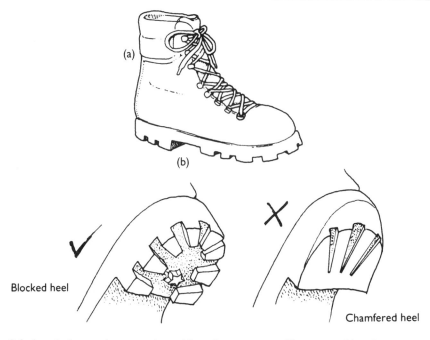

2.1 A typical general-purpose boot. Note the generous ankle support (a) and square-cut sole and heel (b).

give a good amount of support. Some of the fabric boots come with a Gore-tex inner which gives them a degree of waterproofing and breathability.

When choosing boots, look for the following features:

- Well-padded support around the ankles, but beware of the fit being too tight against the Achilles' tendon.

- A reasonably rigid sole which does not bend too much either along the length of the boot or across its width. More than 2cm (1in) when holding the heel and pushing the toes up is too much.

- A substantial sewn-in tongue which will both keep water out and not slip around on top of your foot.

- A good chunky cleated sole, square-cut along all the lower edge including the heel. Be very wary of any substitutes for the traditional sole – many of the newer lightweight materials do not grip at all in the wet. Avoid cut-away or rounded heels even if you are told that they make walking easier; this may be true, but some people find that they make it difficult to get a secure foothold when descending steep grass slopes. The sole should feel solid and substantial, not soft and giving (which is another modern innovation supposedly for comfortable walking).

- A good fit is absolutely essential. As a rule, the boot needs to be just tight enough to hold your foot but not loose enough to slop around in. Try standing on your toes and seeing what happens. Your toes should not be at all squashed into the front of the boot, while at the back there should be just enough room to squeeze a finger down behind your ankle.

- Ensure that both boots fit well. Even minor differences in the sizes of your feet could make themselves felt with unforgiving boots.

Mountaineering boots

Mountaineering boots are made from either a heavier leather or from plastic. They give extremely good support, largely owing to the fact that they are made rigid enough to be used with crampons. These boots are not comfortable to wear for general walking purposes.

Wellingtons

Walking 'wellies' or 'bog trotters' are essentially short wellington boots which are tighter fitting than usual and have walking soles. Although they give only a minimal amount of support, they are ideal for very wet ground.

Socks

Remember that the most expensive boots in the world will be uncomfortable if worn with cheap and nasty socks. A major cause of blisters is ill-fitting, wet or dirty socks; socks with large seams are also a menace. A lot of people still wear two pairs of socks, while others stick to a single pair: the choice is largely a personal one, but you should never need to wear more than two pairs. Using insoles in boots is a good idea, especially the modern shock-absorbing type: not only can they help to give a good fit, but they also provide a surprising amount of cushioning.

Caring for boots

It is worth spending as much as you can afford on your boots – more than anything else, they can make or break a walking trip. Care of boots should never be neglected and a good pair of boots, looked after well, can last a lifetime with the occasional resoling. Your boots should be washed after each trip and dried gently with the laces and insoles removed. Never dry boots rapidly in front of a fire or radiator as this will crack them. Follow the manufacturer's advice for which proofing to use.

Gaiters

Gaiters for walking boots were originally designed to keep out snow, but now many people never walk without them. Essentially, there are three types: the normal calf-length version which covers the top of the boot, a short type which just goes around the ankle, and a third version which completely encloses the boot (Fig 2.2).

Gaiters are useful for everything from keeping water and stones out of boots to keeping trousers clean. If you are considering all-over gaiters, which will keep your feet totally dry, ask yourself if you really need them. They can be very expensive and also the rubber rands which go under the boots can wear out very quickly. If you do decide to go for them, ensure that your boot is the type which will accept them. A workable alternative is to wear ankle gaiters in snow and all-over gaiters in very wet country, but otherwise not bother with them.

Do not make the classic mistake of tucking your waterproof trousers inside your gaiters. If you do, all the water will simply run down your legs and fill up your boots.

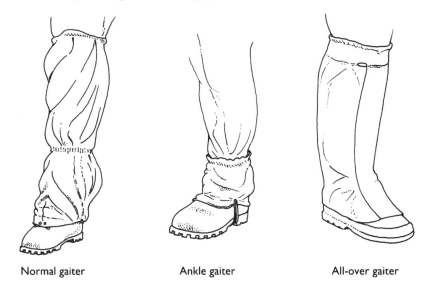

Normal gaiter   Ankle gaiter   All-over gaiter

2.2 Types of gaiter.

Hats and balaclavas

You should never go walking without a hat. In winter it will keep your head warm and in summer it will protect your head from the sun.

A large percentage of body heat is lost from the head so it is sensible to wear a hat or balaclava in cold conditions. Wearing one while in your sleeping bag can make a surprising difference, too. In winter, go for a hat which covers your ears and will not flap around. If it has a peak, make sure that it is stiff. In summer, a wide-brimmed bush hat will be invaluable for keeping the sun at bay.

Gloves

When choosing gloves, ask yourself whether they are suitable for your intended use. A good combination is a thin pair of warm gloves with a heavier pair of waterproof ones to wear if the weather turns foul. Avoid gloves which do not cover the wrist unless you wear very long sleeves or use wristlets: you will be surprised how cold that bare strip of skin can get. If you are expecting stormy conditions, 'idiot-loops' will prevent the loss of a glove.

Equipment

Rucksack

Along with your waterproofs and boots, it is your rucksack that dictates whether you will be comfortable while walking. In the shop it is difficult to tell if a sack really suits you, so seek the advice of friends who already own them. There are several main features to look for in a rucksack.

Size

Weight is rarely a problem with modern rucksacks, but some older ones can be quite heavy.

Choose a sack which is larger than you need so that you have adequate capacity when you progress to bigger trips. Some sacks are

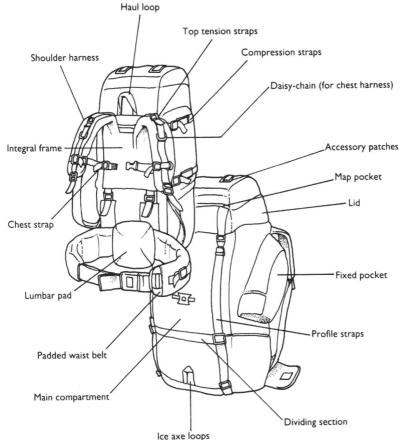

Haul loop

Top tension straps

Shoulder harness

Compression straps

Daisy-chain (for chest harness)

Integral frame

Accessory patches

Map pocket

Lid

Chest strap

Fixed pocket

Lumbar pad

Padded waist belt

Profile straps

Main compartment

Dividing section

Ice axe loops

2.3 Features of a rucksack.

adjustable in size using a bellows system, but you should at least have compression straps so that you can pack the sack down tight after it is loaded. As a rough guide, 65 litres is a suitable size for the average two- or three-day walking trip.

Although many rucksacks have a multitude of adjustments that can be made to them, it is still important that the sack fits you correctly. Most sacks will come in a variety of lengths and the correct length should be your priority when making a decision. Do not compromise on size or you will regret it later.

Carrying straps, pockets and lids

There are essentially two sets of straps for carrying rucksacks: the shoulder straps and the waist strap. There is often a chest strap which brings the shoulder straps in closer together to give a better fit and help to spread the load. When carrying the sack, the waist strap should be sitting on top of your hips rather than around your waist.

Although the actual balance is a personal choice, aim to have around a third of the weight on the waist strap. The waist strap should have substantial padding all round; the padding on the shoulder straps should be cut away from under the arms.

Pockets are a matter of personal choice, but a large pocket in the lid is recommended for small items that you will need during the day. A good compromise is to have detachable pockets on the side so that you can use them when desired and also vary the capacity of the sack. Dividing the main sack into compartments is a gimmick with little real application.

The top of the sack should have a lid which will cover it completely no matter how much has been packed inside. There should also be an extension to the sack which can be pulled over the opening to seal it.

Frames

The development of the internal frame has meant that the days of the pack frame have all but gone. There is now as big a variety of frames as there is of rucksacks, but there is probably not a great deal to choose between them.

Packing a rucksack

Novices never cease to be amazed by how quickly experts pack their rucksacks, but it is simply a case of developing your own system and sticking to it. There are a number of simple guidelines which will help.

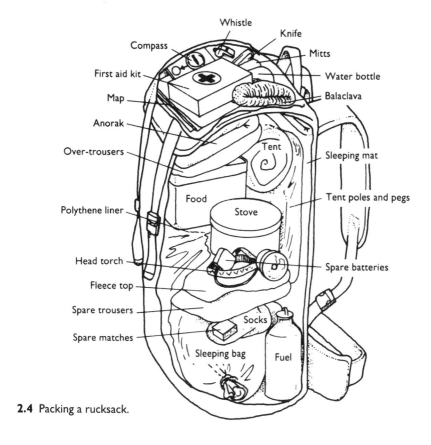

Whistle

Knife

Compass

Mitts

First aid kit

Water bottle

Map

Balaclava

Anorak

Over-trousers

Tent

Sleeping mat

Food

Polythene liner

Stove

Tent poles and pegs

Head torch

Spare batteries

Fleece top

Spare trousers

Socks

Spare matches

Sleeping bag

Fuel

2.4 Packing a rucksack.

Firstly, no rucksack is waterproof, so use a heavyweight plastic bag as a sack liner (a normal bin bag will not be substantial enough). If you want to be absolutely sure, wrap your sleeping bag and spare clothes in another bag as well. Remember that the lid pocket of the sack will not be waterproof either, so it is probably not a good place to store your matches.

The rule to follow when packing your sack is 'last out – first in'. Place things such as your sleeping bag and spare clothes at the bottom of the sack, where they can remain undisturbed until needed. Essential items such as your first aid kit need to be at the top. Perhaps the best place to pack your waterproofs is under the lid of the sack, so that if it starts raining it is not necessary to undo the main compartment. A tent is more of a problem: when it is dry and easily folded it can go in the sack beside your lunch; however, after a couple of days, when it has become wet, it is often a good idea to leave it under the lid.

Ensure that your fuel bottle and stove are well wrapped in extra bags to protect your food and clothes from the smell of fuel. For the sake of balance, try to keep heavy items low and close to your back, although this is not always feasible and it is not so critical with modern sacks as it once was.

The last check is to make quite sure that there is nothing sticking out which is going to dig into you. In Fig 2.4 the sleeping mat has been folded and used to pad the back of the sack. It could also be formed into a lining tube within the sack, with everything else packed inside it. A third option is to roll it tightly and strap it to the outside of your sack.

Make it your goal, however, to have as little as possible on the outside of the sack. There a risk that it will get damaged, and anyway there is nothing more annoying to the group than the clatter of dangling mugs and cooking pots.

Other equipment

Torch
Except in the permanent daylight of the Arctic summer, a torch and spare batteries are absolutely essential.

Whatever torch you carry it must be infallible, because benightment in rough country without a light is unthinkable. If the switch is not foolproof it is bound to get switched on during the day inside your rucksack. Then, when it gets dark and you rummage for your torch you will find that the batteries are exhausted.

To guard against accidentally switching on your torch, you might carry the batteries separately (you should carry spare batteries anyway), but a better method is to remove one battery and reverse it, so that the two positive terminals abut. If you do this, no leakage of current can occur even with the switch on.

As with the rest of your gear, torches should be lightweight. Large, heavy, rubberized torches may be suitable for the boot of a car, but when you are walking the weight of everything becomes important.

Head torches are light in weight and are very convenient for night navigation when map and compass must be handled together. Try lying in a tent in the dark, stirring porridge with one hand and holding the pan handle with the other, and you will realize the value of a head torch. In fact, these are the only torches that can be considered for serious walkers. Head torches are secured to the forehead by adjustable elastic straps around and across the head. They can be worn with or without a helmet. The 4.5 volt type gives a good light, especially with a halogen bulb, but consult your supplier about burning time as these bulbs exhaust a lot of batteries. Alkaline batteries are the only ones worth carrying; cheaper ones and rechargeable batteries do not last long and are unreliable. A converter is available so that three alkaline batteries (AA size) can be used rather than the 4.5 volt flat battery with blade-type brass terminals.

Emergency equipment
A whistle should be carried by every member of the group. You should never blow your whistle unless it is an emergency.

It is also important to carry a pencil and notebook (usually in your first aid kit). In addition to making notes, you might need to write an emergency message in a crisis, to be carried by whoever goes for help.

If tents are not being carried, each individual should have their own plastic survival bag. It is sensible for a group to carry at least two bags that are big enough for two people.

Knife

The Swiss army knife has never really been beaten as the most useful all-round tool when camping. There is no need to carry large knives or machetes unless your trip involves blazing trails or clearing bush. The big advantage of the Swiss army knife is that it contains all the little things that so easily get lost, like a can opener. Beware of cheap imitations: they will be a poor investment in the long run.

Spares and food

Spare matches can be carried in an old film container together with a striker. You can never have enough spare matches.

Spare clothes should always be carried. On a day walk it is enough to carry a spare pair of socks and an extra sweater. For longer trips you need to carry a full change of clothes in case you get completely soaked. A spare set of thermal top and bottoms can be used exclusively for sleeping in.

Although not every person in a group needs a map and compass, there should be at least a couple of spares in addition to the sets being used. The main map needs to be protected by either lamination or a map case.

As well as your normal provisions, carry a small amount of spare food in case you get caught by nightfall or have to spend extra time on the hill. A few chocolate bars and some boiled sweets should be enough.

Water bottle or flask

If you are working hard you need to keep up your fluid intake. Hot drinks are very welcome, but in a hot climate a water bottle of at least 1 litre (2 pints) per person is desirable.

Group gear

The gear that is carried between the members of a party on longer expeditions should include a small spade for digging a toilet hole at the campsite, a 30m (100ft) length of 9mm (⅓in) safety rope and an emergency shelter. The latter, which is simply a large piece of rip-stop nylon, is not strictly needed if members of the group are carrying tents or survival bags, but it does make a good, quick shelter for all manner of stops.

First aid kit
Every walker should carry a first aid kit, and Appendix I provides a list of suggested contents.

Weight

Finally, once you have decided exactly what you need, think again about weight. Almost nothing ruins a backpacking trip more than carrying too much on your back. A general guide is that no one should carry more than a third of their own body weight, but this does depend a great deal on your own experience and ability.

Be totally ruthless. Do you really need a mountain tent which might weigh 5kg (11lb), when a low-level tent weighing only 3kg

2.5 Carrying a packed rucksack correctly. Note that the weight of the sack is balanced vertically, not dropping back from the body. The sack itself is snug to the body, with the shoulder straps and belt well adjusted.

Weight

(7lb) is enough? Do you really need two extra pullovers or three spare pairs of socks? Look closely at the stove you buy: having one which will boil water in five minutes is all very well, but if it weighs 2kg (4lb) when one that boils water in twice the time weighs only half as much, then opt for the lighter one. The same applies to sleeping bags: get one which is appropriate rather than excessive and save another kilo or two of weight.

The biggest enemy of weight efficiency is the 'just in case' factor. While you do need first aid kits, spare clothes and emergency shelters, avoid too much replication within a group.

Tents and camping

The tent

Not so many years ago, choosing a tent was a simple affair. It would be a ridge tent, probably with A-poles at each end; it would be made of waterproofed cotton and weigh half a ton, or at least feel like it after a night's rain.

Today, however, a bewildering array of tents is available, but nearly all of them have certain features in common, as shown in Fig 2.6.

Tent layers

With the exception of single-skin Gore-tex designs, tents will have two layers: the inner tent and the fly sheet. The job of the fly sheet, or outer tent, is to provide weatherproofing. It will probably have guys attached for extra security; there will be a number of loops around the edge for pegs to go through; there will be at least one door and possibly a snow valance, which is a flap of material around the edge of the fly sheet. The valance is useful on hard ground or in bad weather because rocks or snow can be piled on it, making the tent much more secure. The disadvantage is that it can freeze to snow; also, because it reduces the air flow around the tent, it can increase condensation.

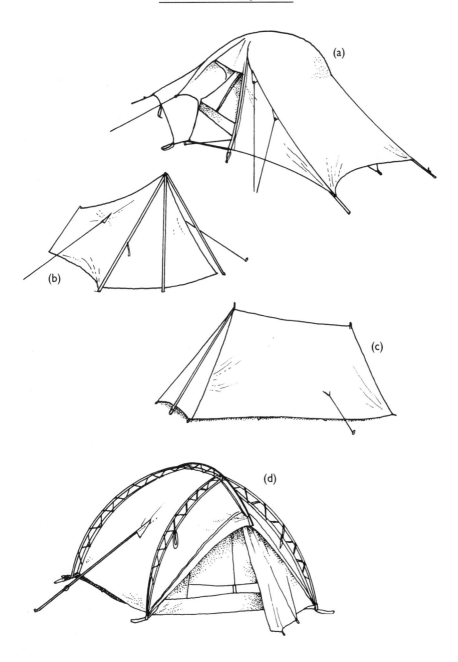

2.6 Four variations on the ridge tent. The differences are purely superficial; the essential features remain the same.

The inner sheet will be of a lighter-weight material, its function being to provide a dry 'room' within the tent. It does this by allowing condensation to pass out into the area between it and the fly sheet, thus preventing drips from forming. It should have a good sewn-in groundsheet, preferably one that curls up around the edges in a 'tray' style. One of the biggest weight savings to be made with a tent is to reduce the quality of the groundsheet, but watch out for this, as keeping the rain out from above is useless if it comes in from below. The inner also usually has a 'no-see-'em', or mosquito net door, in addition to the main one, and you would be foolish to buy a tent without one!

The gap between the inner and outer layers is important: the two must not touch because this would quickly lead to the entry of damp. In modern tents this gap remains small because the two sheets are kept very taut. With older-style tents the gap is larger.

Which layer first? No matter what the design, all layered tents will be erected either inner or outer sheet first. Some makers may claim that the two are erected together for speed but this only means that the two halves are connected in some way – if separated, they will still fit into one of the two categories. Each type has its advantages and disadvantages.

If a tent is erected inner first, it means that the poles are attached to the inner and the outer is thrown over the poles and inner. This gives a very taut tent and means that the gap between the inner and outer can be smaller, giving more space inside. It also means that the tent will not flap as much in the wind and will therefore be much quieter to sleep in. The major disadvantage is that when putting the tent up or down in the rain the inner, which needs to stay as dry as possible, is exposed to the elements for as long as it takes to put the tent up or take it down. If it is raining, the whole tent needs to be put up or taken down very quickly.

In a tent which is erected outer first, the poles are attached to the outer and the inner is then hung from this. The inner is not tensioned and the result is less space, a tent which may flap, and an inner that often sags and looks unpleasant. The major advantage is that, in bad weather, the waterproof outer tent can be put up first and then the inner hung up inside, thus keeping it dry. When taking the tent down it is usually an easy matter to pack up all your gear, take down the inner and put your boots and waterproofs on, all within the comfort of the outer tent.

Tent design

All modern tents fit loosely into one of four designs: the ridge, the tunnel, the dome or the geodesic. Within these loose categories there are endless variations.

Ridge tents　Ridge tents are characterized by having poles at either end of the tent. These can be traditional A-poles or a single pole, a variety of flexible poles or a combination of these. A typical combination would be a high A-pole at the entrance, with a short single pole at the back end and a sloping ridge (Fig 2.6b). This type of tent is often supplied with a choice of A-poles, for convenience, or single poles, for lightness.

Although ridge tents all have a distinct ridge, they do not all have ridge poles. Where they do, these can be either rigid, as in the traditional tent (Figs 2.7 and 2.6c) or flexible, as in the modern tent shown in Figs 2.6a and 2.6d. These flexible ridge-pole tents are often referred to as hoop tents.

Hoop tents are not very strong and need careful erection and tensioning; they must not be side-on to the wind. Their big advantage is that they are very lightweight, and although the inner tents can be quite small the bells (porch areas) are at the side, which makes them very convenient to use. This type of tent is popular for events such as mountain marathons.

Tunnel tents　Tunnel tents (Fig 2.8) were the first development from the traditional A-frame ridge tent. The tent is supported by two

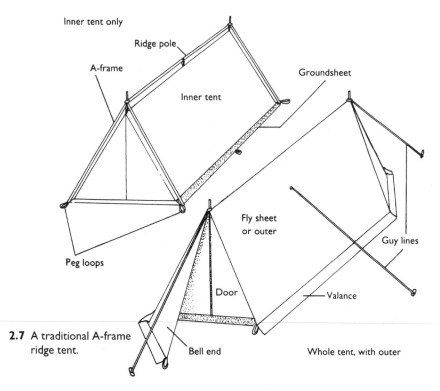

Inner tent only

Ridge pole

A-frame

Groundsheet

Inner tent

Fly sheet
or outer

Guy lines

Peg loops

Door

Valance

2.7 A traditional A-frame
ridge tent.

Bell end

Whole tent, with outer

or three hoops running across the tent. These hoops may vary in size, allowing for head room at the front and tapering at the back. This is a popular design for lightweight tents, but they can be pushed flat by a strong sideways wind and so need careful erecting.

Dome tents   Dome tents (Fig 2.9) are based on the traditional igloo design and can have any number of poles crossing at the centre. They make good base camp or valley tents as they give lots of internal room, but they do not perform well in bad weather. Note that any bell area has to be added to the tent as an extra design feature.

Geodesic tents   This design of tent (Fig 2.10) takes the best features of the tunnel and dome tents, giving a tunnel shape with crossing poles. The tents are very strong and roomy, and they often have sizeable bells at both ends. They will withstand a wind from any

2.8 Tunnel tents.

2.9 Dome tents.

75

direction and will also stand unsupported or pegged, which means that they are suitable for hard or rocky ground. Because of the inherent strength of the geodesic design, manufacturers tend to make this type of tent from stronger, heavier materials for serious mountain use. In addition, they are often fitted with a snow valance and extra guy lines to cope with extreme conditions. These factors, combined with the large number of poles they use, mean that geodesic tents are often heavier than other designs, but versions in lighter materials are becoming available.

Single-skin tents   Single-skin tents are usually made from Gore-tex fabric. Although very light, they do not function as well as a conventional double-skin tent under certain conditions. They are improving all the time, however, and might be worth investigating if you have the money – they are more expensive.

Making a choice

A geodesic tent is a good choice for all-round use, with a hoop tent for occasions where a very light tent is needed that is not going to have to stand up to too much punishment. Your choice should be based on strength, weight, intended use, design features and, in the final analysis, cost.

Strength   How strong do you need it? If strength is a high priority, the A-frame design with its stronger poles has much to recommend it.

Weight   Weight will often be your overriding consideration – either you need a very lightweight tent or you do not. In general, if the tent is to be for two or more people then weight becomes less of a consideration. Be aware, however, that design features such as bell space and strength are often sacrificed for weight.

Intended use   Tents usually have a rating indicating their use, ranging from meadow to expedition tents. This is not only a factor of strength but also includes design features such as guy lines, number

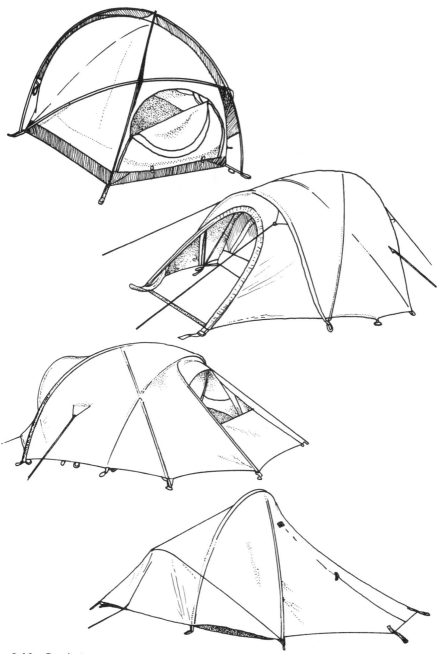

2.10 Geodesic tents.

of pegs needed, height, slope of the top, valance etc. Do not be tempted to go for a tent that greatly exceeds your needs; you will pay for it in both cost and weight. Many tents which are designed or high mountain use suffer from condensation problems that make them unsuitable for valley use.

Care and use of the tent

Despite the strength of modern tents, they still need a degree of looking after and care. They should never be stored wet but should always be shaken out and hung up to air after every use.

When carrying a tents, ensure that it will not get caught or torn: have it inside your rucksack, if possible. In general there is no need to carry the bag that a tent is supplied with. If the tent does get torn, manufacturers usually supply patches which can be glued on with any suitable adhesive. If the repair is in a strategic place or is a large one, the edges should be sealed with a seam sealant.

The obvious place to carry the poles is on the outside of the sack, but be careful of this: modern lightweight flexible poles are not very strong and could be snapped easily. When erecting a tent with lightweight poles, be careful not to bend them more than absolutely essential. Broken poles can usually be repaired on a temporary basis with sleeves provided by the makers.

Erecting the tent

It is always important that you read the manufacturer's instructions and practise with a new tent before you take it out for the first time.

When erecting the tent, check the ground for anything that might damage the groundsheet. Always try to erect the tent with its back into the wind. Pegs are usually designed to be driven in up to the hilt at an angle of about 45 degrees; use skewer types for the inner and outer tents and heavier ones for the guy lines.

As a general rule, if a tent looks good, with no ripples on the fly sheet and the poles up symmetrically when erected, then it is correct. If it looks loose or there are odd pieces flapping, there is something wrong.

Sleeping bag

When you first look at sleeping bags you might wonder how you are going to know which is the right one for you. In fact, the choice is simpler than you might think and you don't need to understand any of the figures thrown at you.

Fillings and ratings

The first choice to make is which filling you want. This is between an artificial filling, usually of 'Hollofil' or something similar, and a natural filling, which will be a combination of down and feathers. Bags with artificial fillings are cheaper and retain their warmth when wet. A down bag can be compressed much smaller and weighs less, but you must take great care that it does not get wet – and it will be expensive.

Many bags will be rated by their seasonal use on a scale of one to five seasons, where a one-season rating is for summer lowland use and a five-season rating is for use in high mountains. The top bags are often referred to as expedition bags.

Construction

You should know a little bit about the construction of sleeping bags. This should not be of the 'sewn-through' type, which would lead to cold spots. Look for a bag which is made in separate compartments, or 'boxes', as this will not only stop cold spots but also prevent the filling from moving around.

Other features

A zip makes getting in and out of the bag so much easier in the confines of a tent. The zip should always have a baffle along the inside of it to protect you from draughts.

Never buy a bag without a substantial hood, and always look for one which has a good shoulder baffle along the top edge to prevent draughts at the neck.

Sleeping mats
Until recently there was little choice of sleeping mats; they were all made of closed cellular foam of differing weights. The only option was whether to go for a full-length mat and comfort or a shorter length to save weight. This has all changed recently with the advent of self-inflating mats, notably the 'Therma-rest'.

Campsites

Factors to look for:

- A site out of the wind, in the lee of hills, woods etc. Be aware that the direction of the wind at the time of your arrival might not be the prevalent one. Think about what would happen to the wind in a storm: will it be funnelled and swirled over a nearby cliff or swirled around a valley? Some wind traps such as high passes are obvious, but others are not easy to spot.

- A site that will not get flooded. Obviously you need a water supply, but watch for streams and rivers which might rise dramatically during the night. Beware also of dips in the ground, which often fill with water during heavy rain, and look out for water run-offs in the hills which might funnel a stream into your site.

- Inherent dangers which might affect the site, such as overhanging loose branches, dry-stone walls in bad repair or scree (talus) slopes. Do not forget cattle, which might be tempted to join you in your sheltered site!

- For comfort, a site which is as flat as possible and free of stones and tree roots. Ten minutes' work on arrival will save a sleepless night, but remember to replace any stones that you moved the next morning.

Choosing a campsite

You cannot always camp wherever you please. It is your responsibility to check the local camping rules and conventions from sources such as tourist offices, national park departments and guidebooks. Once you know that camping is permissible, you can get down to the practicalities of choosing the best site.

The keys to the choice of campsite are wind and water. You need to avoid both, not only at the time when you arrive but also in anticipation in case a storm should blow in during the night.

Rock climbing

With rock climbing, having the right equipment is half the battle. You can climb granite boulders in the California desert or rockfaces on Himalayan peaks at over 7000m (23 000ft) – but you have to match your clothing and equipment to the situation. At one end of the spectrum, you might climb with little more than a pair of shorts and rock boots. At the other, heavily insulated boots and clothing and specialized harnesses might be the order of the day. Most active rock climbers do not operate in an alpine environment, but on individual crags typically between 10m (33ft) and 150m (500ft) in height.

Many people have started rock climbing without any specialized personal equipment, simply using a pair of sports shoes and a direct tie on to the rope, but most climbers will quickly want to acquire the absolute essentials – rock boots, harness and preferably a helmet too.

Rock boots

Climbers on traditional routes or those on long alpine-type ascents might use stiff alpine boots with substantially cleated soles, but the vast majority of active rock climbers will use smooth-soled specialist rock boots.

Legs are very much stronger than arms and one of the first lessons to be learned is that high-quality footwork is essential to make the

2.11 (a) Rock shoe; (b) all-purpose rock boot; (c) rock slipper.

most of your capabilities as a climber. Rock boots (Fig 2.11) provide the crucial link between your foot and the rock and allow you to exploit every opportunity for adhesion that exists.

Rock boots fit very snugly around the foot and will usually have a smooth but high-friction sole of butyl rubber extending for 2.5–5cm (1–2in) over the upper of the boot in what is called a rand. The rand improves the adhesion of the boot when used for foot-jamming in cracks and also, in more gymnastic manoeuvres, allows the heel to be hooked over suitable holds.

Types of boot

The uppers of the boot are usually made from thin suede leather or canvas with laces that extend down close to the toe, although some specialist boots are of slipper construction, rather like a pair of ballet shoes.

Friction boots are soled with soft, high-friction rubber and are deliberately built without excessive stiffness so that they can conform easily to the contours of the rock. This means that they are more difficult to use for 'edging' (using the boot's inner edge) on extremely small holds. In this situation a boot with much more side-to-side stiffness is desirable – an 'edging' boot.

Most modern boots have a toe which is reasonably pointed. If you expect to climb frequently on limestone crags, particularly those with the deep pockets called *gouttes d'eau* in France, a pointed toe that almost allows the big toe to fit into the hold is desirable.

The best all-round choice for the relative beginner is a general boot with sufficient stiffness to allow reasonably comfortable edging. Until you have developed the strength in your feet, the softness of friction boots may present problems. On the most technical climbs, very low-cut boots are used to provide maximum ankle flex, but in general use this style can expose the ankle bones to the rock and, during the descent, to brambles and scree.

The correct fit
Probably the most important aspect of choosing a boot is achieving the correct fit. The best-designed boot in the world is useless if your foot slides about loosely inside it. A well-fitting boot gives a tremendous sensitivity to the contours of the rock and the possibilities of a particular hold. Unfortunately, all boots stretch to a greater or lesser degree in use and so it is difficult at the point of purchase to be sure which size to buy.

Having decided on the broad characteristics of the boot you want to buy, try on several different models before choosing the one that seems to match the shape of your foot. If you buy a boot which is a tight but not quite excruciating fit with bare feet, after a few days' use it will have stretched to a point where it is efficient and acceptably comfortable with very thin socks. If you intend to climb at the highest grades you will be willing to endure considerable pain in order to achieve the most efficient fit, but for climbing at more modest levels on longer climbs, aim for a boot that you do not have to remove every 30 minutes.

Different models of boot stretch to differing degrees and a good climbing shop will be able to advise you on this. Even better, some of them have small sections of climbing wall where you can actually get the feel of how a new boot might perform. If you are able to do this, then pay particular attention to the inside edge of the boot between the big toe and the ball of the foot. This is the part that gets the greatest use and it needs to give you a feeling of confidence in its adhesion to small holds.

Anyone who climbs for a number of years will sooner or later buy a pair of boots which they can hardly bear to wear because they are simply too small – the pair of boots which performs superbly for a couple of days' use on cold, north-facing crags in the Highlands of Scotland will cause agony in the fierce heat of a Californian summer, where your feet will expand much more quickly than the boots. Boulder gullies are not best descended in bare feet!

Soles

Although modern boots give a superb performance on clean, dry rock, they can be lethal unless used with great care on the steep vegetation (particularly dry grass) often encountered during descents. This is a very common cause of accidents and it is all too easy after a difficult ascent to relax concentration during what might appear to be a relatively innocuous descent.

For similar reasons, when starting a climb it is best if the sole of the boot is in a clean condition. Wash any mud off the sole at the end of a day's climbing and, before starting a climb, double-check that the sole is quite literally 'squeaky clean' on its inside edge. Spit and the palm of the hand will do an adequate job, particularly if you avoid standing on damp ground by stepping off a piece of old towel or your empty rucksack. It is crucial to the success of the climb to establish a positive attitude during the first few metres of the route, and slipping from the first holds because the sole of your boot is thinly coated in sheep droppings is not an auspicious start to the climb.

Caring for boots

When you return from climbing, it is worth unpacking your boots and allowing them to dry in a cool, airy place as this undoubtedly extends their life. If the boots have been thoroughly soaked they do tend to shrink, and this can sometimes be used to your advantage with a pair of boots that have stretched more than you would wish.

Harness

It is perfectly possible to tie directly on to the end of the rope by using a knot such as a bowline with a suitable stopper knot. However, a purpose-made harness that takes the weight of the body on the legs and buttocks is not only more comfortable but can also be of life-saving importance. Quite simply, because of the constriction on the diaphragm, a person suspended free (out of contact with the rock) on a simple waist tie will, if unaided, experience so much pain that within three or four minutes they will be unable to help themselves and, shortly afterwards, will lose consciousness and die. It is uncommon for a climber who slips to be totally out of contact with the rock, but it does happen. The investment in a suitable sit-harness or full-body harness (Fig 2.12) can make the difference between a life-threatening crisis and a resolvable, albeit considerable, difficulty.

Sit-harness

A simple climber's belt made from a length of broad and strong nylon webbing with a secure buckle is an improvement on the simple waist tie direct to the rope, but still presents the same

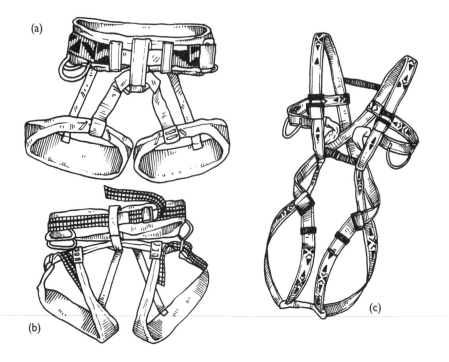

2.12 (a) General-purpose sit-harness; (b) with adjustable leg loops;
(c) Full-body harness.

difficulties to a free-hanging climber. It is strongly recommended that you purchase a sit-harness.

A wide variety of these is available and while almost all will be safe if properly used, it is important to find one that meets your particular requirements. All will be constructed from nylon webbing, which may or may not have some degree of padding and decoration. If you expect to confine your activities mainly to crag climbing, then a simple harness with a buckled waist belt and attached leg loops is likely to be perfectly adequate. If, however, you might be involved in alpine climbing or winter climbing then some degree of adjustment in the leg loops is desirable, to allow for differences in the bulk of your clothing and also for calls of nature on high mountains.

The link between the rope and your harness is crucial and a simple, foolproof system is essential. It is vital to follow the manufacturer's recommendations in buckling the harness and attaching the climbing rope. Most buckles require 'doubling back' and will not hold a fall if this is omitted.

A good harness:

- Allows a direct tie-in of the rope rather than requiring the use of a screwgate karabiner.

- Has a simple and unmistakable buckling system.

- Has a number of equipment loops to allow karabiners and slings to be carried around the waist.

- Has slight padding.

- Is provided with a separate loop built into the system to carry the karabiner for the belay plate.

- Has a loop at the back suitable for holding a chalk bag.

The correct fit

When buying a harness it is important to remember that its prime purpose is to divert the impact of a fall from the vulnerable parts of your body to the stronger regions of your thighs, buttocks and back. For this to happen, the harness design needs to match your particular anatomy. We are all different in the relative shapes and sizes of the parts of our bodies and what can be an extremely comfortable harness for one person can be at best uncomfortable and, at worst, possibly dangerous on another person. Some manufacturers have started to recognize this by bringing out not only different sizes of a harness but also different proportions of the component parts in, for example, a women's version. Most specialist retailers of rock-climbing equipment will allow you to suspend yourself while you literally 'hang about' for a few minutes to find the weak spots of the harness (or, indeed, of your body). Men will probably need little persuasion to ensure that load-bearing pieces of webbing do not threaten the more delicate parts of their anatomy.

Helmet

Whether expert or beginner, anyone who climbs with Outward Bound has to use a helmet. However, go to any popular weekend climbing area and you will see that although helmets are not uncommon the majority of rock climbers will not be using them.

The brain is a particularly vulnerable part of the body and so the protection afforded by a helmet can be valuable both against falling objects and if, in the event of a fall, your head strikes the rock. However, balanced against this are other considerations. For many people, wearing a helmet impedes their sense of balance and there is no doubt that climbers accidentally bang their heads on overhangs much more readily when wearing helmets. Also, helmets can be very uncomfortable, particularly in hot weather.

On some crags loose rock is common, particularly in the areas of easy ground at the cliff top. It is very easy for a passing climber or the rope to dislodge stones. By the time these have fallen some distance they are travelling with considerable momentum and can cause serious injury. The main value of a helmet is in reducing the serious consequences of such impacts. Other crags are very well used and have virtually no loose rock. On these, the hazard is much smaller, although it is always possible that a party climbing above might drop a piece of equipment such as a karabiner, and one can never totally ignore the possibility of rockfall. Most crags are in a state of geological transition, and occasionally massive rockfalls can occur in areas previously considered sound.

Obviously, a helmet provides protection only against small falling stones. It is not the slightest use against the direct impact of large rocks, although it could save your life if you are hit by some of the ricocheted fragments. A word of warning: if you are going to take a break at the bottom of a crag, then choose a spot sheltered from stonefall. If you have a helmet and there is any stonefall danger, then do keep it on.

Each individual must make a choice as to whether to wear a helmet or not. However, it is recommended that people taking up climbing should wear a helmet at all times, not least because the risks of a falling climber hitting the rock are very much greater on easier-angled climbs. When you have more experience and a more informed understanding of the pros and cons, then a proper choice can be made. If you are climbing on difficult overhanging rock with good protection you would be unlikely to bash your head in a fall. Most climbers would leave their helmet off in this situation.

Choosing a helmet
Once you decide to buy a helmet you then, of course, have a choice. The safest helmets are probably the ones constructed of

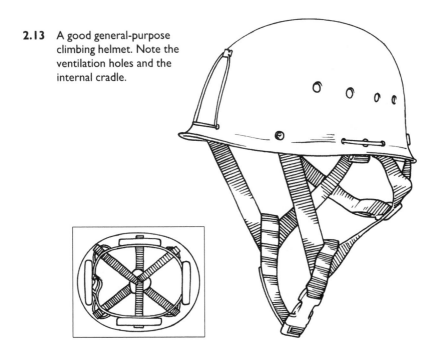

2.13 A good general-purpose climbing helmet. Note the ventilation holes and the internal cradle.

glass reinforced plastic (GRP), perhaps with carbon fibres and a foam lining, but unfortunately they are also the heaviest and the hottest to wear. A plastic-shelled helmet is much lighter and more comfortable; choose a white one in order to minimize the absorption of heat from the sun, and make sure it has some ventilation holes (Fig 2.13).

At least as important as the shell of the helmet is its cradle and harness. An adjustable cradle is useful, but the combined cradle and harness must hold the shell securely on the head. When trying on a helmet, subject it to a glancing blow from the front and back. If, as is depressingly common, the helmet rolls off your head, then you need to adjust its fitting or use a different helmet. A tumbling fall will subject both the helmet and the climber to very considerable impacts and it requires a very securely attached helmet to withstand this.

Clothing

Fortunately, one can climb in almost any type of clothing that allows reasonable freedom of movement. In Britain, people frequently wear stretchy tracksuit trousers and sweatshirts, whereas in the more intense heat of Australia or North America loose-fitting cotton clothing reflects the heat more successfully.

Increasingly, serious climbers wear the kind of heavyweight lycra tights favoured by athletes. These are a powerful statement that you are a 'hard' climber, but are also thought to increase the degree of kinaesthetic feedback from the limbs and thus improve balance and performance. There is also the view that if you dress in a way that makes you feel athletic and dynamic you are more likely to climb in an athletic and dynamic way. So avoid wearing your gardening clothes for that big lead!

Crags that are well sheltered and face the sun can be exceptionally warm; those that are exposed to the wind or are permanently shadowed can be extremely cold. It is a good idea to have enough flexibility of clothing to deal with these extremes, and a lightweight windproof top combined with several thin, insulating layers can be very successful.

Chalk

Athletes' chalk (light magnesium carbonate) started to be used on the hardest climbs in California's Yosemite Valley in the early 1970s. It improves the climber's grip, particularly on smooth, sloping holds, and minimizes the effect of sweaty hands, but you should be aware that there are a number of ethical and environmental considerations relating to the use of chalk and some crags are 'chalk-free zones'. Its use has, however, now spread to all grades except the easiest, and most climbers taking up the sport would buy a chalk bag and chalk either in block or powder form.

Chalk bags

Chalk bags come in various shapes and sizes. Climbers on climbing walls or limestone with small fingerholds might only need a bag large enough to chalk the fingertips, whereas the fierce, hand-jamming cracks of gritstone or granite demand a larger bag so that the hand can be plunged in almost up to the elbow.

The best designs of chalk bag have a wire stiffener to keep the top open, a fleece lining to help the transfer of the chalk to the hand, and an internal sleeve that can be tightened easily to seal the bag. This is useful in preventing chalk escaping while the climber is sitting on stances or scrambling down easy ground.

On water

Sailing

Personal equipment

The dedicated 'gear freak' will march into the biggest outdoor equipment store or chandlery and buy up everything they could possibly need for a whole season of hard sailing. Standing next to them, a lesser mortal with the usual end-of-the-month overdraft might feel that sailing is reserved for those with pots of money who can splash out huge amounts. This really is not the case. Your fellow beginner may be much more comfortable in a drysuit, but if comfort is what you are after then a glass of wine in front of the fire watching television has a lot to be said for it! The drysuit is mentioned as it is one of the most expensive pieces of personal equipment you could buy, not because there is any doubt as to its comfort and value. However, it is by no means essential.

Essential clothing and equipment

Footwear Lightweight training shoes that you do not mind getting wet are usually the best option.

Inner layers Generally, avoid cotton where possible. It is likely that you will get at least a bit damp and cotton tends to stay damp and feel cold. You might be more comfortable in a swimming costume than underpants. Tracksuit bottoms are better if made from artificial fabric rather than the cotton 'jogger' type. In warmer weather long johns, leggings or even shorts might do. On the top half, again avoid cottons if you have the option. Long-sleeved 'thermal' shirts are universally useful across a range of activities.

Mid-layer It is impossible to advise on exactly how much to wear as what you need will depend entirely on the weather, how long you will be out for, the type of boat you are sailing (some are much more energy-sapping than others) and your own ability to retain body heat. Modern fleece tops are much warmer than cotton sweatshirts. Take one with your kit so that you have something warm to put on if you need it. Woollen jumpers can be as warm, but tend to soak up more water and take longer to dry out.

Waterproofs A windproof and preferably waterproof jacket or cagoule will be needed on all but the warmest of days. Ideally it should be not too long, medium weight and have tight-closing wrist and neck seals. You may have something which will do for starting out: what do you normally use when it rains? It may do the job! Waterproof trousers are often useful, too, if only to keep the wind off.

Buoyancy aid   It is *vital* to wear some means of additional flotation while in small boats, and a buoyancy aid is generally accepted as the most appropriate for use in dinghies. It is basically a waistcoat of padded foam, usually secured by a zip and a waist belt. It should fit over your sailing clothing, be quite snug without being too tight, and should not ride up over your head in active use. A whistle is a sensible addition for use in emergencies.

Buoyancy devices are classified as buoyancy aids or life-jackets according to the amount of buoyancy − measured in newtons − that they provide. To qualify as a life-jacket, the device should have

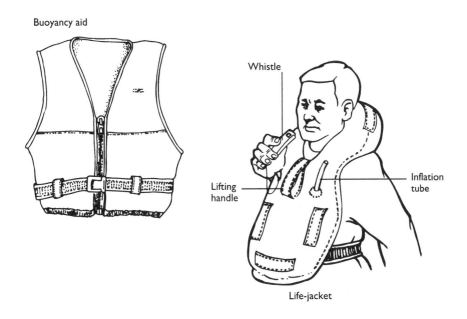

2.14   Buoyancy aid and life-jacket.

at least 150 newtons (15kg/33lb) of buoyancy. Buoyancy aids usually have 50 or 100 newtons (5kg/11lb or 10.5kg/23lb) of buoyancy.

A fully inflated 150 newton life-jacket will keep a person afloat and the right way up even if unconscious. There are two types: those with and those without integral foam in addition to the inflatable section on the front. The type with integral buoyancy tends to be bulky and can be an encumbrance when you are in a dinghy and need to be able to move about freely. When in the water, the bulk of the foam also tends to get in the way when you are trying to swim around the dinghy untangling sheets and organizing the righting. Although less bulky, the type without integral buoyancy is not suited to use for dinghy sailing. It is very bulky when inflated and of no use for short periods in the water.

A 100 newton buoyancy aid does not have enough buoyancy to keep an unconscious wearer afloat the right way up but it does give more support than a 50 newton device, which is only designed to help you stay afloat. Nevertheless, for inshore dinghy sailing where a safety boat is on the water, the most suitable first choice is probably a 50 newton buoyancy aid, which is comfortable to wear and not too bulky.

Hat Much of the body heat is lost through the head, therefore a woolly hat or balaclava does a great deal to keep you warm in cooler conditions.

Helmet This may sound extreme but many courses for beginners offer helmets as standard, particularly for children. They cannot really be described as essential but their use by any beginner should be considered, as a crack across the head by the boom can be very serious. Watersports helmets should fit well and offer protection to the vulnerable areas of forehead and temples.

Spares Do not forget a towel and a full set of warm clothes to change into when you get out.

Upgrading your equipment

This is where you have to start weighing up the priorities. The more sailing you do, the better value decent kit becomes and the more occasion you will have to be glad you bought it. The following list assumes you have something that does the job in each of the essential areas as listed above. The order of priority is based on the assumption that you are sailing a dinghy in which getting wet every now and then is part of the learning process.

Waterproofs Where this appears on your priority list depends on whether you have been able to make do with items you had already and how effective they have been. There is no doubt that a decent set of waterproofs can make a huge difference to your comfort and it is usually worth investing in something appropriate. The one-piece suit is excellent for dinghy sailing and is usually fairly lightweight and comfortable to wear. If you intend to sail larger boats, then a separate set of jacket and trousers may be more versatile. A jacket is generally more expensive than a smock but is easier to get on and a bit more versatile. For dinghy sailing you will not want it too long or heavy, as that would feel restrictive. Salopettes are less likely to start coming down in active use, as trousers with an elasticated waist tend to. This usually happens at a crucial moment when you want to be at your nimblest, such as when dropping the spinnaker or pulling the trolley up the slip at the end of the day with an increasingly eccentric walk on full display to onlookers!

Wetsuit Sailing in wet clothes can get cold and uncomfortable, and a wetsuit can ease this problem on the not-so-sunny days. It will also allow you to enjoy sailing in a greater range of weather conditions. A wetsuit does not keep you dry but works by trapping a layer of water between your body and the suit. Your body heats this up and the wetsuit prevents this warm water from escaping and circulating cooler water around your body.

Wetsuits come in different weights of neoprene and different styles according to what would best suit your purpose. A longjohn covers not just your legs but comes up to your chest and over your shoulders. The arms are not covered, but this allows more freedom of movement and you are less likely to overheat when working hard. A longjohn is an extremely versatile piece of equipment which can be used for a variety of activities, particularly when you want to be able to move freely and do not expect to be fully immersed frequently or for long periods. It can be worn with a T-shirt and fleece underneath if necessary, and with a decent cagoule over the top you should be warm enough in most dinghy-sailing conditions. It can be added to with a wetsuit jacket or bolero top, which provides considerable extra warmth but does tend to restrict movement somewhat. The steamer or one-piece suit is useful for activities where you expect to be in the water more frequently but is less versatile than the longjohn and bolero.

Whatever wetsuit you choose be sure to select one that fits snugly, as too much room inside will make you cold (due to too much circulation of water) and uncomfortable.

Footwear Wetsuit socks are shaped from neoprene and help to avoid that soggy feeling that goes with having wet feet for a while. They have no sole and must be worn inside your wet training shoes or perhaps with a pair of plastic beach shoes. Wetsuit boots have a sole on them, so can be worn on their own. Both of these are more suitable than wellington boots for sailing dinghies, as you will often be beach launching and needing to stand in water deeper than wellies. Wellies can also encumber you in the water, so the use of them is best kept for sailing larger boats, keelboats and (when you are sure you will not be capsizing) dinghies kept on moorings. A good alternative to these is dinghy boots, which are short, snug, laced boots that cannot fill up with a large amount of water.

Gloves A suitable pair of gloves not only keeps your hands warm but helps to protect them from the rigours of rope handling. They should be tight fitting with a good grip and wear-resistant palms. Full-fingered ones are the warmest, while those with cut-away fingers allow for easier rope handling.

Drysuit This is a fully waterproof suit, either in one piece or sealed at the waist, with tight closing seals at wrists and neck. Some have ankle seals, others enclose the feet as well. With a drysuit you can vary the amount of clothing you wear underneath to achieve a comfortable temperature. It must be looked after carefully by rinsing in fresh water after use and dusting with talcum powder after a thorough drying.

Knife Once you decide that sailing is for you, then you should equip yourself with a stainless steel sailing knife. This has a key for undoing shackles and a sharp blade. Ropes surround the sailor and on occasions it is important to be able to cut one free.

Canoeing

Buoyancy aid
Canoeing is a safe sport with very few accidents; however, people do drown even on sheltered water. Some of these would have had a better chance of survival if they had been wearing some form of personal buoyancy. No matter what canoe you choose to go out in, you should wear a BCU-approved buoyancy aid, a British Standards' Institute life-jacket, or, in Europe, one which conforms to the Communité Européenne (CE) regulations.

There are many different types of buoyancy aids and life-jackets and the way to determine which is the best kind for you is to look at what you will be using it for. For example, a compact, manually inflatable life-jacket suitable for use in offshore sailing boats is not suitable for canoeing, because this type of life-jacket has neither built-in inherent buoyancy nor all-round upper-body protection, which also gives extra thermal insulation. Refer to the section on buoyancy aids on pages 93–4 for further information.

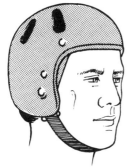

The most common areas for injury are the forehead, temples and nose. These need to be well protected

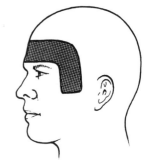

Poorly fitting helmet: temples and forehead are completely exposed. The helmet cradle is either not adjusted properly or the helmet is too small

Well-fitting helmet: the helmet projects forwards enough so that it helps to protect the bridge of the nose

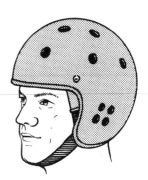

2.15 A helmet that fits correctly is important.

Helmet

For moving water and surf, a helmet is essential. It is not necessary for flat water, such as lakes and estuaries. If you buy one, make sure that it fits well and protects your forehead and temples, which are where most injuries occur.

Clothing

For the beginner, very little specialist clothing is needed. On a sunny, windless day you may get away with shorts, but British weather is not known for its constant sunshine! Canoeing is generally accepted as a wet sport, so some form of insulation is important. Wool is a good insulator when wet, but cotton is not.

Canoe cagoule

Waterproof trousers

Wetsuit boots

Wetsuit

Wetsuit socks

2.16 Canoe clothing.

Several thin layers have more insulating properties than one thick one. Ensure that your trousers will not fall down around your knees and inhibit your swimming ability if you capsize. An old anorak or cagoule will help keep the wind off and should be worn over the layers of wool. For footwear, well-fitting, lace-up shoes such as old trainers are ideal. Large boots or wellingtons are not suitable, as they fill with water and either fall off or are more likely to trap your feet in white water.

As a general guide, old clothing should have good insulation and retain body warmth when wet; it should also be quick to dry and comfortable to wear. Wool and most artificial fibres fit into these categories, but cotton does not.

For more specialist clothing, look in canoeing magazines or visit watersports shops to get an idea of the variety available and the cost. If you are interested, the following are the sorts of things you could enquire about.

Canoe cagoule

Otherwise known as a 'canoe cag', this is a windproof layer for the upper body. It needs to have a loose cut around the shoulders to allow for ease of movement and should be as waterproof as possible. A good, durable material is 170g (6oz) weight nylon with neoprene proofing inside.

Wetsuit

These come in a variety of thicknesses, but 3mm (⅛in) is a good thickness for most conditions. It is better to have the sleeveless variety, known as a longjohn (see pages 95–6), otherwise your arms will be too restricted. Wetsuits only work when they are wet (see also pages 95–6) and if they are a snug fit. You will still need to wear a thin woollen jumper or lightweight, fibre-pile jacket underneath the wetsuit to keep your arms warm. Again, two or three thin layers are better than one thick layer.

When do you need to wear a wetsuit? There is no absolute rule, but if you think you will be swimming a lot or getting soaked by waves and need some extra insulation or protection for your body from scrapes and bruising, then it is a good idea to wear a wetsuit. A wetsuit on its own, however, is not windproof, so you will still need to wear a windproof layer over the top.

Wetsuit boots and socks

These are made of neoprene, the same material as wetsuits. The wetsuit boots have hard soles whereas the wetsuit socks do not, so you need to wear suitable footwear over the socks to give more protection to your feet. Both wetsuit boots and socks are avid collectors of old cheese-like aromas – rinsing them regularly with soap powder or disinfectant helps keep this under control. This is not very practical on a trip, however.

Paddle mitts

These are good in cold or windy weather. They are mitts that fit on to the shaft of the paddle so that you can slip your hands into them and still keep in direct contact with the paddle. They can also be lined with an insulating material for extra warmth – fibre-pile lining is best for cold conditions.

3

Navigation

Knowing where you are on the surface of the planet is a vital skill in the outdoors. When sailing across the Pacific there are occasions when knowing your position to within one nautical mile will be sufficient; when finding a safe descent ridge from a mountain in full white-out conditions, an accuracy of plus or minus 10m (33ft) is sometimes called for; on a rock climb, being off line by a couple of metres will often increase the difficulties dramatically.

Basic navigation skills:

- True north, magnetic north, grid north.
- Reading contour patterns and conventional map signs.
- Scales.
- Transferring bearings from map to ground and vice versa.
- Measuring distance by timing (Naismith's Rule) and pacing.

It is useful to distinguish between *navigation* and *route-finding*. Navigation aims to determine and monitor your position on a map or chart, whereas route-finding is concerned with determining an efficient and feasible route through the terrain with which you are confronted: you may be able to identify your map position on a steep, rocky hillside with some accuracy, but you also need route-finding skills to thread a route towards your destination between the complex outcrops of rock. Several trans-ocean sailors have graphically described how difficult it is to make the transition from offshore navigation to difficult pilotage (the nautical equivalent of route-finding) in a crowded harbour at their port of arrival. Good route-finding is most solidly built on accumulated experience.

In this chapter we concentrate on the strategy and tactics of practical navigation and assume that the reader already has a grounding in the basic concepts and techniques of navigation (for further information, consult the *Map and Compass Handbook* in this series). These would include the basic skills listed opposite.

On land

Fixing your position on a line feature

This is a useful technique when travelling, as one often is, along a linear feature such as a track, stream, bank of a large lake, ridge line or line of crags.

John Hinde, author of the *Map and Compass Handbook*, and two friends were on a winter expedition from Corriechoille, Spean Bridge to Lairig Leacach Bothy. Their experience illustrates the technique.

'We knew basically where we were, climbing south-east up the track. But our packs were heavy (we had overnight camping gear as well as ski-mountaineering equipment) and we wanted to know our exact location on the track. (What we really wanted to know was how much longer we would have to suffer beneath those packs.) So I took a bearing on the swell of the summit of Cruach Innse. Once I had an angle between a line running north and a line leading to a landmark, I knew my position had to be along the line of the angle that passed through the apparent summit. So I placed one long edge of the baseplate on the apparent summit swell and rotated the whole compass, without turning the capsule in relation to the baseplate, until the north/south lines ran north and south, with the direction-of-travel arrow pointing at the landmark. Now I knew I had to be along the line of position defined by that long edge of the baseplate. Since I also knew I was on the track, I had to be at the intersection of my line of position and the track (Fig 3.1). If the edge of the baseplate hadn't reached from the summit to the trail, I would have needed a ruler or pencil to extend it.'

You don't need to be on a track to use this technique: any kind of prominent, linear terrain feature will do. In all cases, the best accuracy comes from picking a landmark at right angles to the terrain feature you are following.

If you can identify two landmarks, you don't even need to be following a terrain feature. Simply take a bearing off one, and pencil in your line of position on the map. Then take a bearing off the second, and pencil in that line of position. Your location is the intersection of the two lines. Fig 3.2 shows you how to do this. If

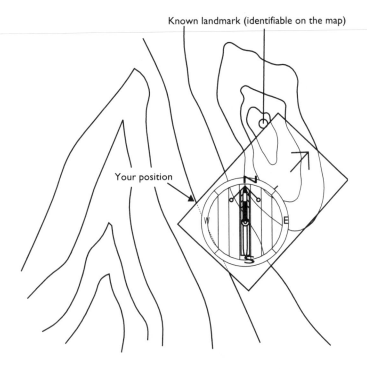

Known landmark (identifiable on the map)

Your position

3.1 Determining your position along a track by measuring a bearing to a landmark identifiable on the map.

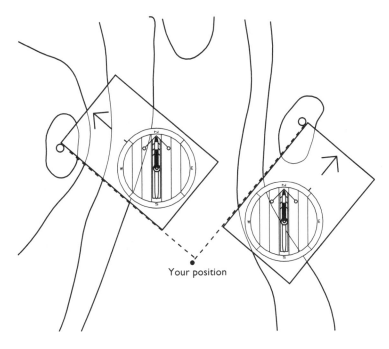

Your position

3.2 Determining your position by measuring bearings to two landmarks identifiable on the map.

you can take a bearing off a third landmark and pencil in that line of position, so much the better. Your true position should lie somewhere inside the triangle formed by the three lines of position.

Once you have identified your location with lines of position, perform a 'reality check'. If the lines cross at a stream, and you are standing on a ridge, something is wrong. John Hinde:

'After we identified our position along the trail to the bothy, we took a close look at the map. We had just walked up a rising section of track and gained a nearly level stretch. Our line of position from the summit crossed the track right where the contours became widely spaced – in other words, where the terrain suddenly flattened out. Our location as determined by a line of position checked with the other information we had about the terrain.'

Whenever you use map and compass together, it is a good idea to perform that kind of reality check on the results, the key to which is being able to visualize terrain from looking at a map.

Navigating round

Basic navigation conveniently ignores the fact that the best route is rarely in a dead straight line, and this is particularly so in the winter months, when cornices (overhanging eaves on the lee sides of ridges formed by the wind-saltation of snow particles) decorate ridges and plateau edges.

Planning winter walks, especially over the high plateaux, you may have to make allowances for avoiding snow cornices. For example, the plateau of Beinn a' Chaorainn above Glen Spean is a fairly serious place because the gentle curves of the corries marked on the map lure people into trying to follow straight-line bearings

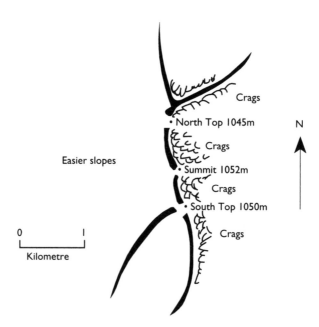

3.3 The ridges of Beinn a'Chaorainn.

106

from tops to summit, or vice versa (Fig 3.3). There are easy slopes to the west, but all the east face is steep and craggy. During the last few years there have been eight or nine separate instances of unroped walkers falling through cornices in poor visibility in this area. Even though in most cases there were no serious injuries, very steep falls of 200m (650ft), halted in soft snow halfway down the cliffs, have caused considerable retrieval problems for the rescuers.

One method of avoiding becoming a rescue statistic is to 'box' the corrie, as shown in Fig 3.4. If the South Top has been gained from Roughburn Bothy on the shore of Loch Laggan, and the visibility is poor, the first thing for the party to do is to rope up. Allow the first person plenty of rope, with the others following in single file tied within a few metres of each other. From your route plan you will know the straight-line bearing from the South Top to Beinn

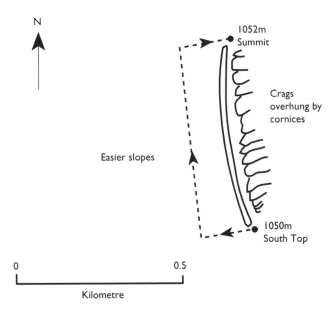

3.4 'Boxing' the corrie.

a'Chaorainn summit. It is probably about zero or 360 degrees magnetic. Find out the exact measurement yourself from the map. Add 270 degrees to the bearing and follow the course at a right angle, pacing out a safe distance – at least 150m (490ft) – from the South Top. The number of double paces must be noted accurately. At the corner of your 'box' add 90 degrees and turn right on to your new course. Now pace out the exact straight-line distance (from your route card) which you have measured from the South Top to the summit. At the second corner add 90 degrees and turn right again.

Now we come to the real 'nitty-gritty'. In theory the summit is exactly 150m (490ft) ahead on the new course, but the leader may be a bit apprehensive approaching the cornice. It is a wise precaution to have a second rope tied to one of the anchor people and loosely held by the leader. In a white-out the rope can be thrown out ahead. If it can be seen lying level on the snow, at least you can see there is something in front.

The latest OS maps mark the spot height of the Centre Peak of Beinn a'Chaorainn as 1049m and the spot height is surrounded by a 1050m contour line. This is impossible, of course, and the Ordnance Survey have admitted that the contour line is incorrect, but that the height of Beinn a'Chaorainn is in fact 1049m. Presumably, therefore, the new 'Munro' will now be the South Top at 1050m. The South Top is much easier to find in poor visibilty than the Centre Top; this may reduce the number of people walking through the cornice.

If the cornice edge can be vaguely distinguished – a variation of pale greys rather than a colour difference – it may be possible to use the edge of the plateau as a 'handrail' (see page 112) to get from one top to another. Movement will be very cautious, and the rope must be kept very tight – absolutely at right angles to the line of the cornice. You must be roped if close to an uncertain cornice, and at all costs avoid moving in single file *parallel* to the edge: if the cornice collapses you may all go down with it.

When theory meets the real world

John Hinde was leading a party of seven hill-walking from a camp near Steall Ruins. For the summit of Ben Nevis, the weather was not too bad. It was snowing, but the breeze was only about 10 knots (18kph/11mph) from the south-west. There was a lot of snow lying but it was on a firm base, well consolidated. Everybody had proved reasonably fit, and although they had ascended through cloud for the final 500m (1640ft) they attained the summit in a little over three hours.

Possibly the most difficult navigation in Britain is to navigate off the high plateaux, such as Nevis, Ben Alder and the Cairngorms, in winter. Great accuracy is required when the conditions make it harder to be precise and there are numerous instances of people falling though cornices.

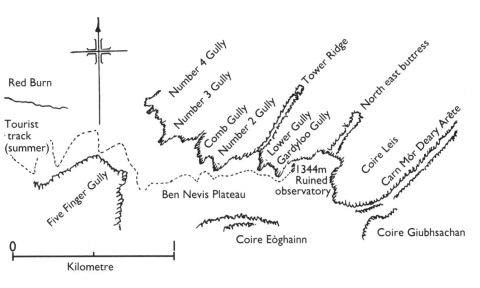

3.5 Ben Nevis.

'There was more snow than I thought, and the cloud was more dense. We were in a white-out. What were we to do? Follow the path? Which path? All traces were buried under 4m (13ft) of snow. Retrace our steps? Our footprints had been wiped out in just five minutes. Follow the cairns? Which cairns? Only the corrugated refuge which at that time topped the tower of the observatory ruins could be seen. The large Peace Cairn and even the triangulation pillar on its 3m (10ft) plinth were nowhere to be seen.

The problem was how to navigate down the Tourist Track. Most of the edge was corniced, with some of the feathery edges sticking out 10m (33ft) over 500m (1640ft) drops. I did not wish to go too close to them.

We needed to hit the zig-zags descending the West Flank and then we would be safe, but the tops of four gullies – Gardyloo, Tower, Number 2 and Comb Gully – lay across the direct bearing, all on the north edge of the plateau. A dog-leg course from the summit was needed. The first bearing south-west for exactly 150m (490ft) would ensure that we did not plummet through the cornices of Gardyloo or Tower Gullies. The second had to be very accurate (I made it 282 degrees grid + 6 degrees west variation = 288 degrees magnetic) because the plateau narrowed about 800m (2600ft) ahead, with Number 3 Gully to the north (right) and Five Finger Gully to the left.

The mountain has a history of people in a similar predicament just heading south. Some get away with it and survivors have said they went south because they knew the big crags were to the north and east. Unfortunately there are also crags of over 200m (650ft) just to the south at the head of Coire Eoghainn.

It was easy leaving the summit. I just set my compass at 231 degrees (225 grid + 6 degrees west variation) from just east of the Observatory Ruin, allowing a little margin for error, and boldly paced out 98 double paces. I knew my natural step over level ground was 65 double paces for 100m (330ft); I had practised it so many times over accurately measured distances.

Then we roped up. The other six tied close together, within 3m (10ft) of one another. I used all the rest of the rope to be way out in front. I wanted to ensure that if anybody fell through a cornice it would be only one of us. Also I needed the separation to concentrate on the navigation. My companions probably wondered why I took so much trouble. It was much easier to follow, as they could see me ahead. I could see nothing but whiteness – the snowfield, the falling flakes and the mist all merged into a blind world of white. I asked the others to do essential tasks. They all had to maintain strict single file, one counting the double paces up to each 100m (330ft) covered, another noting and shouting out the number of hundreds. One person with a stop-watch volunteered to do accurate timing. 'Tail-end-Charlie', on a bit more rope than the others, kept stopping to check the bearing, shouting any corrections.

It was serious stuff. I walked much more slowly than usual, with many pauses, my eyes wide to try and penetrate the void, head sweeping from side to side. I had to try and remember to keep my compass away from the head of my ice-axe, my karabiners, my watch, my camera...

After nearly 500m (1640ft) of nervous tension, 15 minutes of my hesitating grope, I spotted with instant relief a slight shadow hard across to my right, almost behind me. I recognized the shape of Number 2 Gully, with snow fronds of unbelievable delicacy reaching outwards. We still had to clear the top of Five Finger Gully, but that was not so nasty, and probably uncorniced. Now I had a fix, and a much wider angle of error could be tolerated. My second thoughts were of fear and disgust. I had come far too close to the top of Number 2, and I realized I should have made the first leg longer to ensure clearing it.'

Aiming off and handrails

The technique of 'aiming off' introduces a deliberate error in your compass bearing to a point on a line feature, so that when you intersect the feature you know which way to turn. This saves time and anxiety. Imagine that you need to follow a bearing through the woods back to a road where you parked your car. It is impossible to follow a bearing with complete accuracy. If you miss by even a couple of hundred metres, your car may be hidden by a bend in the road and you won't know which way to turn. So, instead of aiming directly for the car, set your course about 10 degrees off. Then, when you hit the road, you know which way to turn (Fig 3.6).

3.6 'Aiming off' to a linear feature.

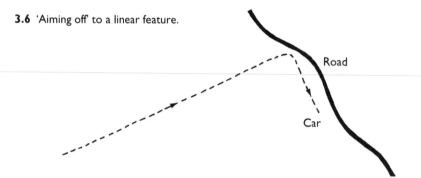

The same principle applies in other situations: finding a bridge or ford across a river, a snow bridge across a lengthy crevasse, a camp you have placed along the shore of a large lake. Road, creek, crevasse and lake shore are all 'catching features': they tell you unmistakably that it is time to change course. Once you have made the turn, they can be considered as 'handrails'. You can follow them without further reference to your map or compass. Thinking about those two concepts can often make your route-finding easier. Instead of heading cross-country for several kilometres, navigating through thick woods with a compass, it may well be easier to walk an extra 500m (¼ mile) to a stream or lakeshore that runs parallel to your course and serves as a handrail. It will almost certainly be easier to walk that far to a track than to beat through a plantation. Then look for a catching feature to tell you when to resume your original course. It might be a prominent side stream, or a particular bearing on a prominent peak that you can see from the handrail.

Attack points

If you are looking for a needle in a haystack, first find the haystack! An attack point is a prominent or easily located feature from which a short bearing or a handrail will lead to a more subtle destination. Your tactics are then directed towards finding the attack point and then making the hopefully simple journey to your real destination.

Check features

'Check features' are anything which can be mentally ticked off as you pass them. They are the key to keeping track of where you are on the map. So, on a long leg of navigation on a single compass bearing it is useful to have a number of checks in mind. Fig 3.7 shows an example of a leg where check features and an attack point can be used to lead to a rather indefinite bend in a wall.

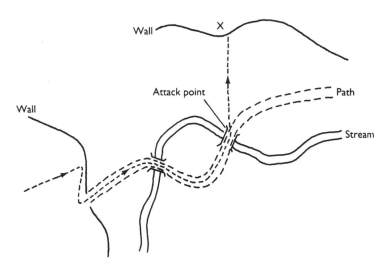

3.7 Using features to break down a complex leg.

Example of check features:

- My first 10 minutes should be descending uniformly on a gentle east-facing slope.
- After 10 minutes I cross a stream running north–south.
- The slope then begins to rise and, visibility permitting, a large crag may appear on the left.
- After 25 minutes I will pass close to a forest corner and it is then only 200m (215yd) to my objective.

Slope aspect

One of the most valuable pieces of information available to the navigator is the slope aspect or, in simpler language, which way the

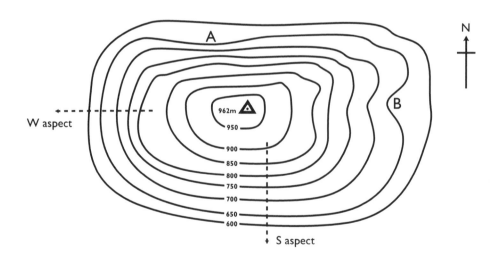

3.8 Slope aspect. If you are on a steep slope of a N aspect you must be at A. If, as you contour in a clockwise direction, the aspect changes rapidly from SE to NW, then you must be at B.

slope faces. Imagine standing on the north slope of a conical hill and then traversing along a contour line right around the hill, walking east to begin. As you walk, the slope aspect will initially be northerly, then north-easterly, then easterly, south-easterly, southerly and so on. The aspect can be read from the map as the bearing of a line cutting the contour lines downhill at a right angle. In the absence of other concrete ground features, you can use the slope aspect to determine your position on your journey around the hill. When combined with an estimate of slope angle from the spacing of contours, a very accurate fix can be provided.

Bad weather and night navigation

There are no additional techniques for navigating in conditions of bad visibility. It is simply a question of practising what you already know and refining it to a higher level. However, there are some useful tips to follow.

In bad weather and at night:

- Concentrate hard and double-check.

- At night use a torch as little as possible – it is often possible to see much more than you think.

- Have a second person checking that you are walking accurately on a bearing – in extreme conditions use leapfrogging.

- Expect to travel much more slowly.

- Do not neglect the well-being of the group – easily done when all your attention is on the map.

- Use a back marker.

Relocation

At some stage in your walking career you are going to get lost – everyone does. This is nowhere near as bad as it might at first seem; indeed, it is usually a question of not knowing exactly where you are rather than being completely lost. The following sequence of actions will usually help you to relocate.

To relocate:

1. Admit you have made an error – the sooner the better.

2. Decide when you were last certain of your position.

3. Using your normal rate of travel and the time elapsed, draw a circle on the map around your last known position to show the furthest you could have travelled.

4. You are almost certainly inside the circle, so now start to narrow down the area of uncertainty even more.

5. Does the slope aspect vary throughout the circle? If so, match the slope aspect and angle of where you are to that on the map: very different aspects and angles can be eliminated.

6. Are there any obvious ground features? If so, match them.

7. From your now narrow circle of uncertainty, plot a compass bearing to a collecting feature (an unmissable line feature) that can then be followed to a fixed location. This may not be in your desired direction of travel, but as long as this does not unduly tire the party your priority at the moment is to fix your position before resuming your journey.

8. Check all your logic, then execute your plan.

Self-deception

Particularly when an admission that you are unsure of your position will result in a loss of face, people can make and compound the most astonishing errors. Take the example of a walker on an expedition to northern Norway, who persuaded himself that he had fixed his position by using a lake that was marked prominently on the map and just visible through swirling mist. All the other map information seemed to fit in with this deduction and he conveniently overlooked the fact that the map showed clearly that he should be on a slope dropping away to the north, whereas he actually stood on one of the opposite aspect. Fortunately, just before he committed himself (and his party) to a dangerously incorrect descent, the mist lifted sufficiently to reveal not a large lake 1000m (3250ft) below them, but a small snowfield that was 10 times nearer.

When all else fails

If you are absolutely convinced that you cannot determine your location, and if you notified someone as to where you were going and when you expected to be back, your best bet is to stay put and wait for searchers to find you.

Nearly all wild areas in Britain are within the response area of a search-and-rescue organization. You will make their job easier if you can move to a nearby location that is easily visible from the air and the surrounding terrain – a ridgetop or some kind of clearing. Brightly coloured gear is easier to spot, or perhaps an orange survival bag held down with rocks. In mist, a rope fully stretched between cairns would be easier to find than persons lying asleep, or worse.

Remember the mountain distress signal: six long whistle blasts, shouts, or torch flashes followed by a one-minute silence, repeated on and on. Keep blowing, shouting or flashing after you think the rescuers have found you, because they will be using your signals as homing bearings. These days, people have been found using mobile phones, but that is something else. Such phones do not work in about 80 per cent of the terrain where you may get lost, but coverage will doubtless improve.

Do not underestimate how serious a bivouac can be, particularly in winter. It is far, far better not to get lost in the first place.

Rock climbing

On rock, usually what is required is a combination of navigation and route-finding. Route-finding is a difficult skill to acquire and is best learnt if you apply careful concentration to finding the best route through a complex area of broken, craggy ground. After a while, you will get the hang of linking together ramps, ledge systems and lines of weakness, but until you are fully confident, take care that you can always retrace your steps.

Rock climbers have often come to grief during the descent from a climb. This is usually down 'easier' ground to the side of the cliff, but such descents can often be very tricky. Before starting a climb, check with the guidebook that you know how to descend and do a visual reconnaissance of the way down. Often, the obvious way is not the best.

When route-finding on broken ground, it is common to look upwards and see the rocky outcrops clearly but not the ledges. This means that things often (but not always) look steeper and more difficult than they actually are. Conversely, when looking down your eye picks up the ledges and misses the intervening crags, so things look much easier than they really are. This can be extremely dangerous and only experience will allow you to judge how difficult such ground is going to be. If in doubt, retrace your steps and try elsewhere. Often, by traversing, you will eventually reach relatively easy ground.

Using the individual route descriptions accurately does require experience. Also, it will take a while to develop 'rock intelligence' and a feeling for the natural lines of weakness on a piece of rock and how to match these to the route description.

Some guidebooks have very detailed descriptions of how to find a cliff, with three-dimensional sketches of the approach terrain. Others unhelpfully assume that anyone who is not totally incompetent will obviously know where the crag is situated. If you are new to an area it is almost always worth investing in a map with a scale of 1:25 000 or 1:50 000, and many guidebooks recommend particular sheets of the map.

On water

Navigating accurately in a small boat at sea must be one of the most demanding activities there is. It has all the complications of bad-weather land navigation but with added complexities.

Difficulties of sea navigation:

- Tidal streams will offset the boat from its anticipated position and direction.

- The navigator must allow for underwater obstacles such as sandbanks or rocks and the differing depths of changing tides.

- In bad weather, complex navigation must be undertaken on a wet, pitching platform.

- The state of the sea will vary enormously with changing winds and tidal streams.

A comprehensive description of small-boat navigation is beyond the scope of this book, but the following sections outline some of the main areas to be understood for inshore, coastal navigation.

Charts and pilotage

Part of your preparation for a day sail will be to make sure you have a good knowledge of the area you are planning to sail in. A large-scale chart provides an ideal source of information about the areas of shallows, dangers, navigation marks and other features. Standard charts are expensive, however, and on a small boat the size of some can make them difficult to use; small-craft versions are also available which are folded into a more manageable size and contain navigational information printed on the reverse. If you are buying charts, check to see which types best cover the area you sail in.

For cruises away from familiar waters charts become essential, but for the purposes of dinghy day sailing in familiar and straightforward waters it is possible to manage without one. The information they contain is nevertheless very important and looking at a chart of your intended sailing area should hold no surprises. Look carefully at the area you are going into and check for dangers such as rocks and shallows, building a picture of where they are. Charts are interesting to look at and so are often found on the walls of bars, marina offices, chandlery shops and sailing clubs. You may wish to make some notes in a form you will be able to understand and refer to – a notebook of waterproof paper is handy for jotting down tides and other information. You could also annotate maps with all the necessary information, or write information on white acrylic boards using waterproof felt pen or chinagraph pencil.

Scale and distance

The first consideration on a chart is probably the scale and this varies from chart to chart. A large-scale chart shows a fairly small area in large detail, an example being a scale of 1:25 000. This means that 1cm on the chart represents 25 000cm (250m) of actual distance (or that 1in = 25 000in, ie 694yd). Charts can come at even larger scales and 1:20 000 or 1:12 500 are also fairly common. Large-scale charts usually have a scale drawn on them showing the length of a nautical mile split into tenths that are called cables (Fig 3.9).

As well as the scale line, you can also judge distance on a chart by measuring it off the latitude marks up the side of the chart (Fig 3.10). These mark the latitude in degrees and minutes, and as one minute of latitude is a nautical mile this is the usual method of measuring distances on a chart. You may come across charts that do not have a separate scale line, in which case the latitude scale is used. If you progress to longer-distance cruising and use smaller-scale

3.9 Some chart projections allow the inclusion of a scale line.

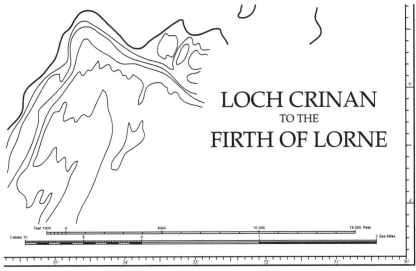

DEPTH ɪɴ METRES

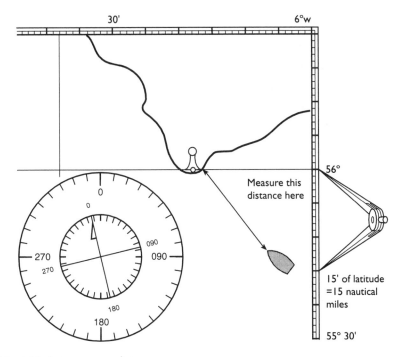

3.10 Using latitude to measure distance.

charts, you will find that the projection can cause a difference in the latitude scale from one part of the chart to another. For this reason, it is necessary to measure your distance from the latitude scale to the side of your position. This is a good habit to get into even if your chart only covers a distance of a few miles from top to bottom.

Chart datum

Once you have got an idea of the scale of the chart you are looking at, then take a look at some of the detail. It provides a wealth of information and one of the most obvious is the depth of water. In tidal waters this changes, of course, and so the depths indicated relate to a specific level of tide that is called 'chart datum'. This can be taken to be a low level, below which the tide rarely falls, so

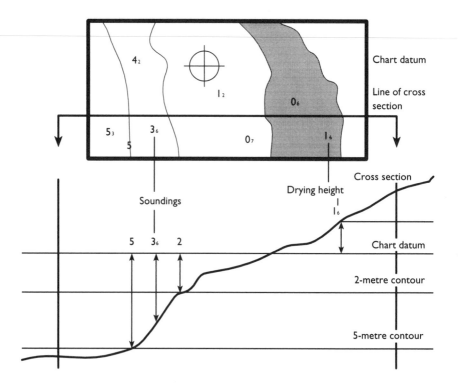

3.11 Chart soundings.

generally there is at least the depth of water indicated by the 'soundings', which are given in metres and dotted around the chart (Fig 3.11). Certain lines of equal depth are joined together to produce depth contours. These vary according to the scale of the chart but typically might be at chart datum, 2m, 5m and 10m. The shallower soundings are in tenths of a metre, so 25 would be 2.5m. The edge of the land is the mean spring high-water mark and the area between this and chart datum, like a beach which covers and uncovers with different tides, is called a drying area. Soundings here are measured above chart datum and called 'drying heights', denoted by an underline 1̲3̲.

Dangers

The chart is full of other information, showing features both at sea and on the land which are useful to the sailor. Dangers are probably the most important, and Fig 3.12 shows the most common ways in which rocks are indicated. Most charts have a key to their symbols printed on the reverse; others – such as UK Admiralty Charts – have a separate booklet that provides the key.

Rock which does not cover. Numbers refer to height above the mean high water springs.

Rock with a drying height above chart datum.

Rock awash at the level of the chart datum.

Rocks or ledges covered by less than 2m of water at chart datum or those considered to be dangerous to surface navigation.

3.12 Some charted dangers.

The dangers in your area may well be marked by buoys, so get to know the buoys and markers and make sure you know which side of the danger they are. In Europe the colours and shapes all conform to the IALA system, which tells you where the safe water is in relation to the buoy. If you want to sail into new areas you will need to learn this system, but for now you can just get familiar with the buoys in your area. Buoys mark the main channels for larger vessels, so are often marking something that just is not a danger to a shoal draft boat like a dinghy. Check the detail on a chart and if in any doubt keep well clear.

On the other hand, you may be sailing closer to unseen dangers that are not marked by a buoy or beacon and you will have to avoid them by using other means. The simplest is by remembering them in relation to features ashore such as a building or a particular section of coastline. You could remember that a rock lies 'about two cables offshore of the chimney', but this can be a little vague and it can be hard to judge distance across the water. It is much more accurate to use a couple of features on the shore to make a line that you avoid crossing. This is called a 'transit' and can be printed on the chart or in pilot books, or you can figure them out for yourself (Fig 3.13). Transits provide the quickest and most

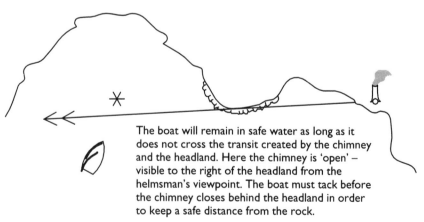

The boat will remain in safe water as long as it does not cross the transit created by the chimney and the headland. Here the chimney is 'open' – visible to the right of the headland from the helmsman's viewpoint. The boat must tack before the chimney closes behind the headland in order to keep a safe distance from the rock.

3.13 Transits.

accurate aids to the pilotage necessary to keep your boat in safe water. It is often necessary to combine more than one transit to use them to best effect.

Tides

The main difference between inland and coastal sailing is the tide and how it can affect just about everything you do. If you are heading for tidal water then you must be able to look up the tide and work out when you can launch, where you can go, how fast you might go and also where you should avoid.

Tides are caused by the gravitational pull of the moon and the sun and their effect on the earth in conjunction with the earth's rotation. When the moon, sun and earth are all in line they cause the larger spring tides; when the sun and moon are offset then smaller neap tides occur (this is illustrated in Fig 3.14). It takes about 28 days for

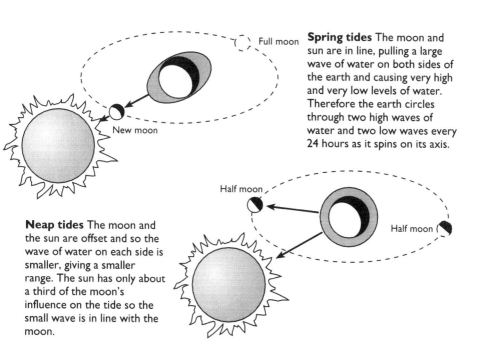

Full moon

Spring tides The moon and sun are in line, pulling a large wave of water on both sides of the earth and causing very high and very low levels of water. Therefore the earth circles through two high waves of water and two low waves every 24 hours as it spins on its axis.

New moon

Half moon

Half moon

Neap tides The moon and the sun are offset and so the wave of water on each side is smaller, giving a smaller range. The sun has only about a third of the moon's influence on the tide so the small wave is in line with the moon.

3.14 The moon's cycle.

the moon to orbit the earth, so there are about seven days between each of these different phases of the tides.

Tidal information

Tide times can be looked up in almanacs, local papers or booklets which are usually available in chandler's shops, bookshops and newsagents. The way this information is laid out is normally as follows or similar:

0009	0.6
0609	4.3
1235	0.6
1826	4.1

Here the times are in 24-hour clock and the heights are in metres. You need to know whether the time given is local time or if you have to correct it for the relevant zone or for seasonal time changes. Often tide tables mark the days on which the moon is full or new, usually denoted by a circle for a full moon and a solid spot for a new moon. This is useful information, as you will see that the spring tides follow these moon phases by about a couple of days. The above example shows a spring tide for Oban and has a morning range of 3.7m (12ft). A neap range can be as little as 1m (3ft) in Oban. It is worth examining the tables for your area to see what your average spring and neap ranges are.

Tidal information is specific to a place and will need to be adjusted if you are any distance away. The adjustments to be made to these standard port times and heights are usually listed for a variety of other local places as well. It must also be remembered that these are predictions and that strong wind conditions and unusual weather patterns can affect them. For your purposes initially this approximate information is probably sufficient, but take local advice from other sailors or fishermen as to the quirks of the tide in your particular area.

Bear in mind that tidal information can be considered as two separate but entirely related subjects. So far we have only really considered the height of tide, or tidal rise and fall. This is likely to be most important when considering where and when to launch a boat. Some slipways cannot be used at all states of tide so you have to plan your launch and recovery accordingly. Another aspect of the rise and fall that may affect you is whether at low tide you have enough of an area to sail in!

At Outward Bound Aberdovey in Wales the broad estuary at high water becomes rather a narrow ribbon at low water, and this brings into consideration the second aspect of tides – tidal stream. This is the horizontal movement of water that can cause a real problem to a low-powered vessel such as an engineless sailing boat in light airs. As the tide falls at Aberdovey the sandbank is exposed and the ebbing tidal stream is concentrated in the remaining narrow channels. This increases the rate of the tidal stream to such an extent that sailing against it is often impossible. Such a place can be dangerous for an unsupervised beginner, so if you are in tidal water take local advice, have someone ashore keep an eye on you and get your timing right.

When you are sailing on the coast it is important that you always know the state of tide – whether it is rising or falling and the times of high and low water. Knowledge of whether you are in a spring or neap tide period is also important, as the greater the range the faster the tidal stream. Most (but not all) places have tides with a time difference of approximately six hours between high and low water. The tide does not fall evenly during that period, however, and it can be seen from Fig 3.15 (overleaf) that during the third and fourth hours the tide falls a lot more than in the first and last hours. A general rule of thumb as a guideline is the Twelfths Rule (see the chart overleaf).

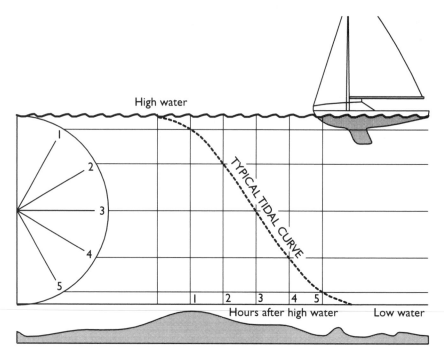

3.15 Tidal curve for a theoretical tide with a 6m range, a midday high water and 1800 low water. It would appear in the tide tables as: 1200 6.5, 1800 0.5.

Twelfths Rule:

- In the first and last hour the tide drops one twelfth of the range (here this is 0.5m).

- In the second and fifth hours it drops two twelfths of the range (= 1m)

- In the third and fourth hours it drops three twelfths of the range (=1.5m)

Pilot books and almanacs

Although usually written for larger vessels, pilot books contain an enormous amount of information about anchorages, harbours, tidal streams, particular hazards and other relevant data. Almanacs are usually published annually and provide information on tides, lights, buoyage, radio frequencies, coastguard services and so on. Making the most of the data available on the chart and in pilot books and almanacs will require training and dry land practice before they can be used in a small boat in difficult conditions.

4

Avoiding Danger

This section is a mosaic of different potential hazards which are presented across a range of land- and water-based activities. When a hazard is identified, some guidance is given as to possible strategies to avoid, diminish or eliminate the problem. Some hazards, such as bad weather, can affect a wide range of activities; others, such as being trapped in a capsized kayak, are confined to a particular sport. However, even though the same hazard may affect a number of activities, it tends to do so in different ways: a stiff breeze may be very welcome to the sailor but undesirable for the rock climber balanced delicately on small holds; a good downpour can greatly improve river kayaking, but at the same time can provide lethal flood conditions in the underground passages of caves. In this chapter hazards are considered under several activity headings, but it is, of course, recognized that overlap often exists.

On land

It is possible that you can spend your entire walking career without ever coming across a dangerous or emergency situation, but it is unlikely. Your first step away from the waymarked paths and tracks takes you into an environment where you need to be able to recognize hazards and a wide variety of potential dangers. In different parts of the world you may have to contend with heatstroke, be badly bitten by sandflies and mosquitos, mauled by a water buffalo, or swept away by a spate river – although you are very unlucky if you are exposed to all these simultaneously!

Avoiding problems

Perhaps the most important factor that will affect the outcome of any expedition is the frame of mind of the walkers themselves.

An over-ambitious walk can lead to poor decisions, and no walker should ever regard turning back as failure. Modifying your objectives in the face of adverse weather conditions, the indisposition of members of the party or equipment deficiencies and failures is only sensible. There is an expression 'the first domino', and once the first domino of a standing line has fallen we become more aware of the imminence of further setbacks. A tummy ache, a broken anorak zip or hood draw-string, a lost map or spectacles, a warning of a westerly gale or freezing level down to 300m (1000ft) may not seem to be major problems, but any one of them might be the metaphorical first domino which causes the whole line to collapse. Even when an expedition has been carefully planned and a detailed route card left, the arrangements must be sufficiently flexible to cope with illnesses, changes in the weather and even changes in the motivation of the individuals. The route card has columns for alternatives and escape routes. The very task of filling in the form will ensure that these things have been considered, but the plan has not been written in tablets of stone, and no blame should result from changing it if unforeseen problems arise.

Changing a plan to something more ambitious if the weather improves, the group is more highly motivated than originally thought or difficulties have been over-assessed should be undertaken less readily. The original plan should have been designed for the benefit of the least fit and experienced in the group, not for the gratification of the ambition of the leaders.

Hazards and emergencies

Steep grass slopes

Steep grass slopes are slippery when wet, and surprisingly slippery when very dry. You must have good purchase with a pair of good stiff boots (see pages 58–9), which must either bite into the slope or rest on secure ledges. If your boots have chamfered heels, throw them away unless you are well insured. You may have to go down grassy slopes when it is raining, but avoid anything that is other than gently sloping. Wet waterproofs on wet grass have a practically negligible coefficient of friction, so you might slide faster than you would think possible. If you do slip, trip or stumble, try immediately to get your hands and feet, or anything else, rammed into the slope, before you slide or your speed accelerates. Avoid carrying anything in your hands, such as cameras, hats, gloves or maps, if there is the remotest danger of falling. Not only may these objects cause you to slip if you drop and try to grab them, but also your carrying hand will not be available to stop you if you slip for some other reason. Your rucksack must be securely and compactly packed for similar reasons, without any trailing or dangling objects.

Separation

Separation incidents are commonplace. Typically, a walker will descend on one side of a hill range to report a missing companion, and wonder why rescuers do not immediately pull out all the stops to start a major search. They will, of course, do so if the person reported lost is ill-equipped in foul weather, completely inexperienced or with learning difficulties, suffering from a medical condition that may cause collapse, or very young or old, but what usually happens is that the overdue person turns up after an hour or two in another valley – sometimes not even telephoning, being unaware of the alarm caused.

It is surprisingly easy to lose companions on a walk. Afterwards the explanations always take the same form: 'I thought he would carry on and meet me on top' or 'I was sure she would wait for me'. It is usually too late to guess the other party's intentions and reactions after separation. They will probably think the opposite of what you expect them to think. Good communication, both ways, before the accidental separation is the key. If it has been discussed, it will probably not happen. Great care should be taken to avoid splitting up unless a contingency plan has been agreed. With groups, frequent head counts are needed. Often the missing person is the least experienced, poorest equipped and weakest.

Weather

Weather is one of the most important factors to be considered before any walk is undertaken (see pages 17–20), and the task of checking the weather forecast should always be undertaken by the group leader.

Wind direction

Generally routes are planned for fair winds, and it is easier to walk with the wind on your back. Consider the weather forecast carefully, planning the route with that consideration in mind, allowing for later veering or backing winds. (The wind veers when its direction changes clockwise – directly from south-east to south, for example – and it backs anticlockwise – from north-west to south-west, say.) If your route is circular, plan not to face a headwind late in the day when you may be tired.

The prevailing winds in Britain are from the south-west. For longer walks, it is best to plan to have prevailing winds behind you if your overnight stops are inflexible – you may have to book youth hostels well ahead in the holiday seasons, for instance. If you are camping or using hotels or bed-and-breakfast stops, get a five-day forecast at the start of the walk and be flexible enough to change the overall direction of the route.

Beware of wind traps. Going downwind may be all very well if you are able to continue the full planned distance and there are no mishaps. However, say you are walking to the top of a hill with the wind on your back, which is easier, when one member of the party gets exhausted or slightly sprains an ankle, making it imperative to descend to the starting point. This would mean a fight all the way back into a headwind, perhaps with face-flaying hail or sleet in it.

Remote, deep valleys are even less escapable: you cannot simply sidle around the other side into the lee of the hill. A case in point happened some years ago. A group of 10 walking east up the Uisge Labhar from Loch Ossian in the Central Highlands of Scotland (Fig 4.1) had a strong breeze behind them. There was some rain at times and the cloud base was not all that far above them. After a few miles, one person started to wilt and complain, but the group continued beyond the point of no return. The path became less evident, the slope got steeper, the tailwind stronger. Stopping to camp in those conditions was not a pleasant prospect, and the group felt compelled to press on over the top of the pass to reach Culra Bothy on the east side. The further they went, the more

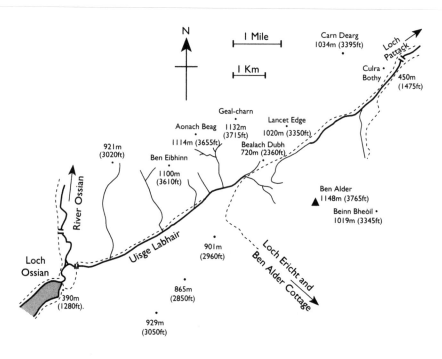

4.1 A wind trap between Loch Ossian and Cultra Bothy.

134

daunting would have been the task of returning by their outward route. Fortunately, the apparently exhausted member, the weak link, rallied when the seriousness of the group's predicament became evident. They struggled on through the gap, the Bealach Dubh (Black Pass), and coasted downhill to the bothy, sheltered from the main force of the wind, which was still on their backs.

A word of caution. British winds can be among the world's worst, and speeds of over 250kmph (156mph) have been recorded. Walking is impossibly dangerous at less than half this velocity, with gusty winds being more upsetting than steady airflows. It is not always possible to gain shelter by going down behind a ridge. Imagine a ridge running south-west to north-east with a steady, storm force (96kmph/60mph), south-east wind blowing across the ridge at right angles, making walking very difficult on the windward slopes. Eddy currents and down-draughts on the lee side of the ridge, and even down in the valley, coming in violent, dangerous gusts, can be of greater velocity than the steady storm. A party of 10 walkers, all roped together and trying to descend gentle snow slopes, could all be blown back uphill. Of course, strong winds by themselves can be not only a major impediment to walking but also a hazard in their own right by causing a slip or fall.

You should also be aware that the wind will reduce the air temperature in a dramatic fashion. A mild day of 5°C (41°F) will be reduced by windchill to an equivalent of −2°C (28°F) in winds as light as 10kmph (6mph).

Persistent heavy rain

Most modern walkers are well equipped with good boots, breathable rainwear and emergency gear. They may have travelled a long way by train or car to achieve a long-cherished route, and they are unlikely to be deterred by rainy weather on waymarked paths, which have been well maintained with good bridges across all the streams. Walking in heavy rain can be interesting, especially on safe paths beside spate rivers and waterfalls.

Dangers and delays are more likely in remoter areas with less clearly marked paths and fewer bridges. Tiny streams can become unfordable in an hour or two. The biggest spates occur in Britain with warm south-westerlies and persistent heavy rain, which rapidly washes the big spring accumulations of snow off the mountains.

Lightning

Lightning strikes are rare but they do happen. Apart from the obvious signs of a storm, if you are about to get caught in a major electrical storm you will notice that the air becomes charged and you will feel it in your hair and on metal objects. The first and most important rule is to get away from any exposed position you may be in, be that on a mountain top or standing under a tall tree. Some people will tell you to discard metal objects such as ice axes, but this would be foolish as you might need them after the storm has passed. Instead, place obvious metal objects away from you and if possible untie yourself from wet ropes, which are good lightning conductors.

The best place to sit out a storm, although it may be unpleasant, is on the open ground. Sit on your rucksack and tuck your knees up to your chin to reduce your target size and provide a short path for lightning should you get struck. Avoid sitting in cave entrances or under boulders where you might act as the electricity conductor in a spark gap.

White-outs

Many people refer to low visibility as being in a 'white-out', which is not the case. A true white-out is where the ground and air become indistinguishable from each other, such as in wind-blown snow. The best answer to a true white-out is to put up your tent and sit it out. The second, and riskier, solution is to navigate through it.

In this case, have a single person on the rope well out in front of the group, with the rope taut and tied to the rest of the group. If you do decide to navigate through a white-out it will the best test of your micro-nav skills you will ever experience and should not be underestimated.

Floods and rivers

One of the biggest dangers that the weather brings is that of flooding. As well as affecting your choice of campsite, it makes the crossing of rivers a major problem (Fig 4.2).

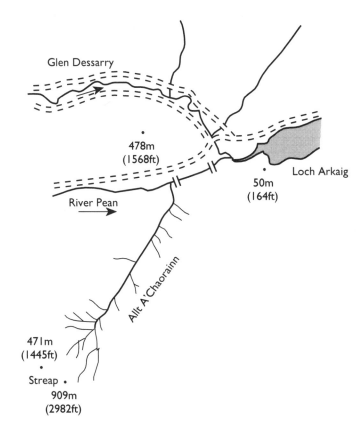

4.2 A river trap. When the river is in full spate it is unwise to try to descend the Chaorainn at all, and safer to return to Glenfinnan.

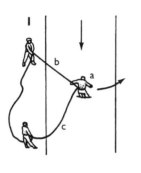

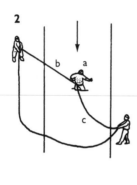

4.3 Crossing a river. The person crossing (a), leans back on the top rope (b) for support. This rope is fixed and swings across like a pendulum. The lower rope (c) is paid out and is used to pull the crosser back to shore should they fall in. The first person, once across, can take over the role of controlling the lower rope, while the second person across can take over the control of the top rope. If there are more than three in a group, it is important that someone keeps hold of the rope on the first bank in order to pull it back each time.

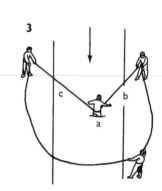

The three rules to be observed when crossing rivers in spate are:

1. Don't.
2. Don't.
3. Don't.

If at all possible, avoid crossing any river which is fast moving and higher than your knees. Trying to cross a fast-flowing river which is higher than your waist is approaching the suicidal. If you have decided that a river *must* be crossed, there are a number of procedures which can help.

First, keep your boots on, although you could remove your socks. Take off any baggy waterproofs which are going to catch the water. If possible, pass rucksacks across, but if they have to be carried you should loosen the shoulder straps and undo the waist and chest straps so that the sack can be dropped if necessary.

Although there are many ways of crossing without a rope, they are all better suited to slower-moving water because they require a number of people to move together, which is extremely difficult in a fast-moving river. Look for a suitable spot at which to cross; it should have low banks, no obstacles such as boulders or trees, and should not be on a bend of the river, where the current runs faster.

Fig 4.3 shows a method of using the rope to aid crossing in which the aim is to keep the rope in a triangular shape over the water.

However, you should only use a rope to cross a river in spate as a last resort. If you must, remember to give support from upstream, pull out anyone who has fallen in from downstream, and never let the rope jam. If it does, be prepared to cut it. A person attached to a jammed rope in fast water will be swept under and is very likely to drown.

Loose rock

Loose rock is found in a number of places. The biggest area is found on scree, or talus, slopes where the main dangers consist of falling over yourself and sending stones down on top of someone else. In any case, scree slopes are valuable botanical sites where many (often rare) plant species make their homes, so for this reason, if no other, they should be avoided if possible.

Other dangers associated with loose rock are walking under it and tripping over it. It is only common sense to avoid camping or taking a break under a crag with loose rock on it, and especially when the sun is loosening frozen rocks or a gully is channelling stonefall. However, the hazard is not always easy to spot and care does need to be taken in mountain regions. Loose rock underfoot is usually safe to walk on with care – if you can see it. When hidden by high bracken it is hard work, time-consuming and a potential area for sprained ankles.

Snow, ice, cornices and crevasses

Ice, cornices and crevasses are hazards that you will probably not encounter in the passage of a normal walking trip. Some trails do, however, cross the lower levels of glaciers, where you should always stick to the marked trails and seek local advice. On ridges and mountain plateaux, avoid lee slopes if there is snow on the ground. These are frequently the accumulation zones of slab avalanches. Further information on snow cornices and navigation is given on pages 106–11.

Wildlife

Wildlife is usually more of a nuisance than a hazard and most wild animals will leave you alone if you leave them alone. Be aware of the habitat and habits of any local nasties. For example, avoid holes under stones and boulders if you are in snake country, and find out from local people in advance the best way to act in bear country, including what precautions need to be taken when cooking. A good tip is to copy the locals: staff working at Outward Bound Hong Kong all carry large sticks, not only to keep the packs of semi-wild dogs at bay but also to swing in front of their faces to avoid a surprise encounter with woodland spiders.

If confronted by dogs, the answer seems to be to stay calm and back away. Shouting just gets animals excited, although throwing stones will often disperse a pack of agitated dogs. If the worst happens and you get bitten while in a rabies area, you must get to medical help with all speed. Rabies immunization does not actually prevent the disease – it merely slows it down to give you more time to get help. In the event of a dangerous close-up attack by a large dog, thrusting your fist and arm down the attacker's throat is said to kill the dog.

Midges

Midges – no-see-ems in the USA – are sometimes less than 1mm ($\frac{1}{32}$in) long, and the word is a loose term meaning 'biting fly'.

Any pursuit, such as rock climbing, which demands concentration and limited movement should be avoided if the midges are bad. It is better to charge about or dive into the loch (midges are a particular problem in the Highlands and Islands of Scotland). You may not even get relief indoors.

Canadian black flies and tropical mosquitoes can be mild by comparison with midges. Clegs (horse-flies) hurt more with the initial jab, but at least you get the satisfaction of killing them. There are various insect repellants available, but these are often more repellent to the walker than they are to the insects. None of them seems to be effective for as long as they claim, probably because the fluids are washed away by sweating.

There are two methods of dealing with midges. Firstly, try to avoid them, as the red deer do in summer, by keeping high on the windy ridges. This method is useless in calm, humid weather, and it is perfectly possible to be pestered above 915m (3000ft) on the islands of Skye and Rum and over 1220m (4000ft) on the Scottish mainland. Sheltered, cosy, winter campsites can be truly horrendous in summer; camp on any breezy knoll or eminence you can find, ensuring that your inner tent insect screens are in good repair.

The second method is to cover up, and open-weave summer clothes will not afford you adequate protection. Make sure your midge-proof socks are long enough to pull up over your midge-proof long trousers. Wear shirts that can be tightened at the collar and wrists and that go well down inside your waist belt. Get yourself a good, long midge net: dark ones are best because they are easier to see through. Unfortunately, you cannot eat through a net, but it is possible to eat and drink under one. Do not try to be sociable or even communicative, as the midges are bad enough to excuse civilized manners.

Midges are not usually active in bright sunshine (strong breezes will also help), but you will often see people with large areas of naked skin, suffering from bad sunburn, compounding their agonies by the application of powerful insect repellents. Antihistamine creams and pills may be useful for those who are not only infuriated by midges but suffer allergic reactions. Really bad cases may be forced to return home.

Foul water, food and disease
In many parts of the world, disease is spread in alarming ways via water and food.

Water
Always regard water with a degree of suspicion until you know for certain that it is safe to drink. Just because locals drink it does not mean that you can. At best, it takes time to get used to different water supplies; at worst, they can carry all manner of unpleasant surprises. If you are unsure of it, water should always be well boiled for several minutes. If you want cold water, boil it at night and leave it to cool – but not in plastic bottles as it will taste awful. Water-purifying tablets are of limited benefit but will often be enough, although they do make the water taste like a swimming pool. Adding iodine is another method which works but leaves the water tasting awful. There are some good filters on the market which are very effective, although the cheap ones will not be up to the job. In truly remote areas water above the level of habitation is usually safe, but in many places, notably North America, Giardia (a waterborne gut infection) is almost universal.

Food
Unless you are sure of your food, follow the simple maxim: 'Peel it, cook it or leave it.' Avoid leaving food to cool and then reheating it, as this could lead to infection. Unless you are an expert, do not experiment with food harvested along the trail. In particular, be careful with seafood such as cockles and mussels: sea creatures contain some of the strongest poisons known.

Hypothermia

Hypothermia, or exposure as it is commonly known, is one of the great killers in wild country. It is a condition where the core temperature of the body falls to a level where the correct functioning of the brain and other vital organs is impaired. A distinction is often made between rapid-onset (or immersion) and slow-onset (or exhaustion) hypothermia. The former occurs within minutes of unprotected immersion in very cold water, while the latter follows the gradual cooling of a progressively more exhausted individual in cold, wet conditions and can be aggravated by factors such as inadequate clothing or diet, and physical and mental attitude. Prevention is largely a matter of common sense and careful observation.

Before going on the hill ensure that:

- All members of the group are correctly clothed and equipped.
- Everyone has had a decent breakfast and has an adequate supply of food and drink (including emergency rations).
- The weather conditions are suitable for your planned trip.
- The planned route is within the physical and mental capabilities of all members of the group.
- No group member has a severe cold, flu or any other condition which makes the planned trip unsuitable for them.

During the trip, the members of the group should always keep an eye on each other. No matter how bad the conditions get, it is vital to keep talking to each other. Hypothermia often goes unnoticed until too late because everybody in the group walks along enveloped in their own private world.

How do you know if someone is hypothermic? There have been times when someone has been rescued by helicopter only to be immediately discharged from hospital with nothing wrong with them. Sadly, the reverse is more often true and people have pushed too far and succumbed.

The signs of hypothermia include:

- Shivering and cold, pale, marble-like skin.

- Apathy, confusion and irrational or 'drunken' behaviour.

- Complaining of tiredness, coldness, cramp (particularly in the calf muscles) or blurred vision.

Many of these symptoms could also be attributed to being merely 'cold, wet and tired'. The key to early recognition of hypothermia depends upon knowing the members of your group and detecting behaviour that is out of character.

There is detailed advice on recognizing and treating both mild and severe hypothermia on pages 287–95.

Frostnip and frostbite

Frostnip, and the more serious condition of frostbite, can be treated by gentle rewarming if spotted early. The first signs are tingling in the affected parts, which become pale and numb. Frostnip is quite common and not a problem if treated. People rarely notice their own frostnip – watch out for waxy yellow patches on the ears or noses of your companions.

Frostbite, however, goes deeper into the body tissue, which turns hard, white and stiff, then mottled blue and eventually black. Deep frostbite, like third-degree burning, is completely painless, so if you get numb you had better check your fingers and toes for circulation.

You can even get frostbite indoors. Cooking in a freezing bothy, still with your boots on and with your damp socks not changed, has led to some bad cases.

Some people suffer from swollen feet after the first day or two of a walking holiday, and they may be so keen to continue that they reduce the number of pairs of socks that they wear, or wear thinner socks so that they can get their boots on. Tight boots restrict circulation, so if the thinner socks get wet on lower boggy ground and are not changed above freezing level, the wearer is risking frostbite from two sources – frozen socks and tight boots. It is essential to have dry socks with you in winter, and they must be kept dry until you are above freezing level. Do not change into dry socks as soon as your feet get wet or you will just end up with two sets of wet socks. Similarly, in the mornings, if you are below freezing level, it is best to start off wearing your damp gear from the previous day and keep your emergency clothing dry. The moment of truth comes when you have to change back into damp clothes from a warm sleeping bag, but it is soon over, if you do it quickly!

You must have good-quality socks and gloves that are in good condition. If you wear darned socks, or socks or gloves with holes at the toes or fingertips, you are really asking for trouble. Mitts and gloves are easy to lose, so it is worth carrying spares. Make sure that your old-fashioned breeches meet your socks or gaiters below the knee, because that is a common site for second-degree frostbite blisters. These are not all that serious, but they may be painful and awkward for weeks.

There is detailed advice on recognizing and treating frostnip and frostbite on pages 295–8.

Blisters

Blisters are there for a reason: the liquid they contain serves to protect and cool the wound. This is the body's way of coping with an injury such as a friction burn.

Blisters can be caused by badly fitting, inadequate or damp socks, so carry spare pairs. Another item that is well worth carrying (if you can justify the weight) is a pair of thongs or flip-flops so that you can get out of your boots in the evening and let your feet relax. Look after your feet and they will look after you.

Blisters never completely cripple anybody unless they become infected, but bad ones cause real pain and can easily ruin a holiday. Walking causes a climax of agony to build up, which levels out and then remains constant until you stop walking. As soon as you start again you have to return through the pain barrier.

There is detailed advice on treating blisters on pages 273–4.

Illnesses

It is an individual responsibility to decide whether or not to tell your walking companions if you have a medical condition that might affect your performance. Most group leaders would probably prefer to know if you suffer from asthma, heart conditions, epilepsy, diabetes or, indeed, if you are just feeling off colour that day. Many people have enjoyed a long lifetime of outdoor activities with these conditions; many carry medications and know exactly what their reactions will be if they do a lot of physical exercise or fight for hours against a freezing wind. People with asthma may be able to walk at high altitudes much better than they dreamed they could, and those with diabetes will know that they may need to take a lot of extra sugar if their energy output is higher than they had expected, due to weather conditions or other unexpected difficulties.

However, it might be best if the acknowledged leader, or some responsible members of the group, or even everybody, knows as much as possible about everyone else's capabilities, not only to avoid surprises, but also to help in important decision-making. As an illustration, illnesses caused 49 casualties to be evacuated by affiliated rescuers from Scottish mountains, forests and moors during the three-year period from 1990 to 1992. Of these 49 casualties, just over half (26) were fatalities, and a very high proportion of the fatalities were heart attack victims. They were mostly walkers as distinct from climbers.

Sunburn

Remember that exposure to the sun has been identified as a cause of skin cancer, so always apply good sun-block creams and wear protective clothing, even when you think the day is fairly overcast. Prevention is always better than first aid.

Wear a lightweight hat and a scarf if you are travelling on snow, and apply sun-protection creams or oils frequently. Sunburn on areas other than the hands and face can be classed as self-inflicted and inexcusable.

There is advice on treating sunburn on page 274.

Snow blindness

This condition can be extremely painful, like sand in the eyes, and complete blindness can ensue for several days. It can occur very quickly, even in mist, especially at high altitudes. The sunglasses that you wear for, say, driving are not necessarily effective against the strong ultraviolet rays encountered on mountains. Goggles or side-screened glasses should be worn and spares carried.

There is advice on treating snow blindness on page 316.

Dehydration

Even when you are conscientiously drinking more than you think you need, you can still become badly dehydrated. Drying winds with high temperatures, especially at high altitudes, are the worst. On one expedition in high mountains, a walker had deliberately tried to drink in excess of what he thought he needed, but in fact lost so much fluid from sweating and breathing that he had to be helped back up to his tent from a glacier. He lay there for 36 hours while friends brought him over 7 litres (about 12 pints) to drink, and he did not have to urinate once. He was lucky enough to make a full recovery.

There is advice on recognizing and treating dehydration on pages 284–5.

First aid kit

You have to be selective when you are choosing what to carry in a first aid kit, and in the field you must be ready to improvise splints, dressings, slings and so on. If your first aid kit is too heavy you might get benighted from exhaustion. A list of suggested contents for a personal first aid kit is provided in Appendix I. Check that personal medication is carried by each member of the party, especially by anyone who suffers from asthma, diabetes or epilepsy.

A Swiss army knife is an essential item of kit for a group (see page 68). The small blade should be kept in its pristine condition, so that you have a razor sharp scalpel for use, not necessarily by you, in emergencies. Other useful pieces of equipment incorporated in the knife are scissors, tweezers and a saw (for sawing splints, not bones).

Rock climbing

All the techniques of movement and ropework in climbing are aimed at controlling a potentially hazardous environment, but some other hazards can be anticipated.

Weather

The weather has a powerful effect on both crags and climbers. Each winter wreaks subtle changes to the rock, levering off a small flake here, loosening a boulder there, but most of this happens when the crag is unfrequented and the most obvious effects of weather are felt more directly.

Rain

Rain has a dramatic effect on most climbs and increases the standard of difficulty enormously. If you commonly climb at Very Severe standard in the British grading system, you will find that in wet conditions many Difficult and Very Difficult climbs are at least as difficult as Very Severes in the dry. Rain breaks down the friction between boot and rock and also, to a lesser extent, that of hand on handholds. If the crag is covered in lichen, a film of water converts it to a surface like a skating rink in a matter of minutes.

Few people deliberately climb in such conditions, but once you have made the effort to go out you can have a very entertaining day if you choose a climb that is much easier than your normal standard. Do not underestimate the difficulties you are likely to meet, for a simple move on sloping holds that you would barely notice in dry conditions can become a formidable obstacle. If possible, choose a climb with relatively sharp-edged and positive holds rather than a friction slab, and it is also worth trying to climb in heavyweight walking or climbing boots with cleated soles. A useful dodge is to climb with old socks over your rock boots, as this greatly improves their adhesion on wet rock. Incidentally, a side effect of climbing on wet rock is that your hands become very soft and much more prone to cuts and abrasions from the rocks. This can be a serious problem on multi-day climbs, even in dry conditions, and climbers will often guard against this by taping their finger ends and knuckles.

If the rain starts while you are on a long climb, you have a number of choices, none of which is particularly attractive.

Sitting it out
You can sit out the rain, keeping your fingers crossed and hoping that it is a passing shower. On clean, south-facing cliffs the rock will dry out very rapidly after rain if there is any trace of sun and/or wind. However, lichenous, north-facing crags are likely to take several days to recover.

Abandoning the climb
You can abandon the attempt and descend. If the climb is one of some difficulty, you are unlikely to be able to down-climb in the wet and so your descent is likely to be by abseil. Be alert to the fact that heavy rain is likely to affect your concentration during the

descent and guard carefully against this. Your rope is likely to become saturated with water, and as you abseil your friction device will neatly squeeze most of this over your legs.

Forcing an ascent

You can force an ascent. Although you would not claim it as a normal ascent, it is sometimes better to escape upwards than downwards. Generally, this would consist of using every form of assistance at your disposal to complete the climb. It is worth trying to climb, perhaps with socks over your boots, with the frequent placing of runners to assess how feasible the ascent will be. It is unlikely that this will succeed for the whole climb and you may either have to find an easier route, perhaps where your route and a less difficult one cross, or use direct aid from runners.

At its simplest, this involves using runners as handholds, but when this becomes too strenuous it is worth standing in single-length tape slings clipped into the runners on difficult sections. The most common mistake is to make these slings too long. The best approach is to place the sling so that you can just get your foot into it after raising your leg in a kind of can-can manoeuvre. From there you can strenuously stand up, but in so doing gain a reasonable amount of height which, after all, is the object of the exercise. In your enthusiasm to pull on your runners, do not forget to clip the rope into some of them for protection.

On an autumn day in Glen Etive in Scotland a group of climbers made a number of mistakes. They started rather late in the day on a climb of about 250m (820ft). It had been wet all week, but as they started to climb the crag appeared to have dried out. Unfortunately, all the cracks were still weeping water and this made the climbing both slow and difficult. They decided to press on regardless but near the top of the climb a steep, overhanging corner had them resorting to all-out aid climbing techniques in the gathering gloom. By this time, it had started to rain again. The climbers, of course, had no waterproofs with them and arrived at the top of the crag in pitch darkness, shivering cold, soaking wet and with a very difficult descent ahead of them. One of the odd things about climbing is that the intense memories of that sort of day are remarkably satisfying (in retrospect) and linger long after the recollections of warm, sunny days have passed!

Loss of body heat

Climbing in the wet is very slow. It is also very strenuous and tiring. If you are on a long climb and conditions are cold, you can find yourself in a dangerous situation as heat drains from your body to a point where your performance starts to be affected. If you are on a long climb and the weather is unsettled, it is worth carrying a light waterproof and perhaps a fleece jacket with you. If these are put in a light rucksack, the second can carry it without undue difficulty and it will greatly strengthen your position should the weather break.

There is a vogue in the Alps and elsewhere for very rapid ascents of long rock climbs. People often go on climbs of perhaps 1000m (3300ft) with little more than the clothing and equipment they would use on a roadside crag. This is wonderfully lightweight climbing when things are going well, but should a storm break – and unpredicted storms are common in high mountains – then you are extremely vulnerable. A few years ago two very experienced climbers who had chosen to make a rapid ascent of the North Face of the Piz Badile (a classic rock climb in Switzerland) succumbed to the cold of a sudden storm and perished.

Snow

Sometimes if you are climbing in a high mountain area, it will start to snow. In cold, dry conditions this can sometimes leave the rock dry and you can climb reasonably successfully as long as you keep your fingers warm – perhaps by using thin gloves or fingerless mitts ('miser mitts'). Normally, however, the rock will become wet and, of course, the lower ambient temperatures increase the problems unless you are very well clad.

Heat

Excessive heat is rarely a problem in Britain but is more common in Australia, California and southern Europe. You will find it very hard to concentrate if you are too hot, so get round the problem by choosing to climb on shaded cliffs during the heat of the day, or make an early start and then take a long siesta before resuming climbing in the cool of the evening. On a long climb, you should carry water with you and take care that you do not become dehydrated. Becoming seriously overheated (heat stroke) is an extremely dangerous condition (see pages 285–6).

Weather forecasts

Weather forecasts are useful as long as you take care to translate them according to the conditions that will prevail on the crag. If you are in a mountain area, winds will be higher and temperatures generally lower than those forecast for low ground. There will also be an increased likelihood of cloud cover and increased precipitation. If you are climbing away from regular weather forecasts, then regular inspection of the sky can give many clues, as can the carrying of a pocket altimeter or a barometric watch.

At its simplest:

- A rising atmospheric pressure is a generally favourable sign.
- A decreasing atmospheric pressure spells a message of probable bad weather.
- A steady barometric pressure suggests little immediate change.
- Rapidly changing pressure should lead you to expect high winds.

Meteorologists will probably be horrified at this over-simplification, but if you are guided by this and regularly compare atmospheric pressure with the weather around you, you will quickly learn to predict with a good degree of accuracy.

Be aware that changing altitude also affects pressure and allow for this by readjusting your altimeter at any known spot-height.

Adverse conditions
Weather is the main source of these, but others exist.

Earthquakes and stonefalls
Recently climbers in California were horrified to experience an earthquake during which they could feel the cracks flexing and changing in width. More mundane but actually more dangerous is the risk of stonefall. As has already been mentioned, this is commonly caused by other climbers, but can also be caused by the sun's loosening ice-cemented stones on alpine climbs during the heat of the day.

There is no safe approach if stonefall is prevalent. Start early to avoid the heat of the day, and keep away from gullies and chimney systems that tend to funnel stones. If you must cross such an area, cross it rapidly, be vigilant and be grateful if you are wearing a helmet.

Sea cliffs
Sea cliffs provide their own hazards and more than one heavily laden climber has drowned in a so-called 'freak' wave. Most people believe that waves are regular in size. They are not, and if you watch a set of waves for long enough a particularly large one will come along.

If a very large wave arrives when you are standing unroped at the foot of a sea cliff you can be washed away with little chance of being able to swim.

Insects

In warmer climes, snakes and swarms of bees can detract seriously from the enjoyment of a climb, but of course none of these are as ferocious as the Scottish midge. Climbing on the Etive Slabs on a moist August day, the fresh breeze that had kept the midges away all day suddenly dropped. All across the crag, parties could be seen rushing to set up abseils. One or two unfortunate leaders, high on unprotected pitches, desperately tried to maintain maximum contact with the rock while simultaneously yelling for top ropes and scraping the carnivorous midges off their faces.

Mountain safety

Safety in the mountains is largely an attitude of mind. You are much more likely to be well prepared if you take the problem seriously and make a sensible assessment of what the risks might be. A broken ankle may be a relatively simple problem if it occurs in a car park; the situation is much more difficult if you are half an hour's walk over rough ground from help, and is a very serious one if you are several days' able-bodied walk from assistance.

Suggested mountain safety checklist:

- Proper clothing to deal with changes in weather conditions.
- Survival bag.
- Emergency rations.
- Map and compass.
- First aid kit.
- Helmet.
- Torch.
- Dark glasses, sun block, insect repellent.

The best recipe for mountain safety is to keep asking 'What if?' and to equip yourself for a moderately pessimistic scenario. You may sometimes meet groups from the armed services who come to climbing areas equipped with stretchers and large first aid rucksacks. This is clearly safe, but does tend to detract from the spontaneity of the day.

Obviously if you are climbing five minutes' walk from your car you hardly need a survival bag or, indeed, several of the other items. If, however, you are caught out in the wilds by darkness or bad weather, a strong but lightweight polythene bivvy sack and a couple of chocolate bars can be lifesavers.

On water

Sailing

A kind of constructive pessimism pays dividends in sailing. Always consider the worst that might happen and either amend the plan or make a conscious decision to proceed having noted the danger, although it must be stressed that sailing is a very safe sport when conducted properly.

As you learn more you will decide which side of the sport is for you and you will become comfortable in operating in the new environment. The racing sailor needs to be happy that their equipment is in good order and can stand up to the stresses that a hard racing season imposes. A racer needs to be confident operating at high speed, in close proximity to other craft that might be fast and powerful, and will be intent on getting the upper hand. The cruising sailor will wish to be more independent in order to sail safely away from the cover of the club rescue boat.

Many people enjoy both racing and cruising and find both activities rewarding. They will make a boat go faster and more efficiently when racing and extend the boundaries of their adventures when cruising.

Safety considerations:

- Make sure your personal kit is in good repair and that you foresee eventualities or a change of plan. Have with you everything that you need.

- Are the boat and equipment in good repair? Gear failure can be serious so good maintainance is essential. Develop a maintenance checklist and keep everything in good working order.

- Is your planned activity well considered and thought through? Have you got all the information? Have you considered the potential ways and occasions where things could go wrong? To do this, think through the immediate factors of you, your boat, your crew and your equipment, and the external factors of weather, tides, hazards, and other vessels etc.

Possible problems to consider:

- **Anticipated events**
  Immediate factors
  Hunger, thirst, coldness, tiredness, avoiding injury, gear failure avoided by maintenance.

  External factors
  Tidal constraints and dangers, onset of darkness, lee shores and shoreline hazards, weather (eg forecast wind change), avoiding vessels in busy shipping areas.

- **Unpredictable events**
  Immediate factors
  Coping with injury/illness, gear failure, capsize.

  External factors
  Weather not as forecast, danger from other vessels.

As well as immediate and external factors, there will be both anticipated events and unpredictable events. The relation between these can be shown by the examples in the list opposite.

These are some examples of potential problems to consider and you may well think of more that are relevant to your specific situation. Not everything in life can be categorized and some things here fall into more than one area. Weather conditions, for example, can be anticipated through forecasts and an understanding of local effects, but might turn out to be rather different. You therefore have to plan bearing in mind both the forecast and how things would be for you if the weather turns out differently. Perhaps we should call this an area of 'anticipative unpredictability'!

Considering the potential problems is useful, but you should also look at how to avoid them or be prepared to cope with them if they occur.

How to avoid or minimize anticipated problems:

- Thorough preparation – being properly equipped with boat and gear in well-maintained condition.
- Good planning – which keeps you aware of the external factors and helps you to operate within safe margins.
- Good judgement and careful operation – ensuring that things remain in your control and within the bounds you had planned.

Unpredictable problems are obviously harder to avoid. As two examples, the likelihood of injury or gear failure can be lessened but not ruled out.

Consider the potential outcome of problems to give some way of judging the seriousness of the activity. For example, a capsize during a club race has little risk with a safety boat ready to give assistance if necessary. A capsize when cruising away from a patrolled area could carry a much greater risk.

How to reduce the risk of unpredictable problems:

- Reduce the possibilities of such problems occurring by careful operation and good maintenance.

- Lessen the impact of problems should they occur by awareness (noticing problems at an early stage) and training (capsize recovery, first aid etc).

Training and awareness – some specific situations

Many situations can be prepared for by practice. If you have practised sailing without a rudder, for example, it will not be such a disaster if it ever breaks, and you should be well practised in capsize and man overboard recovery (see pages 322–6). Some other potential problems need further explanation.

The lee shore

This inspired dread in sailors of old, when ships might founder by failing to make to windward. We must still look on this with similar caution, despite the efficiency with which most modern boats now sail close hauled. If the wind should rise beyond the level you can sail with smallest mainsail, if the waves stop you from making to windward, or if something goes wrong and you lose drive, then you would quickly drift downwind. If that takes you towards a rocky shore with breakers you are in big trouble. Even a gentle, sloping shoreline in moderate wind should be regarded with caution, so always think through the considerations of a lee shore when sailing.

Being towed

If you need a tow, unless it is a simple situation with the club rescue boat it is usually better to use your own painter or towline. Generally people are keen to help, but if an unknown boat gives you a tow then salvage laws could give them a claim, so you should to bear this in mind. The failsafe is to negotiate a fee before passing the towline.

A towline should be made fast to a strongpoint on the boat – the foot of the mast is often a good place. You should be able to undo the line when it is loaded. A round turn and two half hitches would be suitable. Ideally, the painter should go through a fairlead on the bow. The sails should be lowered, the centreboard raised at least halfway and you should steer to follow the boat towing, sitting towards the stern.

Other vessels

This comes into a fairly predictable category as a straightforward hazard where danger is avoided by a defined set of rules. These are the International Regulations for the Prevention of Collision at Sea (collision regs for short). The result of a collision with another vessel could vary from a minor embarrassment to a tragic loss of lives and boats. Every boat user should therefore have a working knowledge of the priorities between vessels and how to avoid collisions.

International Regulations for the Prevention of Collision at Sea (IRPCS)
The first priority in any close quarters situation is to assess whether a risk of collision actually exists. In the case of two dinghies this is fairly easy, and once you are experienced you can allow them to come fairly close to one another. When racing, sailing boats come particularly close together and use International Yacht Racing Rules to avoid contact as well. For the moment, though, a basic knowledge of the collisions regs will suffice. If you are judging risk of collision with a larger vessel some way off, then hold a steady course and line up the vessel with a part of your boat. If the ship continues to be in line with that shroud or rowlock or whatever you have used, then there is a risk of collision.

Collision avoidance basics:

- You are required to keep clear of a ship manoeuvring in a narrow channel. This might be a stretch of water that seems quite broad to you but may be fairly tight for a ship with deep draught. You should keep clear of larger vessels anyway and do not expect ships to give way to you in restricted waters.

- If you are proceeding along a narrow channel then you should keep to the starboard side. If you wish to cross a channel you should do so by heading straight across at right angles.

- An overtaking vessel is required to give way to one being overtaken. This includes you if you are sailing past a motor boat slower than you.

In any other situation where risk of collision exists a list of priorities determines who gives way to whom.

Who has right of way?

- The simplest of these is that power gives way to sail (do not forget the above rules, though). Be aware that some water users are not very good at responding to this or might not even know the rules at all!

- Between two sailing vessels the right of way is with the boat on the starboard tack.

- If sailing vessels are on the same tack, then the boat to windward gives way. This is best done by passing astern of the boat to leeward.

The boat with right of way must hold a steady course to enable the give way vessel to avoid it. If the give-way boat does not take action in time, then the boat with right of way should take avoiding action. There is no point in being obstinately in the right if you end up getting run down!

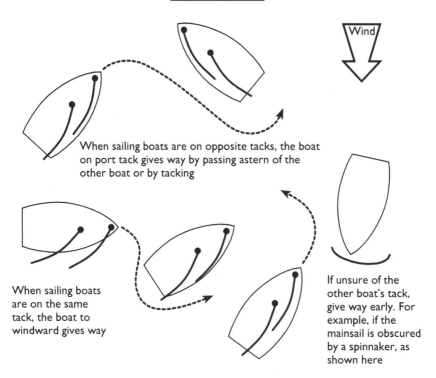

When sailing boats are on opposite tacks, the boat on port tack gives way by passing astern of the other boat or by tacking

When sailing boats are on the same tack, the boat to windward gives way

If unsure of the other boat's tack, give way early. For example, if the mainsail is obscured by a spinnaker, as shown here

4.4 Right of way.

Gybing problems and refinements

A common occurrence after a bad gybe is when the boat turns up towards the wind and heels over alarmingly. This is called a broach and can easily result in a capsize.

If you are suffering a broach and looking at an impending capsize, then quick action to remedy the first three of these points might keep you dry.

Factors which can cause or compound a broach:

- The mainsheet gets caught and is therefore effectively sheeted in tight once it fills with wind on the new side. This causes excessive heeling, which in turn makes the boat turn even further to windward.

- The tiller was not centred soon enough, causing the boat to turn much more than planned. This is the most common cause of gybing problems.
- The weight of helmsman and crew might not have been moved at the right time to balance the boat effectively and keep it level.
- The centreboard may have been down too far, causing the wind to have greater heeling force.

Quick action to avoid a capsize:

- Free the mainsheet from whatever might have obstructed it. (In future, sheeting in a little as you gybe can help by leaving less slack in the system to get caught. It is then sheeted out again as the sail fills on the new side, and letting it run through the mainsheet block provides an effective shock absorber. The sheet must be free to run out through the block, however, otherwise you just create the same problem by different means.)
- Sit out on the new windward side and pull the tiller towards you to bear away from the wind.
- Crew weight helps to keep the boat level.
- Check the centreboard position for the new point of sailing.

Canoeing

So long as our evolutionary development requires us to breathe air in order to survive, then there will always be inherent risks with any water-based activity such as canoeing.

Life is full of risks and so is canoeing. That is what makes canoeing exciting and challenging. Some of the risks are obvious, like canoeing over waterfalls, or capsizing and swimming down a nasty rapid. Others are less obvious but potentially as serious, such as going out alone, not wearing enough warm clothing, changes in the weather, cold and hungry paddlers with no warm drink or food available, not checking your equipment, being put under pressure by friends to do something you are not comfortable with and so on.

Safety is about minimizing risks. It is *not* about making lists of 'dos and don'ts'. Being safe means being aware of the dangers and taking the necessary precautions to guard against them before they happen. People who are trained and well prepared can have fun and excitement in challenging situations where an untrained or inexperienced person could drown.

The best way to learn to canoe is with other people who are suitably experienced. Getting out on the water safely in the right place, at the right time, with the right people and the right equipment, without overestimating your ability may sound unexciting, but you will live to repeat it. There is evidence that canoe fatalities which occur on what is considered to be very 'easy' water seem to show a correlation between inexperience and not wearing personal buoyancy.

Ask yourself:

- Can you swim?

- Do you have the right personal equipment?

- Have you got the necessary skill level for what you are doing?

- What experience do you have? Is it relevant?

- Do you know what hazards are involved in what you are doing?

- Are you prepared for (and do you have) equipment for an emergency?

- Is what you are doing your idea or someone else's?

- Is your canoe safe enough for what you intend to do?

- Does anyone else know what you are doing or where you are going?

There are lots of questions that you should ask yourself (and answer honestly) before taking to the water. Even if you are on a beginner's canoe course, by asking these questions you can see how other people prepare for canoeing activities and so begin to educate yourself. Education is an important part of the art and skill of paddling.

Fear of capsize

It is natural to be afraid of capsizing and being stuck in your kayak. A good way to come to terms with this fear is to play lots of games in, and on top of, swamped boats and so on. Practising capsizing will help you to come to terms with fears and anxieties, can also be fun and will help you gain confidence and increase your ability as you come to know what to expect (see page 331). Being relaxed with your canoe is important. Take your canoe for a swim and see how it responds.

Looking after your equipment

Taking care of your equipment is an important aspect of safety. If you look after your equipment it will serve you well when you most need it.

Remember, one mistake on its own is not normally fatal. Recognize the potential for mistakes to build up – not looking after equipment is one.

Do not compromise yourself and others with poorly looked-after equipment and by thinking 'It will be all right, just this once'. You may find that your equipment is not as effective as it ought to be just when you most need it.

Safety equipment

Good practice is to carry enough equipment to use or improvise with in the event of an emergency. This may depend on what you are going to do, where you are going, how long you will be out and the time of year.

Examples of not looking after equipment:

- Using your buoyancy aid for anything other than that for which it was intended, such as sitting on it or using it as protective padding for your canoe, is not to be recommended. All it does is cause wear and tear to your most vital piece of equipment and it may seriously damage it.

- Sitting on your canoe while it is on the shore can damage the seams and hull, because body weight compresses the boat when it is on the ground. When the canoe is on the water, the water provides support for it in all the right places. You may not notice the damage, especially if it is made of fibreglass, but even polyethylene boats can be severely gouged or dented if treated in this way.

- Sea water and grit or dirt of any form needs to be rinsed off everything. Sea water is a good corrosive, and grit and dirt get into and jam movable fittings.

Safety equipment you should carry:

- Extra food (chocolate).

- Means of making a hot drink (flask or stove with fuel, water, matches and flavouring ingredients).

- High-insulation spare clothing.

- Means of making an emergency shelter (bivvy bag or exposure bag).

- First aid kit.

- Small repair kit including knife, string, Sylglass duct tape (see page 168), nuts and bolts for foot rests.

- Means of towing a canoe (towline and clip for attaching to canoe).

- Whistles.

Each person in the party should also ensure that they have adequate personal clothing, including waterproof and windproof layers for themselves.

Waterproof containers

Keeping everything dry is a big challenge. There are two basic kinds of waterproof container: rigid or semi-rigid containers that have waterproof lids, and waterproof bags.

Rigid or semi-rigid containers   These come in a variety of shapes and sizes and are useful for carrying such things as cameras, repair kits, first aid kits and anything else that is fragile, has sharp edges that need protecting, or you do not want to be squashed. These containers are durable but bulky.

Waterproof bags   These are better for maximizing space as they can be squeezed into small places. Several small ones are better than large ones, and better for obtaining a more even weight distribution. When lined with a well-sealed polythene bag, rip-proof nylon bags are effective, cheap substitutes for the more expensive but durable heavy-duty waterproof bags.

Whatever the container, however, you should never rely on them being 100 per cent waterproof. Use a good-quality, heavy-gauge plastic bag as a liner, even inside the more expensive bags, with strong elastic (called shock-cord) or car inner-tube for sealing up the top.

What equipment to pack where?

Knowing what equipment you have put where, and in which container, is especially important with safety equipment, so that you can find what you want when you want it. A combination of containers is therefore useful.

The equipment should be packed so that the heavier items are as close to the centre of the canoe as possible. This makes turning

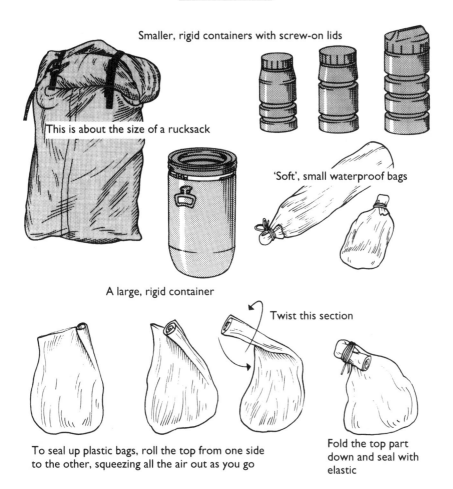

Smaller, rigid containers with screw-on lids

This is about the size of a rucksack

'Soft', small waterproof bags

A large, rigid container

Twist this section

To seal up plastic bags, roll the top from one side to the other, squeezing all the air out as you go

Fold the top part down and seal with elastic

4.5 Waterproof containers come in various sizes and types with different methods of closure on top. Any container is suitable for an open canoe, but only the smaller ones are suitable for kayaks.

and manoeuvring easier. There should never be anything loose in the boat. Everything should be tied in or secured firmly, and nothing should be in the way of the area in which you sit or kneel.

Remember that, despite the canoe being much slower to respond with all the extra equipment, the bags add to the internal buoyancy because they are airtight and will keep water out should you capsize.

Repairing canoes

The kind of repair kit you need will depend on your canoe and what material it is made of. Looking after your equipment is the best form of prevention. However, there always comes a time when you will need to fix something.

Temporary repairs

Temporary repairs to canoes still on the water, with holes or cracks in them, can best be carried out using plumber's tape or Sylglass, available from hardware stores. It comes in large rolls, with or without a foil backing, and is about 5cm (2in) wide. Although it is messy to handle and not very aesthetic, it makes a good short-term repair. The great advantage with Sylglass is that it will stick to anything, wet or dry. A small hole can be filled and covered with the tape inside and out, while a larger hole can be covered with a piece of more rigid plastic, from containers such as catering-size squash bottles, then sealed with the tape on both sides.

Handling Sylglass (plumber's tape)   The best way of handling Sylglass is to prepare pre-cut strips about 15cm (6in) long and lay them between two pieces of plastic bag, which are then trimmed all the way round to within about 2cm (1in) of the tape. Roll these strips up and they are then ready for use. Peel off one side of the plastic, put the tape on to the canoe where you need it, and press the tape down firmly through the other piece of plastic, which is then removed when you have finished. In this way you stand less chance of getting your hands messy. You could also carry polythene gloves.

Duct tape   Duct tape (or carpet tape) is also a universal tape used, in the short-term, for repairing anything that is dry: canoes, paddles, tents and other equipment that has holes, tears or breaks. It has also proved very versatile for people who need patching up for scrapes, blisters, stings and so on, and is therefore a must for all repair kits. Duct tape is available from hardware stores in various-sized rolls.

Permanent repairs

Fibreglass For more permanent repairs, a fibreglass canoe is easily patched with resin-soaked pieces of chopped strand mat, but this does require a dry, warm environment. The area around the patch will first need roughing up with a grinder or equivalent, to allow the patch to stick properly. Make sure you wear a mask, goggles and ear protection.

Polyethylene Repairing polyethylene canoes can be more difficult. Linear polyethylene can be heat welded, but some canoes are made of cross-linked plastic which is harder to damage and harder to repair. A number of manufacturers and retailers offer a repair service.

ABS (Acrylonitrile-butadiene-styrene) ABS canoes are incredibly robust and are rarely holed, but they are also difficult to repair. Among other uses, the very slippery, hardwearing outer plastic covering is also used for protecting the layers underneath from ultraviolet damage (a good reason for not dragging your canoe over abrasive surfaces). If this outer layer of plastic is damaged (that is, only the colour disappears) then it can be covered with fibreglass and polyester resin. Kevlar and polyester resin are also good for making a 'bang plate' on the keel-line at the bow, both above and below the waterline, to prevent surface damage in this vulnerable area.

You will need to find out what materials your canoe is made of and which types of resins and catalyst hardeners they are compatible with. If they are *not* compatible the resin and catalyst may well eat up or dissolve materials, such as the foam in the walls of your canoe. ABS is a styrene-based plastic, so polyester resin is all right. Royalex repairs can be made with epoxy resin repair kits that include 'putty' for outside scratches. The manufacturers are the best people to ask for advice.

Aluminium Open canoes made of aluminium usually dent if they hit something hard. This can be straightened out best by being knocked back into place. Just beware of the limitations that an alloy has in terms of metal fatigue, if the same place is damaged repeatedly. Pop riveting or welding may be other alternatives for repairing worse damage.

The advice for long-term repair is to look after your boat and as far as possible prevent unnecessary damage – then it will probably outlast you or your use for it.

PART II

COPING WITH ACCIDENTS AND EMERGENCIES

Introduction

This weekend scores of paddlers will overturn their boats, climbers will fall, and walkers will become lost. The perceived risk involved in this is usually much greater than the actual danger.

Nevertheless, most of us understand that in many worthwhile activities there are real dangers. In Outward Bound courses, we strive to balance these dangers against the joys and benefits of intimate experience with wild country and natural forces. This is the sensitive balance known as 'acceptable risk'.

Hazards are not sought for their own sake, but neither are they completely avoided. For wilderness travellers, an important part of striking the balance is preparation for handling dangerous situations when they occur. This includes a logical, common-sense approach to personal injury which takes into account all aspects of the environment. Once you leave the civilized world behind, the situation changes dramatically. Techniques and equipment developed for the emergency room or ambulance are often inappropriate or impossible outside the hospital setting. An indication of the variety of injuries and incidents that can occur is given in the table overleaf, which shows an analysis of British mountain accidents over a two-year period. Multiply this by several other countries and activities and you will have an enormous list.

Summer conditions	1991	1992
Slips	88 (2)	85 (7)
Illness	18 (6)	15 (10)
Sea cliffs	16 (7)	10 (5)
Exposure, heat trauma, exhaustion	11 (2)	22 (1)
Rockfall	3	5 (1)
All terrain vehicle accidents	4 (2)	1
Blown over	2	2 (2)
Loose rock/heather, hand/foothold fail	7 (3)	2
Pulled muscles, cramps, strains	3	3
Abseil point failure/misuse abseil gear	2	2
Wire broke when climbing deer fence	1	–
Duck-boarded path failed	1	–
Burn injury	–	–
Suicide	1 (1)	1 (1)
Not known	1	2 (2)
Swinging on tree, fell through loop	–	1 (1)
Friends pulled out – rock climbing	–	1
Stuck in brambles	–	1
Drunk – lost, presumed dead	–	1 (1)
Paragliding – insufficient take-off speed	–	1
River crossing	–	1 (1)
Stumbled and fired gun	–	1 (1)
Mountain motor cycling	–	1

Winter conditions (snow, ice, frozen ground)	1991	1992
Slips	41 (9)	33 (7)
Avalanche	14 (3)	2 (1)
Exposure, exhaustion	9	7 (2)
Illness	4 (2)	–
Ice tools pulled out	5 (1)	–
Glissading without crampons	3 (1)	1
Glissading, trip over crampons	2 (1)	1
Skied over cornice	2 (1)	–
Ski slips	9 (1)	–
Blown over	2	1
Walk over cornice	1	2
Fall through thin ice	1 (1)	–
Fell in bog	–	1

Numbers of injuries

	1991	1992
Summer hill walking non-fatal	79	85
Summer hill walking fatalities	1	8
Summer climbing non-fatal	22	10
Summer climbing fatalities	4	2
Winter hill walking non-fatal	30	25
Winter hill walking fatalities	7	4
Winter climbing non-fatal	24	7
Winter climbing fatalities	9	5
Totals (fatalities in brackets)	176 (21)	146 (19)
Percentage of winter injuries	40%	28%
Percentage climbing of total injuries	27%	16%

(excluding sea cliff incidents, skiing, illnesses, hypothermia, mountain biking, suicide, etc but including injuries from slips, avalanche, rockfall, abseiling, loose rock, equipment failures, glissading and cornice incidents)

II.1 Contributory causes of some injuries (fatalities in brackets).

Getting an injured person out to civilized medical care is rarely easy. Even when performed by skilled rescuers, an evacuation from wild country is difficult, expensive, and often hazardous. The popular television image of helicopters swooping to the rescue bears little resemblance to reality. Even where available, safe helicopter operation is limited to a fairly narrow range of weather and terrain conditions. The 'heroic' rescue is usually an arduous, sweaty, muddy scrabble that disrupts the lives of dozens of people.

The object, therefore, in preparing for wilderness medical problems is not to find more and better ways to scream for specialized help, or to stuff your pack with first aid kits. It is to develop a good basic understanding of the body's structure and functions, and to learn some basic techniques for preserving these functions in the presence of injury.

It is, of course, important to recognize that there are considerable limits to your ability to affect the outcome of some medical emergencies. There are times when screaming for help is absolutely the right thing to do – and there are times when all the help in the world will not make any difference. The vast majority of situations, however, are well within the capabilities of every wilderness traveller.

Like all things remote from civilization, wilderness medicine is elemental. The most important skill is improvisation, and good improvisation requires a solid understanding of the principles behind the treatment. It is a skill like reading a river, or picking a route through steep rocks: the technical information is important, but it is the gut feeling for the subject that gets you through.

The material in this section is arranged to emphasize this concept. We start by covering generic principles which are common to all injury and illness, and outlining a system for organizing your response. After developing a general level of understanding, we look at some of the most common specific problems you might possibly encounter.

In each topic, the path to effective treatment begins with understanding the *cause of injury*. This refers to the cause of the problem at the anatomic level. For example: the cause of injury for a broken leg could be trapping your foot briefly in a violent rapid; the cause of injury for nerve damage could be displaced bone fragments in a broken leg.

The next step is *assessment*, which is the process of identifying the problems and their relative severity. For example: leg fractures are associated with a positive cause of injury followed by pain, deformity, and tenderness; nerve impairment is revealed by loss of sensation in an injured extremity.

The goal is effective *treatment*. Stabilizing and realigning the fragments of a leg fracture would be the best way to prevent nerve damage and other long-term disability.

Sometimes the principles and procedures are quite specific, such as in the management of a dislocated shoulder or the treatment of an allergic reaction. More often, though, they are general in nature and adaptable to a variety of situations.

We hope that this format will succeed in sharing some of our experience with you. We also hope to stimulate your own interest in developing greater competence and self-sufficiency in the wilderness. You are, after all, your own responsibility.

A note on the ⊞ 'treatment' symbol:

We have added the ⊞ symbol to help you pinpoint quickly specific treatments for the medical problems discussed in this book. This has been done to save time in an emergency. Remember, however, that no treatment can be completely effective without a thorough knowledge of the overall issues involved. We recommend close reading of the entire text *at home* before attempting any wilderness first aid procedures.

5

The Approach to Medical Problems

Organized thinking

In the dreadful quiet that follows an accident far from help, the vital priority is to think clearly and act properly. Your success in balancing apparently conflicting demands and solving an apparently intractable problem will be enhanced if you have a system that can impose order on chaos.

In the hospital casualty department, clear priorities are established whereby the most life-threatening conditions are dealt with first, even though a specific diagnosis is often unavailable. What happens is a generic process of stabilizing and supporting the vital functions of the circulatory, respiratory, and nervous systems. The 'BIG 3' body systems (Fig 5.1, overleaf) include the most important and sensitive organs – heart, lungs, brain and spinal cord – the critical machinery most essential to life. Only after the immediate threats to the patient's life have been stabilized can the process of more specific diagnosis and treatment begin.

The same principle is followed in the wilderness setting. However, because we have only basic diagnostic equipment (our hands, eyes and ears) and limited options for treatment, the medical problems and treatment plans remain general in nature. These limits are imposed by the environment, not your training or intelligence.

This makes things a great deal easier from a medical point of view. For example, you do not need to memorize 12 different causes of abdominal pain: you only need to know when to consider abdominal pain to be potentially serious. Even if you could distinguish an acute appendicitis from a perforating ulcer, you are not going to operate in either situation.

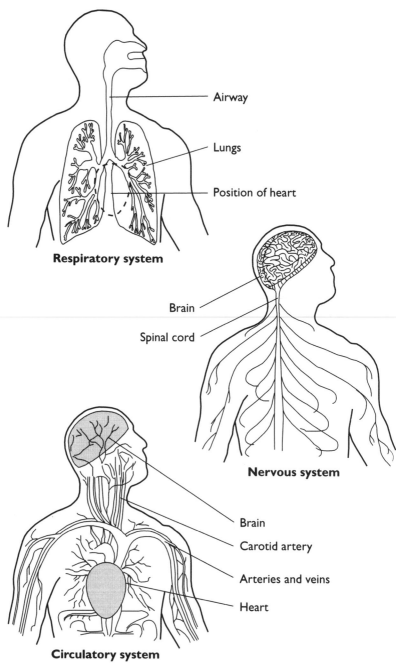

Respiratory system

Airway

Lungs

Position of heart

Nervous system

Brain

Spinal cord

Brain

Carotid artery

Arteries and veins

Heart

Circulatory system

5.1 The BIG 3 Systems – are all intact?

In the hospital emergency department, the patient's medical problem is all the doctor needs to worry about. He or she is working in a stable environment with the resources and time to focus on specific medical problems. In a remote wilderness setting, however, the patient's medical problem is only a small part of a much larger picture, which includes weather, terrain, the condition of the group, available assistance, and a number of other factors.

You may be caring for an injured partner for hours or even days. Your plan needs to address not only immediate problems but problems which can develop later. All these additional factors reinforce the need to keep the medical part of the response simple and generic.

Patient assessment

The main tool for organized response is *patient assessment*, based on information gathered in a series of surveys and organized in a standard format. It consists of three important steps: gathering information, organizing a response, and anticipating problems which may develop over time.

Gathering information

1. Scene survey

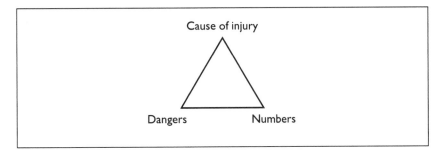

Danger to rescuers and patient: Before rushing to the rescue, be sure that you are not going to become another casualty. You cannot help anybody else if you are out of commission yourself. It can take tremendous discipline to overcome the powerful urge to come to the immediate aid of a friend in trouble, but this is exactly what you must do, at least for the moment. Stop, look around, and ask yourself: 'What's trying to kill me?' It may be freezing water, another avalanche, or further rockfall. Whatever it is, if it can disable you, it must be stabilized before you do anything else.

Once you are safe, or relatively so, look for any further threat to the injured person: 'What's trying to kill him?' Stabilize the scene by moving danger from the patient, or the patient from the danger. This has priority over everything else. So, get the patient out of the water, out from under the cornice, or secure him with a rope before proceeding with evaluation and treatment.

Clearly, a difficult decision must be made if the injured person is in a dangerous position and, for instance, spinal injuries are suspected (see page 249).

Cause of injury: Another important element in the survey of the scene is determining the cause of injury. This may be quite obvious, but occasionally more investigation will be necessary. For example: how far did he fall? Was it enough of a tumble to cause injury? Are there other factors, such as exposure to weather, which might be the cause of the patient's condition?

Number of patients: How many people are injured or at risk? Casualties are often overlooked in the rush to treat the most obvious and uncomfortable problems. This is especially true of environmental injuries where most or all expedition members can be in danger of hypothermia or dehydration, and where sufferers can be extremely inconspicuous.

2. Primary survey

This is the initial patient examination. You are checking the status of the BIG 3 systems, looking only for conditions which represent

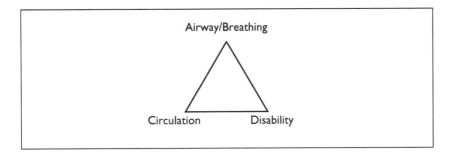

an immediate threat to life. Check that the mouth and nose are clear to allow the passage of air, and that air is actually going in and out. Confirm that blood is circulating, and not running out all over the ground! Finally, ensure that the patient's spine is stable, and that the central nervous system is functioning normally.

Primary survey:		
A – **Airway**	Nose and mouth clear	**RESPIRATORY SYSTEM**
B – **Breathing**	Air moving in and out	**RESPIRATORY SYSTEM**
C – **Circulation**	Check for pulse	**CIRCULATORY SYSTEM**
	Severe bleeding	**CIRCULATORY SYSTEM**
D – **Disability**	Spine stable	**NERVOUS SYSTEM**
	Level of consciousness	**NERVOUS SYSTEM**

Performing a primary survey may mean hanging upside down in a crevasse listening for breath sounds in your unconscious partner, and feeling inside bulky clothing for blood. On the other hand, it may be as simple as asking 'How are you?' and getting a 'Fine' and a smile. Whatever form it takes, it is a critical step in your organized approach to the situation.

Any problems encountered in the primary survey must be addressed immediately, before worrying about less critical things. You will have to fight the natural tendency to focus on the obvious injuries like deformed fractures and messy scalp wounds. This can keep you from finding the life-threatening problems like airway obstruction or severe bleeding.

The immediate management of life-threatening problems found in the primary survey is referred to as 'basic life support' and is covered on pages 194–5. If the situation requires basic life support, you may never be able to go any further with your patient examination. However, in most cases you will be able to determine that no life-threatening problem exists and go on to the secondary survey.

3. Secondary survey

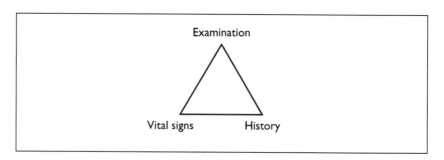

By now you have decided that neither you nor the injured person is in imminent danger. The patient has no medical problems which are going to kill him or her right now. The scene is stable. The patient is stable.

Examination: This stage is a slower, more deliberate examination of the whole patient. It is less urgent than the primary survey, but speed and detail change with circumstances. Unless your primary survey missed something, it is not necessary or efficient to stop and treat problems as you find them. Complete your list, then return to treat later in order of priority.

Although it really makes no difference in what order you proceed, most examiners start with the head and neck, moving to the chest, abdomen, pelvis, back, legs and arms. You are looking, touching and feeling for abnormality – that is, tenderness (pain caused by touch), swelling, deformity, discoloration or bleeding.

You should be gentle, moving the patient as little as possible. Your examination should be as comprehensive as the situation allows. In wild country you do not need mystery and surprises. Touch and look at everything.

Vital signs: These measurements provide another way of assessing the function of the BIG 3 body systems. The major parts of the circulatory, respiratory and nervous systems are hidden from our view. We need to rely on indirect methods of watching them work.

Vital signs are like the gauges on the dashboard of your car. Every time you drive you are looking at the same standard gauges: oil pressure, charge indicator and engine temperature. You can evaluate the health of your car without opening the bonnet and taking the engine apart. You might not know what the exact readings are supposed to be, but you will certainly notice if they are different from normal. And, depending on which gauge it is, you will gain some idea of where the problem lies.

The value of vital signs is not only to distinguish normal from abnormal, but to observe the direction of change over time. By measuring the same standard signs at regular intervals, you can get a sense of improvement or decay in a patient's condition. Is your treatment working? Are things getting better or worse? Is it time to panic, or sit back and have a cup of tea and another bar of chocolate?

The detail with which you measure vital signs will depend on the equipment available. Vital signs are listed overleaf, with the ranges of normal values in brackets.

Vital signs:

T **Time** when vital signs are measured.

BP Blood pressure in mm of mercury (140/90–110/60).

P **Pulse** in beats per minute (60–100).

R **Respiratory** rate in breaths per minute (12–18).

C **Consciousness** and mental status (AVPU).

T **Temperature** of the body core (36.4–37.6°C/97.6–99.6°F).

S **Skin** colour, temperature, moisture.

Now, if you would rather devote the precious space in your pack to peanuts and chocolate than to blood-pressure cuffs, stethoscopes and clinical thermometers, you are not alone. Even if a watch is too much technology for you, you can still make a valuable assessment of vital signs. Measurements become relative: for example, pulse is 'fast' or 'slow', temperature is 'cool' or 'warm'. Blood pressure can be assessed as 'normal' or 'low', based on signs of adequate or inadequate blood flow (more on that later).

Level of consciousness is a measure of nervous system (brain) function for which no special instruments are required. It is related to one of four letters on the 'AVPU' scale.

AVPU scale:

A **Alert.**

V Responsive to **verbal** stimulus.

P Responsive only to **painful** stimulus.

U **Unresponsive** to any stimulus.

This is a widely used and relatively precise description which avoids confusing terms such as 'semiconscious' and 'in and out'. Alert patients are further distinguished by their mental status. This refers to the patient's level of orientation and anxiety. People with normal mental status generally know who they are, where they are, what day it is and why they are where they are.

History: The final act in the process of gathering information is to obtain a relevant history.

History assessment:

A **Allergies** to insect stings, foods, medications etc.

M **Medication** that the patient is currently taking.

P **Past history** of similar or related problems.

L **Last meal**, time and content.

E **Events** leading up to the incident.

Of course, the entire primary and secondary survey may not always be necessary. A simple laceration of the finger by a knife blade while slicing an apple does not warrant a full body examination. However, many accidents are unwitnessed, confused by pain and anxiety, and involve hidden injuries. Even in a very straightforward situation, your own level of anxiety as a rescuer makes it advisable for you to have a structure within which to function. An orderly system will do a lot to put your mind at ease and stabilize an uncomfortable situation.

Organizing your response
The system of organization commonly used by the medical profession is: subjective, objective, assessment and plan. It is a simple and effective management process, from gathering information and identifying the problems, to forming a plan to deal with each problem. It is the way medical records are written, and the order in which medical information is communicated. The headings are summarized overleaf:

Response summary:

S **Subjective**: What happened? Where does it hurt? Relevant history.

O **Objective:** Information gathered by observation and examination. Include vital signs.

A **Assessment:** Based on the subjective and objective findings, what is the problem? If more than one, list in order of priority.

P **Plan**: What are you going to do about each problem?

Using this system, a typical response summary would be made as follows:

Subjective: A nine-year-old boy fell off his bicycle. He complains of pain in his right wrist and tingling in his fingers. He has no complaints of pain anywhere else.

Objective: An alert, oriented but uncomfortable boy. The right wrist is swollen and tender to touch. The patient refuses to move the wrist voluntarily. The fingers are warm and pink and can be wiggled with slight pain felt at the wrist. The patient can feel the light touch of a cotton swab on the end of each finger. He has no other apparent injuries.

Assessment: Fracture of the right wrist.

Plan: Splint wrist. Follow up with a visit to a hospital casualty department.

This format paints a nice picture of the situation. You get a sense of who the patient is, what happened, what field treatment has been given and what the doctor is going to do about it. There is also a brief description of problems which might occur, and what the response should be.

The format is perfectly adaptable to the wilderness setting, and it performs the same vital function as it does in the hospital. It organizes your thoughts, renders order from chaos, and allows you to communicate your ideas and plans.

But we need to expand the format a little to take into account where we are. We must consider the problems created by weather, terrain, distance and time. These factors are just as important as the condition of the patient.

Anticipated problems

In long-term care, we add a section called 'Anticipated problems'. This is a list of problems which may develop over time, something which often relates to a wilderness scenario. They could be complications of the injury itself, or the potential result of exposure to environmental factors. By including them you will be in a better position to prevent problems from developing, and be ready to deal with them when they cannot be avoided.

Watching for change (monitor)

As your patient's condition, the weather and your logistical situation all change with time, you will need to revise your plans. The best way of doing this is to repeat the relevant parts of your surveys, and revise your plans accordingly at regular intervals. This is where you watch for the anticipated problems which you have listed in your original assessment.

Patients with potential BIG 3 problems should be re-evaluated most often, at least every 15 minutes if possible. The circulation, sensation and movement of injured extremities can be checked less frequently, at one- or two-hour intervals. Conditions which develop slowly, such as wound infection, might be monitored adequately every six hours.

Now let us take that previous case, concerning the nine-year-old boy, into the wilds.

GATHERING INFORMATION – SURVEYS

1. Scene survey

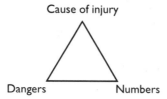

2. Primary survey

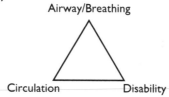

3. Secondary survey

Response
        Subjective
        Objective
        Assessment
        Anticipated problems
        Plan

Watching for change (monitor)
        Repeat surveys
        Anticipate problems
        Revise response

Case study

Subjective: A nine-year old boy falls on to his outstretched right arm while crossing a burn by Corrour Bothy. He complains of pain in his right wrist and tingling in his fingers. He has no complaints of pain anywhere else. He does not feel cold or hungry. He is known not to have allergies, be on medication or have any significant medical problems. He has just finished a snack. The fall was due to slipping on wet boulders, and not from a significant height.

It is now sunset. The air temperature is 15.6°C (60°F). It is raining lightly.

Objective: An alert, responsive but uncomfortable boy is found sitting on a rock holding his right arm. He is warm, dry and adequately dressed. His right wrist is slightly swollen and tender to touch. He can wiggle his fingers and feel the light touch of the examiner's hand. His skin colour is normal. There is no other injury.

Assessment: Fracture of the right wrist.

Anticipated problems:
1. Swelling and ischaemia (inadequate blood flow to the extremity).
2. Difficult to walk out.

Plan:
1. Splint the wrist, keep the patient quiet and the arm elevated.
2. Monitor right hand every hour for circulation, sensation and movement.
3. Shelter here tonight, walk out in daylight tomorrow.

Even in complicated cases where a patient may have more than one problem, the format remains the same. Under 'Assessment' we would list the problems in order of priority, and have a plan for each one. By checking each problem for a plan, and each plan for a problem, we can avoid missing anything. We can also avoid making plans for problems that do not exist.

General principles of wilderness medicine

Simply memorizing treatment procedures or carrying a set of instruction cards in your pocket is far from acceptable preparation for medical emergencies. Unless you frequently use or practise memorized procedures, you will forget them. Your instruction card will never be there when you need it, and you will not have time to read it anyway.

Practical preparation for medical emergencies involves developing a full understanding the principles behind the procedures. If you can accomplish this, you will never 'forget' what to do – you will

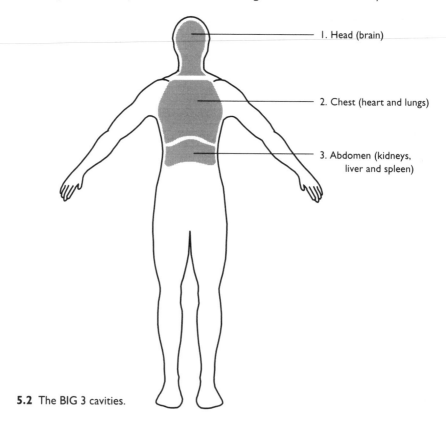

1. Head (brain)

2. Chest (heart and lungs)

3. Abdomen (kidneys, liver and spleen)

5.2 The BIG 3 cavities.

understand what needs to be done. Your response may not be in quite the right order, but it will be as appropriate and effective as the situation allows.

The BIG 3 body systems

Injury or illness which is life-threatening involves a major problem with the circulatory, respiratory or nervous systems (BIG 3). These three systems exist in an interconnected triad. Problems with one are quickly reflected in the other two. For example, serious respiratory problems, such as asthma, produce an increased heart rate (circulatory system) and changes in mental status and consciousness (nervous system). If any of the BIG 3 actually stops functioning, death occurs within a matter of minutes.

The vital organs of these BIG 3 systems are contained within the BIG 3 body cavities – the head, chest, and abdomen. These organs are not generally accessible to direct examination. We must therefore use indirect signs and symptoms to assess the status of the BIG 3 systems.

Functions and responses

Perfusion: The function of the circulatory system is to force blood through the beds of tiny blood vessels (capillaries) in all body tissues. This brings blood in close proximity to living cells to allow oxygen, nutrients and waste to be exchanged between the cells and the blood stream. This is 'perfusion', and it is essential to any living tissue.

Considerable pressure is required to push the blood through the capillary beds. This 'perfusion pressure' (blood pressure) is generated by the pumping action of the heart, balanced by the ability of the larger blood vessels to constrict. Adequate perfusion requires adequate pressure.

Oxygenation: It is the task of the respiratory system to supply outside air to the lungs where, in the alveoli (air sacs), it comes into close proximity with the perfusing blood. This allows oxygen from the air to enter the blood stream, in effect 'filling up' the blood with oxygen. Oxygenation of the blood is as critical to life as perfusion. It would be of no use to perfuse tissues with blood that had no oxygen to deliver.

Compensation: The nervous system regulates the function of the circulatory and respiratory systems to maintain adequate perfusion and oxygenation under a variety of conditions. Heart rate, respiration, and blood-vessel constriction are manipulated by the brain to compensate for the effects of exercise, cold, heat, injury and other factors. Adequate compensation requires an intact and functioning nervous system.

The best way to watch compensation in action is by observing vital signs. Minor changes will occur as the healthy body adapts to the various stresses of normal life. Major changes indicate that the body is compensating for abnormal stress, such as injury or illness, which may be life-threatening.

Shell/core effect: One of the primary compensation mechanisms seen in stress and injury is the shunting of blood from the less vital organs of the shell to the vital core of the body. The 'shell' comprises the skin, digestive system and skeletal musculature. The 'core' includes the brain, heart, lungs, liver and kidneys.

The shell/core effect accounts for the cool, pale skin observed in volume shock or cold response. It indicates that the body is trying to preserve the core at the expense of the shell. This can be a normal response to a minor, self-limiting problem, or the early sign of a more serious condition.

Swelling: Swelling is an increase in the pressure within body tissues due to the accumulation of excess fluid. This can come in the form of blood escaping from ruptured blood vessels (bleeding), or serum oozing from damaged capillaries (oedema). It is a general response to injury or infection which occurs in all tissues. It may be localized, such as the swelling of a sprained ankle, or systemic, such as the swelling of the whole body that occurs in allergic reactions. Swelling can develop almost instantly, or slowly over the course of several hours.

Swelling which develops to the extent that it obstructs the flow of blood or air is the primary mechanism for most life-and-limb-threatening emergencies. It can be an immediate threat to life if the tissues affected are the vital organs of the BIG 3 (circulatory, respiratory or nervous systems).

Anticipating or controlling the development of swelling is one of the keys to successful emergency care. Most of the swelling that occurs following injury develops during the first six hours. It then

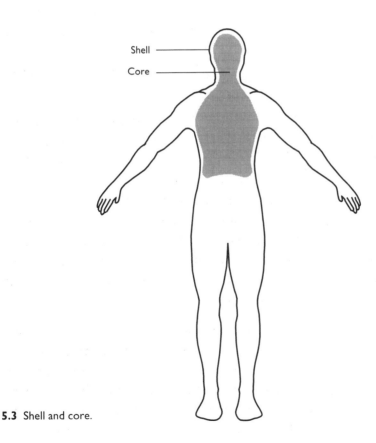

5.3 Shell and core.

tapers off over the next 18 hours, with very little swelling occurring after 24 hours. Re-injury can start the process over again.

Ischaemia: This is the term for inadequate perfusion. It can occur when the perfusion pressure is too low to force blood into the tissues, or the pressure within the tissues is too high to allow the blood in. The most life-threatening examples of these problems occur in shock and head injury.

Ischaemia can, of course, occur anywhere where perfusion is inadequate. If you were to wrap a string around your finger tight enough to reduce blood flow, the end of your finger would become 'ischaemic'. If you left the string there long enough, the end of your finger would die.

Decompensation: In the presence of injury or illness, the nervous system (brain) will make whatever changes are necessary in the functions of the circulatory and respiratory systems to maintain perfusion and oxygenation. Early on, this compensation mechanism may work well enough to hide the problem. However, if the problem is serious the normal compensatory responses will ultimately be overwhelmed. This is the condition known as 'decompensation'.

Hopefully, however, by observing changes in vital signs in the context of other survey findings, you can detect compensation at work, and intervene to prevent decompensation. Recognizing the subtle changes of early compensation is another important key to saving lives in remote areas.

For our purposes, the most sensitive and useful vital sign is level of consciousness. This is because the nervous system is exquisitely sensitive to oxygen deprivation, and problems with perfusion and oxygenation are quickly indicated by changes in brain function.

The 'evolutionary onion': To understand nervous-system functions as an indicator, picture the brain as an onion with increasingly complex layers of function from the inside out. The basic 'vegetative' functions of body regulation, breathing and consciousness are contained in the deeper, more primitive layers. Higher functions, such as personality, judgement and problem solving, would be located in the outer layers, added later in human evolution.

These outer layers, most recently acquired, are also the first to be lost when problems develop. The earliest vital sign changes seen are the first stages of 'peeling the onion' – altered mental status. Patients remain conscious and alert but may become anxious, uncooperative or respond in ways that do not fit the situation. They may act in an apparently intoxicated, belligerent or confused manner.

More extreme injury affects the deeper layers, causing a decreased level of consciousness. When the onion has peeled this far, the situation has become more serious. Patients progress from being alert (A) to lower levels of responsiveness (V, P) and unresponsiveness (U) as oxygen deprivation in brain tissue becomes more severe. The progression can also be reversed, if the underlying problems with perfusion and oxygenation are corrected.

Acute stress reaction (ASR): Acute stress reaction is a normal, self-limiting nervous-system response to acute stress of any type. The problem is that ASR can be mistaken for the symptoms of life-threatening conditions such as shock and increased intracranial pressure. The difference is that it is harmless and goes away with time. It can also occur along with true shock, and cause problems by masking the symptoms of serious injury. Acute stress reaction comes in two basic forms:

1. Sympathetic – this is the 'adrenaline rush' known so well to those of us who push beyond our limits in the great outdoors. Adrenaline is the hormone released by the nervous system that produces what is sometimes called the 'fight or flight' response. Its effects speed up the pulse and respiratory rates, dilate the pupils, and generally get the body ready for action. It also stimulates the release of natural hormones which serve to mask the pain of injury.

This type of acute stress reaction certainly has value to human evolution. It allows heroic survival efforts even in the presence of severe injury. However, it also makes the immediate accurate assessment of injuries difficult for the rescuer following the accident.

2. Parasympathetic – feeling faint and nauseous in response to stress is another familiar feeling. It is caused by a temporary loss of perfusion to the brain due to a slowing of the heart rate. The evolutionary value of this response is more difficult to work out. This, too, is harmless except in its ability to mimic the consciousness and mental-status changes seen in shock and head injury. It is highly desirable to be able to distinguish acute stress reaction, which is self-limiting, from these serious conditions.

Basic life support

Discussing serious problems first has its drawbacks. You might get the feeling that every accident is going to produce some tragic and overwhelming injury. It can make you a bit shy about taking risks, or even letting yourself get more than a mile or two from the nearest road. So keep in mind that we cover the big problems first because they are big, not because they are common.

General principles

Requirement for life

Adequate perfusion of vital organs with oxygenated blood under all conditions.

Life-saving treatment

Perfuse the brain. Any condition which has the potential to interfere with the flow of oxygen to the blood, or blood to the brain, must be corrected.

Basic life support is the immediate treatment of life-threatening BIG 3 problems discovered during the primary survey. It should be your automatic response to conditions which are likely to cause death or severe disability. It is designed to provide temporary support for only the most vital functions of the circulatory, respiratory and nervous systems while patient assessment continues, or until the patient is transferred to advanced treatment. For basic life support to be effective, it must begin immediately at the scene.

Although basic life support is outlined in a specific sequence, the reality of field treatment requires flexibility. In terms of saving lives, all components are equally important. It is often necessary to change the order in which things are done, or to manage several components at the same time.

Most of the procedures used in basic life support are covered by the 'Resuscitation' section of the *First Aid Manual* of St John's and St Andrew's Ambulance Associations and the British Red Cross. We strongly recommend that you attend one of their courses to learn the vital skills of resuscitation. However, remember that it will require some flexibility to adapt what you learn there to the wilderness environment.

Primary survey
You will remember from the section on patient assessment (see pages 177–88) that the primary survey is a quick look to see if the circulatory, respiratory and nervous systems are functioning. The simplest and most elegant way to conduct a primary survey is to ask your patient 'Hello, how are you?' If they give an appropriate verbal response such as 'Fine, will you help me get this rock off my foot?' you can be satisfied that there is no immediate life-threatening BIG 3 problem. The airway is intact, they are breathing, their heart is beating and their brain is functioning. You have done your primary survey. In cases where the patient is unable to respond, or has responded abnormally, you will need to look a little more closely. This is the process known as 'checking the ABCDs'.

A – Airway

Airway problems in the primary survey are caused by obstruction of the upper airway (pharynx or larynx). Obstruction may be complete or partial. Complete obstruction is rapidly fatal, but can often be treated effectively, with dramatic results. Possible causes of airway obstruction include:

Causes of airway obstruction:

Position – unconscious states produce relaxation of soft tissues ('swallowing the tongue').

Vomit – most patients vomit at or near death.

Foreign body – conscious people can inhale food. Children can inhale anything (coins, peanuts etc). Unconscious patients can also have their airway obstructed by a foreign body (vomit, teeth, injured tissue).

Swelling – caused by trauma, irritants such as smoke or chemicals, or allergic reaction (anaphylaxis).

Spasm – sudden exposure to water can cause the throat to spasm. This accounts for infrequent cases of 'dry drowning' where the lungs do not fill with water.

Primary survey assessment of A – Airway: The assessment of A – Airway has common elements with the assessment of B – Breathing. If the patient is not breathing, the problem may be in the airway, or with the ability to breathe. The airway is assessed first.

Air going in and out = Airway OK
No air in and out = Airway problem

If the patient is able to speak, the airway is OK. In the absence of speech, observe other signs such as a vapour cloud in cold weather, the sound of air moving, or the rise and fall of the chest. Look also for an obvious airway obstruction such as a mouth packed with snow or other foreign material.

⊞ *Primary treatment of A – Airway obstruction:* Treatment of obstruction is a progression of actions from the most simple to the most desperate. Your hope is that the obstruction will be cleared without the need for significant movement of the patient.

The airway is opened using a jaw thrust, chin lift, or direct pull on the tongue, while the neck is held in the in-line position to protect the spinal cord (Fig 5.4). Cervical-spine stabilization is a component of basic life support, so whenever there is the possibility of neck injury, positioning is done with minimal neck movement. Hyperextension of the neck, although taught in the past as an airway opening technique, adds little or nothing to the effect and can be extremely harmful if the spine is injured.

Try moving air into the patient's lungs with mouth-to-mouth breaths. If air does not go in, reposition the airway and try again. If air does go in, the airway is not obstructed, and the problem is B – Breathing.

If positioning and test breaths do not succeed in moving air, the cause of the obstruction is assumed to be foreign material. You

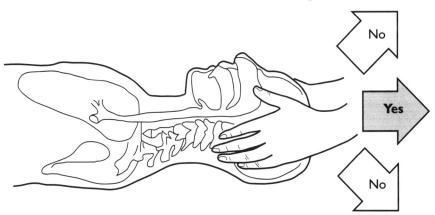

5.4 Gentle and steady 'in-line' position protects the airway and the spinal cord.

must clear the airway manually. Try first to use gravity to clear obstructions. The usual method is simply to roll the whole patient to the side, keeping the spine in line, and 'finger sweep' the mouth. If there is no evidence to suggest spine injury, roll the patient prone and pull up at the waist. This is effective in clearing vomit.

Another method is to use residual air to help clear obstructions. A sudden thrust to the abdomen or chest can force the air left in the patient's lungs out under pressure, blowing any obstruction out with it (Fig 5.5). The abdominal or chest thrust is done with the patient on his back. In cases where an obstructed patient is still conscious and standing, it is done from behind by grasping your own arms around the patient and squeezing. It really doesn't matter whether you are squeezing the abdomen or the chest, the effect is the same. For infants, the best method is to pound firmly on the patient's back between the shoulder blades while holding them head down.

B – Breathing

Even with an open airway, the patient may not ventilate adequately. Inadequate ventilation means not enough air is moving in and out to support life. This can be the result of the lack of nervous-system

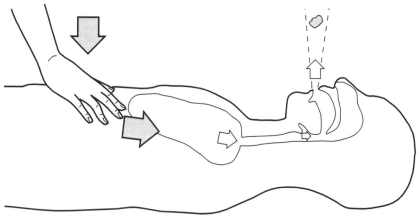

5.5 Abdominal or chest thrust – air trapped in the lungs can, under pressure, dislodge an obstruction.

drive due to an injured spinal cord or the loss of brain function. It can also occur when the bellows mechanism of the chest wall and diaphragm is damaged.

Primary assessment of B – Breathing:

Adequate ventilation = Breathing OK
Inadequate ventilation = Breathing not OK

'Not OK' and 'Inadequate' are inexact terms. They generally refer to ventilation that is absent, very slow or extremely irregular in an unconscious patient. Light-skinned individuals may turn pale or blue. If you are in doubt, consider the breathing inadequate and begin to support the ventilation. Ask a conscious patient for a verbal response. A person who is able to speak generally has ventilation adequate for the primary survey.

⊞ *Primary treatment of B – Breathing:* Inadequate or absent ventilation is treated by blowing into the lungs through the airway. This is called 'mouth-to-mouth ventilation' or 'artificial respiration'. This technique must be practised. Training sessions run by First Aid societies, using sophisticated dummies, are invaluable.

Mouth-to-mouth ventilation for an adult patient:

1. Ensure airway is open and pulse is present.

2. Pinch nostrils and seal your lips on patient's mouth.

3. Give 10 quick inflations.

4. Then inflate at about 10 breaths per minute, watching the chest rise and then deflate for each inflation.

5. Check pulse every minute.

6. When casualty is breathing normally, put in recovery position if unconscious.

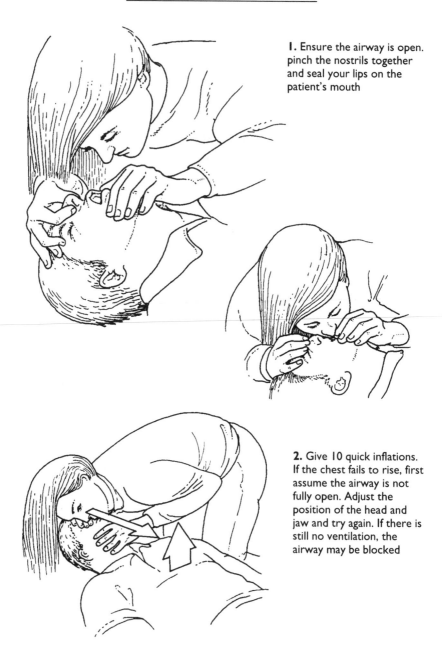

1. Ensure the airway is open. pinch the nostrils together and seal your lips on the patient's mouth

2. Give 10 quick inflations. If the chest fails to rise, first assume the airway is not fully open. Adjust the position of the head and jaw and try again. If there is still no ventilation, the airway may be blocked

5.6 Mouth-to-mouth ventilation.

C – Circulation – Pulse

Cardiac arrest refers to the loss of effective heart activity. No pulse can be felt. Cardiac arrest immediately leads to loss of consciousness and respiratory arrest due to loss of brain perfusion. A patient who is at all responsive (A, V, P on the AVPU scale), breathing or moving spontaneously is NOT in cardiac arrest.

Primary assessment of pulse: Pulses can be very difficult to find under adverse field conditions involving fear, cold hands, dangerous places etc. The pulse is very weak in the presence of shock, and very slow if the patient is in profound hypothermia. It is extremely important to take the time to find a pulse. The carotid pulse is the easiest to get to, and the strongest to feel. It is located on either side of the Adam's apple (larynx) in the neck. If the carotid pulse is absent, the heart is not beating.

> **Pulse = Circulation OK**
> **No pulse = Circulation not OK**

⊞ *Primary treatment for lack of pulse:* Cardio-pulmonary resuscitation (CPR) is a combination of chest compressions and mouth-to-mouth ventilation which produces some perfusion of the brain and vital organs. The generally accepted procedures for chest compressions and ventilation are outlined on page 203. CPR has limited application in the wilds. The patient's own natural heart activity must be restored quickly if the patient is to survive. This usually requires drugs and electrical defibrillation.

Although ventilation can support breathing for hours or days, chest compressions cannot support the circulation for a prolonged period of time. Most medical authorities are in agreement that the chances of survival are minimal if spontaneous heart activity is not restored within approximately 30 minutes. The exceptions to this are in cases of severe hypothermia, and in cases of cold-water drowning.

Chest compressions cannot preserve life where the cardiac arrest occurs as a result of massive trauma to the chest, severe blood loss, spinal-cord transection or massive head injury. In these situations it is best to accept that the patient has died. It is not necessary nor useful to start or to continue CPR when these conditions are discovered.

Therefore, although the procedure for CPR is summarized opposite, first aiders must accept that unless specialist help is nearby the chances of saving the patient's life may be very small.

CPR is used only for an unconscious patient whose heart has stopped. It combines the oxygenation of the patient's blood by the exhaled air of the rescuer (mouth-to-mouth ventilation) with the mechanical compression of the patient's chest. This drives the

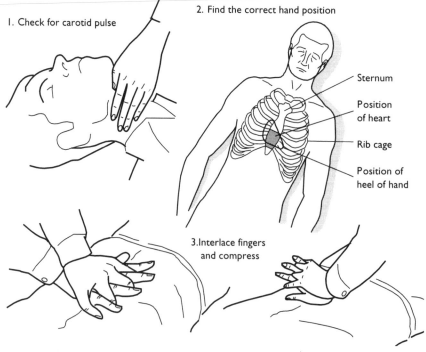

5.7 Cardio-pulmonary resuscitation (CPR).

patient's blood from the inactive heart to the oxygen-starved brain. As with mouth-to-mouth ventilation, training and practice in CPR are essential.

CPR for an adult casualty – a summary:

- If at all possible, expert help should be summoned immediately – this gives the casualty the best possible chance

1. Ensure airway open.
2. Check no spontaneous breathing.
3. Give two quick inflations.
4. Check no carotid pulse.
5. Single sharp blow to centre of sternum may restart heart. Check for restored pulse.
6. Place casualty horizontal or slightly head-down on a firm surface.
7. Find correct hand position.
8. Interlace your fingers and compress slightly faster than one per second ('One and two and three...').
9. Give 15 compressions, then two full ventilations.
10. Check for pulse only if there are signs of returning circulation.
11. If pulse returns, stop chest compression but continue ventilation if spontaneous breathing is not restored.
12. If both pulse and breathing are restored but patient remains unconscious, put in *recovery position* to protect airway.

Two practised rescuers can work effectively with coordinated compression and breathing in a 5:1 sequence.

These instructions are for adults. For children, the rates of compression and inflation need to be somewhat increased and less pressure applied.

The recovery position

The recovery position prevents patients from choking on their own vomit or ingesting the acids produced by the stomach. It cannot be used for casualties thought to be suffering from a spinal injury.

Kneeling beside the casualty, straighten the legs. Place the arm nearest to you at right angles to the casualty's body, then bend the upper arm parallel with the body, with the palm facing up. All the time ensure that the head is kept tilted back and the airway clear. Bring the arm furthest away from you across the casualty's chest and place their hand against the cheek nearest to you, with the palm facing outwards. This will cushion the patient's face and head when they are rolled over. Using your other hand, hold the thigh furthest

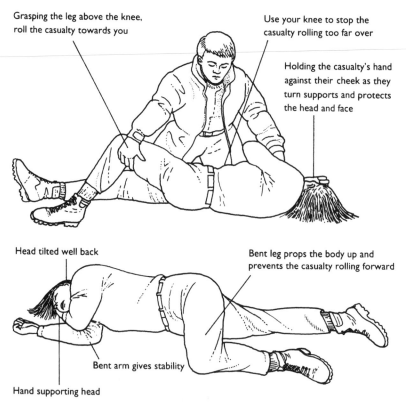

Grasping the leg above the knee, roll the casualty towards you

Use your knee to stop the casualty rolling too far over

Holding the casualty's hand against their cheek as they turn supports and protects the head and face

Head tilted well back

Bent leg props the body up and prevents the casualty rolling forward

Bent arm gives stability

Hand supporting head

5.8 The recovery position.

from you and, keeping the casualty's foot flat on the floor, draw up the knee. Keeping the casualty's hand pressed against their cheek, pull the raised thigh towards you. This will roll the casualty neatly into the correct recovery position.

Ensure that the head is kept tilted back and supported on the casualty's hand. Once in this position the casualty should never be left alone but should be closely monitored for breathing problems or their state of consciousness.

C – Circulation – Bleeding

Adequate perfusion requires sufficient circulating blood volume. Blood loss must be controlled as part of the basic life support process. Bleeding can be external and obvious, or internal and more difficult to detect and stop.

Primary assessment of severe bleeding: External bleeding is usually obvious, but can be missed when a full examination is not done. Snow can make bleeding less obvious because blood tends to melt through quickly and disappear. Bulky clothing can absorb or obscure blood with the same effect.

Bleeding from an artery is usually the most immediately life-threatening. It will be under pressure, and may spurt with the pulsing of the heart. There is no easy rule for deciding when bleeding is severe. Generally, if it looks like a lot of blood, it probably is, but a little can go a long way.

Internal bleeding is not so obvious, and will generally not be discovered in the primary survey. It can usually be inferred if the patient has suffered trauma, and is developing shock. Severe internal bleeding is frequently associated with fractures of the femur and pelvis, and blunt abdominal and chest injury.

⊞ *Primary treatment of severe bleeding:* All bleeding stops eventually – ideally we would like it to happen while the patient still has enough blood to appreciate our efforts! External bleeding is controlled by well-aimed direct pressure over the bleeding site. Pressure can be applied with the bare hand if necessary, but a bandage or cloth is preferred if available. This is not to absorb blood, but to provide even pressure across the damaged vessels.

If bleeding continues, remove the bandage and look again for the source of blood, and re-aim your pressure. You should expect to apply pressure for 10 minutes or more before a clot will form. Once bleeding is controlled, a pressure bandage should be applied. Beware, however, of obstructing circulation by creating an accidental tourniquet. Tourniquets are used only for major amputations if direct pressure is not effective.

D – Disability – Spine

Injuries to the vertebrae of the spine can damage the spinal cord with dramatic, devastating, and permanent results. It is essential that management of spine injury be considered part of basic life support. The most dangerous movement of the cervical spine is flexion (movement of the chin toward the chest). Moderate extension is usually safe. Hyperextension (tilting the head back) is dangerous (see Fig 5.4 on page 197, showing the 'in-line position').

Primary assessment of spine injury: Any event that could possibly produce spine injury is a positive mechanism. This is one of the factors you determine in your survey of the scene. Examples include a fall from a cliff, being tumbled by an avalanche, or a long swim over a short waterfall. No further examination is necessary, as these are all treated as spine injuries during *the primary survey*. The spine itself will be examined during the secondary survey and the possibility of injury can then be re-evaluated.

⊞ *Primary treatment of spine injury:* If no movement of the spine is required for treatment, or is likely to occur during your examination, leave things as they are while you complete your patient assessment. If you must move the spine, do so with an absolute minimum of rotation and no flexion. This will usually require three or four well-coordinated helpers (see page 253). Spine splints are applied after the patient assessment.

The airway can be managed effectively and safely with the neck held in position. If it is necessary to roll the patient to clear vomit, hold the head, neck and trunk in line as a unit (log roll). In the field, stabilization of the casualty's position with rucksacks, boulders or sandbags may be all that can be done until specialist equipment arrives.

D – Disability – Abnormal consciousness

Abnormal consciousness indicates nervous-system problems severe enough to affect the brain. Because it is an indicator of BIG 3 function, consciousness is included in the primary survey.

Primary assessment of consciousness: AVPU (see page 182) is a relatively precise and universally understood scale. It replaces subjective terms such as 'semiconscious' that are often vague and confusing.

⊞ *Primary treatment of level of consciousness changes:* There is no specific treatment in basic life support for the nervous-system problems indicated by AVPU changes. Treatment is aimed at the life-threatening airway/breathing/circulation problems which are causing the nervous-system changes.

6

The Big 3 Body Systems

The circulatory system

Structure and function

The circulatory system requires adequate pumping action from the heart and integrity of the vessels to maintain the pressure to perfuse the body tissues effectively with oxygenated blood. It also requires an adequate volume of blood. To complete its part in the BIG 3 triad, the circulatory system must have oxygen faithfully supplied to the lungs by the respiratory system, and good nervous-system control of heart rate and blood-vessel pressure.

There are three major components of the circulatory system:
1. Heart – maintains blood flow and pressure through pumping action.
2. Blood vessels – contain blood volume. Able to help maintain pressure through constriction controlled by the nervous system.
3. Blood – fluid and cell mixture contained within the circulatory system.

Normal function of the circulatory system requires:
1. Adequate pumping action from the heart.
2. Integrity and muscle tone of the blood vessels.
3. Adequate volume of blood.

Circulatory-system problems

Shock

Shock is often misunderstood and misrepresented. True shock is *not* caused by fatigue, disappointment, surprise, grief or any other reaction to *psychological* stress. These factors often cause a condition called 'acute stress reaction', which can look like shock but has none of the serious consequences. True shock is a *physiological* condition, caused by an acute loss of perfusion pressure in the circulatory system. Shock can be the result of failure of the pumping actions of the heart, dilation or leaking of the blood vessels, or loss of blood volume.

True shock always indicates a life-threatening physical condition which requires specific, aggressive treatment, preferably in a hospital. It does not improve spontaneously in the field. Without treatment, the patient will die.

The classic symptoms of shock are pale skin, elevated heart rate and elevated respiratory rate, all caused by the body's attempt to compensate for loss of normal perfusion pressure. Shock develops along a spectrum of severity from mild to severe. Progression can be stopped at any given point, but it is more common for shock to progress from bad to worse. There are various types of shock, but the most commonly encountered in wilderness emergencies is *volume shock*.

In trauma, sudden loss of circulating blood volume is usually the result of internal or external bleeding. However, blood volume can also be lost indirectly over the course of hours or days through dehydration. The fluid that one loses as sweat, vomit, or diarrhoea will ultimately result in reduced fluid volume in the blood stream.

Assessment of shock: A history of trauma sufficient to cause severe internal or external bleeding should make you think immediately of volume shock. This is also true of severe fluid loss from diarrhoea, vomiting or sweating. The classic sign of cool and pale skin is caused by the shell/core effect during compensation. This particular sign may be less than useful in cold environments, as the shell/core effect is also part of the body's normal protection against heat loss.

Signs of shock

The late George MacKenzie of Forres used to teach how to remember the signs of shock by using all the Ps.

The signs of shock:

- **Pallor** – pale due to low blood volume available in system (hypovolaemic shock).

- **Pulse** – fast heartbeat (due to low blood volume) and weak pulse; it feels thready.

- **Panting** – air hunger; the brain needs more oxygenated blood so the breathing rate is increased.

- **Pleading for water** – thirst due to reduced blood volume; patient probably needs a drip set up, but not all rescue teams have this capability.

- **Pain** – one cause of shock.

- **Panic** – casualty is probably very anxious.

- **Plucking at garments** – anxiety.

- **Perspiration** – a cold sweat.

- **Puking** – a feeling of nausea.

- **Proper poorly.**

- **Passes out.**

The vital-sign pattern shows the compensation mechanisms at work. A loss of blood volume or of other body fluid results in an emergency effort by the body to maintain perfusion to vital organs. The degree of change in vital signs reflects the severity of the fluid loss.

The first vital sign change to occur as shock develops is an increase in heart rate (P), followed closely by an increase in the respiratory rate (R). If you are able to measure blood pressure (BP), you will observe that it remains near normal early on, which shows that the compensatory mechanisms are working. In long-term care, urine output is a good measurement of available fluid in the core circulation. Reduced blood volume will be reflected in greatly reduced urine output.

In the early stages of shock, this compensation mechanism may work so well that it prevents symptoms from being noticed. As long as the brain remains adequately perfused, the patient's mental functions will be fairly normal. However, as the shell/core compensation mechanism is overwhelmed (decompensation), perfusion to the brain is reduced and the 'onion' starts to peel. The higher brain functions (personality, problem-solving ability etc) are the most sensitive to decreased perfusion. As shock progresses, compensation will fail, perfusion pressure will fall, and level of consciousness (C) will decay.

Vital signs in volume shock:

	Normal	Mild	Moderate	Severe
BP	>110/64	Normal	Decreased	Decreased
P	72	<100	100–120	>120
R	12	14–20	20–35	35
C	Alert	Anxious	Anxious	V, P or U
T	37°C (98.6°F)	Normal	Normal	Normal
S	Normal or pale	Normal Cool	Pale Cool	Pale
Urine output	>30ml/hour	Decreased	Decreased	None

⊞ *Treatment of shock:* Shock is generally a serious BIG 3 problem that you cannot treat effectively in the wilds. The traditional 'treatments' of reassurance, elevating the feet and keeping warm

⊞ **Generic temporary treatment for shock**

Stop volume loss

Maintaining full volume is helpful for any type of shock. In the field, this usually means the control of external bleeding. Internal bleeding and other types of fluid loss may be impossible to control in the wilderness setting.

All external bleeding can be stopped by well-aimed direct pressure, with or without bandages. If direct pressure on the bleeding site does not seem to be working, you are either not applying enough pressure or you are in the wrong place. Take your hand and the bandage away, look for the source of the blood, and try again. Pressure points and tourniquets (except in cases of complete amputation) are much less effective, and may do harm.

Position

Lying flat with legs elevated works with gravity to perfuse core organs. This is the textbook 'treatment' for shock found in every first aid book. This position may be helpful, but it is certainly not definitive treatment. Warmth and reassurance are also helpful, but are not definitive either. Protection from heat loss is important for any patient exposed to the environment and unable to exercise to maintain body heat.

Fluids

Sometimes brought to the scene by rescue teams, intravenous fluids infused rapidly and directly into the circulatory system can help restore volume. This is only a temporary measure to stabilize the patient during evacuation.

In cases where mild shock is developing slowly due to sweating or diarrhoea, drinking fluids may reverse the problem. However, this is a very slow method of fluid replacement which will not be very effective if shock is more severe or fluid loss is rapid.

Oxygen

Supplementary oxygen may be brought to the scene by rescue teams if weight and time constraints allow, but is also only a temporary measure, and has limited effect in the field setting.

are certainly good for any patient in shock, but do nothing to address the real problem of low blood volume. A patient in shock needs intravenous fluids, surgeons and a hospital. This is a bona fide emergency and you are justified in recruiting whatever help is necessary to get the patient to advanced medical care. The only real field treatment for shock is evacuation. There are, of course, temporary measures which may help stabilize the situation long enough to reach medical care.

Acute stress reaction (ASR)

Following sudden stress or injury (which may or may not be serious) a variety of reactions, including extreme anxiety, feeling dazed or disoriented, fainting, hyperventilating and pain masking – sometimes called 'psychogenic shock' or 'acute stress reaction' – commonly occur. Because these reactions are also under the control of the nervous system, they may appear similar to true shock or the compensation mechanism of volume shock.

The use of the term psychogenic 'shock' for this phenomenon can be confusing and misleading, because the consequences are very different from true shock. It is important to distinguish true shock, in its various degrees of compensation and levels of severity, from an acute stress reaction, which might look similar but is not at all life-threatening.

In the hospital or ambulance setting the difference is less important, since both are managed as shock. For long-term management in the wilderness, however, recognizing ASR for what it is, when possible, can save a lot of emergency resources, not to mention your peace of mind.

Assessment of ASR: The key to recognizing acute stress reaction is in the cause of injury and the progression of symptoms. ASR can look like shock, but can occur with or without any mechanism of injury which can cause shock. Also, with the passage of time ASR will get better, especially with calm reassurance.

We have all seen people with only minor extremity sprains or superficial wounds become lightheaded, pale and nauseated. Although they look 'shocky' there is no cause for alarm, and certainly no need for helicopters and emergency surgery. They have no mechanism for sudden volume loss. We let them lie down and get better.

It is important to remember that acute stress reaction can co-exist with true shock. In cases where the patient has both a good reason to be in true shock, and the signs and symptoms to go with it, you must treat it as such.

⊞ *Field treatment of ASR:* Allowing the patient to lie down, providing calm reassurance and relieving pain by treating injuries should result in immediate improvement in symptoms. This is the traditional 'treatment for shock' that is described in many first aid texts.

Case study

Subjective: An 18-year old man skiing off-piste fell against a stump, injuring his left upper leg. He was unable to move without extreme pain, and was forced to lie in the snow until he was discovered about an hour later.

The skier who found him was also alone, and immediately left the scene to report a 'dead body' on the slope. By that time it was just past sunset. The air temperature was -5°C (23°F) with a moderate north wind.

Objective: Ski patrollers found the patient lying on his back in the snow. Ski tracks in the powder exposed a large spruce stump. The patient's airway was clear and he was breathing. The only response noted was a weak grimace when the patroller doing his secondary survey touched the patient's left thigh. Even through ski clothing, the patroller could feel that the leg was quite swollen. Vital signs at 17.40 – BP: unknown; P: 120; R: 24; C: P on AVPU scale; T: feels cold; S: pale.

Assessment:
1. Volume shock.
2. Fracture of the left femur.
3. Unreliable examination; cannot rule out spine injury.

Anticipated problems: Severe hypothermia.

The patient's neck was immobilized using a blanket roll. The limbs were aligned using 'traction into position' (see pages 239–40), and the patient was wrapped in blankets and a plastic sheet and immobilized in the toboggan. During the ride down the mountain, the patrollers stopped every minute to check airway and breathing. They arrived at the first aid station 20 minutes later. The patient was transferred immediately to an ambulance for the one-hour ride to hospital.

Discussion: This fellow arrived at the hospital, alive, with a body core temperature of 34.7°C (94.4°F), in compensated volume shock. His left femur was fractured, and the femoral artery lacerated – the cause of substantial internal bleeding.

The respiratory system

Structure and function

One of the BIG 3 body systems, the respiratory system performs the task of bringing adequate quantities of outside air into close proximity with blood (circulatory system). This takes place in alveoli of the lungs, where only a thin membrane separates air from blood, allowing the diffusion of oxygen into the blood, and carbon dioxide out of it.

The rest of the system consists of semi-rigid tubes to conduct air to the alveoli, and a bellows system for moving the air in and out. Like the circulatory system, respiration is under nervous-system control. Under normal conditions, the brain measures the pH (acidity) of the blood, which is a reflection of the amount of carbon dioxide dissolved in it. Too much carbon dioxide in the blood causes the pH to drop. The brain responds by increasing the rate and depth of respiration to 'blow off' the carbon dioxide until a normal pH is re-established. Conversely, too little carbon dioxide is corrected by decreasing the rate and the depth of respiration.

The respiratory system consists of five major components:
1. Upper airway – consists of the mouth (oropharynx), nose (nasopharynx), and the throat (larynx).
2. Lower airway – composed of large tubes (trachea), smaller tubes (bronchi), and the smallest tubes (bronchioles).
3. Alveoli – the terminal membraneous air sacs at the end of the system, adjacent to blood-filled capillaries where oxygen and carbon dioxide exchange occurs.
4. Chest wall and diaphragm – in normal function, the action is similar to a bellows. Inspiration (the intake of air) is caused by the active contraction of the diaphragm and chest-wall muscles, which expand the rib cage, sucking air into the lungs. Expiration (air out) is a passive process which occurs when these muscles relax and the natural elasticity of the lungs and chest squeeze out the air.
5. Nervous-system drive – the nervous system (brain) controls the rate and depth of respiration in response to the amount of carbon dioxide and oxygen in the blood.

Normal function of the respiratory system requires:
1. Clear upper airway.
2. Clear lower airway.
3. Alveoli with membranes exposed to air.
4. Functioning bellows.
5. Intact nervous system.

Respiratory-system problems

There are dozens of different respiratory system problems which can develop directly, or be the indirect result of circulatory- or nervous-system problems. They all have the same effect: reducing oxygen supply to the blood (except hyperventilation syndrome). We can condense these problems into five broad categories, which are given the same generic treatment, with a few additional specifics. Since the generic treatment applies to all respiratory problems, we will outline it first.

⊞ **Generic treatment for respiratory distress**

Position
Any patient in respiratory distress, who is able to move, will already have found the best position in which to breathe. This is usually sitting up to allow gravity to assist the diaphragm, and to help keep fluids out of the airway tubes. In unconscious or immobile patients, special care must be taken to position them in a way that prevents airway obstruction from secretions, vomit, or the collapse of their own airway. This is usually on the patient's side, with the head and neck in the 'in-line' position.

Reassurance
Encourage the patient to breathe more slowly and more deeply rather than panting like a dog. This brings in fresh oxygen rather than moving the same old carbon dioxide back and forth in the tubes.

Ventilation
A patient in respiratory distress will fatigue rapidly. Assistance to respiration may be given by use of an AMBU-type resuscitator or, in principle, by use of mouth-to-mouth ventilation coinciding with the patient's own breathing. This can be problematical.

Oxygen
If available, giving supplementary oxygen will increase the concentration of oxygen getting into the blood, and ultimately, to the brain.

Upper airway obstruction

The upper airway may be obstructed by the tongue, a piece of food, or the fact that the patient's head is under water. Obstruction can also be the result of swelling from trauma or infection.

Assessment of upper airway obstruction: If the primary survey reveals the absence of respiration, even if the patient is still conscious, basic life support procedures should be instituted immediately (see pages 194–207).

If airway obstruction is not complete, the patient may have noisy and difficult respiration. The ability to swallow is often impaired, and the patient may dribble. Talking may be difficult or impossible.

Assessment of partial obstruction is directed at determining whether the patient is getting enough air to support life until medical care can be reached. You are looking for signs that oxygenation of the blood is adequate: good skin colour, minimal changes in consciousness and mental status (A on the AVPU scale), and no worsening of the respiratory distress.

⊞ *Treatment of upper airway obstruction:* For the treatment of complete airway obstruction, or partial obstruction with inadequate oxygenation, refer to page 198.

In cases where a foreign object is lodged in the throat for a brief time and successfully removed before the patient gets into difficulties, you may certainly congratulate yourself on a real 'save'. However, be aware that the object may have caused sufficient irritation to result in later swelling, which is another form of obstruction. Such a patient should be watched closely, and an evacuation begun if necessary.

In cases of partial airway obstruction with adequate oxygenation, the rule is 'do no harm'. Apply the generic treatment of respiratory distress and evacuate quickly. In almost all cases of partial obstruction, breathing cool air will reduce swelling of the airway temporarily. Be prepared to perform the airway-opening manoeuvres detailed on page 197 if it becomes apparent that the airway is closing. A partial obstruction frequently becomes worse over time.

Lower airway constriction

Spasm, swelling or the accumulation of mucus or pus can cause narrowing the lower airway tubes (bronchi and bronchioles). This is what happens in asthma, bronchitis and anaphylaxis. The effect is to slow the movement of air in and out of the lung tissue.

Assessment of lower airway constriction: Expiration is often prolonged, with wheezing and gurgling. In some patients, the lower airway noise is loud enough to hear from a distance. At other times you may need a stethoscope or an ear to the patient's chest.

The patient may recall exposure to smoke, inhaled water or other irritating substances, indicating a generalized swelling. They may have been exposed to something to which they are allergic, indicating anaphylaxis. Or there may be a history of slowly worsening illness and fever, pointing to respiratory infection. Whatever the cause, the patient usually develops a cough as the respiratory system tries to clear itself. There may be an obvious increase in respiratory effort as the system struggles to move air against increased resistance.

Vital signs may show increases in the compensatory mechanisms, with elevated heart and respiratory rates. The presence of fever may indicate a respiratory infection.

⊞ *Treatment of lower airway constriction:*
1. Generic treatment for respiratory distress (see page 217).
2. In the field, this is largely confined to the use of an asthmatic's own inhaler.

Pulmonary fluid

Excess fluid accumulates in the alveoli (air sacs) blocking the exchange of oxygen and carbon dioxide between air and blood. This may come from outside the system or from within.

Sources of pulmonary fluids:

- **Aspiration** – vomit or other foreign material is inhaled.

- **Drowning** – water is inhaled in 'wet drowning'.

- **Pulmonary oedema** – fluid may leak from circulatory system capillaries into the alveoli (air sac). This can be the result of too much pressure in the capillaries from congestive heart failure, swelling in reaction to irritants like water and smoke, or the effect of high altitude.

- **Bleeding** – contusion or laceration of the lung tissue may cause alveoli to fill with blood.

- **Pneumonia** – infection fills the air sacs with pus.

Assessment of pulmonary fluid: Large amounts of fluid in the lungs will cause gurgling which can be heard at a distance. Fluid may actually froth at the mouth. Small amounts of fluid may be heard with an ear to the chest as 'crackling' on respiration. Vital signs will show that the body is compensating for partial loss of lung function with an increase in respiratory and heart rates. The development of fever indicates infection.

In less severe cases, this loss of lung function may not be noticed while the patient is at rest. However, with the increased demands of exercise, reduced lung capacity will become obvious as the patient becomes short of breath much more easily than normal.

Coughing is common with the accumulation of pulmonary fluid. It may produce sputum tinged with pus or blood. There may have been an injury to lung tissue through exposure to smoke, infection or near-drowning. Or you may be experiencing the beginnings of high-altitude pulmonary oedema.

⊞ *Treatment of pulmonary fluid*
1. Generic treatment for respiratory distress (see page 217).
2. Specific treatment for pulmonary fluid. Evacuation to medical care. In high-altitude sickness, immediate descent.

Chest trauma

Trauma to the chest wall or airway tubes can interfere with the function of the respiratory system in a number of ways. The injuries are usually complicated and severe, and cannot be managed effectively in the field. Chest trauma with respiratory distress is best evacuated without delay.

Lung contusion is the term applied to the development of generic swelling in the lung tissue following injury. The chest wall remains stable with the bellows system intact, but pulmonary fluid begins to accumulate in the alveoli. This can occur along with suspected rib fracture, or any severe blow to the chest.

An unstable chest wall, also called a 'flail chest', indicates that the bellows system is damaged to the point where it is no longer rigid. The chest wall collapses with inspiration, causing incomplete lung expansion.

Haemothorax and pneumothorax are terms used to describe the presence of blood (haem) or air (pneumo) in the chest cavity (thorax). This blood and/or air occupies the space between the lungs and the chest wall, preventing full expansion of the lungs even though the bellows may continue to operate. In the case of an open pneumothorax, sometimes called a 'sucking chest wound', air may enter the chest cavity through an injury in the chest wall. In a closed pneumothorax, air may enter the chest cavity through an injured lung. It may affect one side or both. Flail chests are common in motor accidents due to impact with the steering wheel.

Assessment of chest trauma: There will be evidence of significant blunt trauma to the chest, or of penetrating injury. There may be bruising, fractured ribs or other evidence of potential injury to lungs or chest wall. In the presence of chest-wall injury or haemopneumothorax, there may be a radical decrease in respiration even though the patient is obviously making a great effort to breathe. It will be apparent by level of consciousness, mental-status changes and other vital signs that the patient is not getting enough oxygen. Significant

6.1 A flail chest. The flail segment is sucked IN when the chest expands and pushed OUT when the chest contracts.

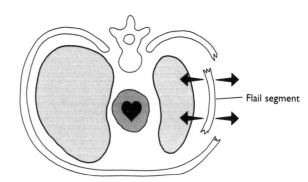

Flail segment

injury to the circulatory system also often occurs with severe chest trauma, and will result in volume shock.

⊞ *Treatment of chest trauma:*
1. Generic treatment for respiratory distress (see page 217). Like the treatment for shock, this is limited and temporary only. The patient with chest injury significant enough to cause respiratory distress requires immediate evacuation.
2. Specific treatment for chest trauma. Lying on the injured side reduces pain, and may reduce instability. Gravity can help prevent blood from building up in the uninjured side of the chest. In the case of a simple rib fracture, a wide bandage wrapped around the chest can make the patient more comfortable and thus better able to control bleeding.

In cases of open chest wounds, the injury should be covered with an airtight seal, such as a piece of plastic bag. This will stop the 'sucking' chest wound from allowing air into the chest cavity instead of the lungs. If the patch works the way it should, respiration and oxygenation should improve. If symptoms become worse, the patch should be removed.

Decreased nervous-system drive
Breathing is controlled by the nervous system. If the nervous system ceases to function, breathing will stop (respiratory arrest). The

causes include toxins and drugs, head injury, altitude sickness, lightning strike and hypothermia.

Assessment of decreased nervous-system drive: As respiratory drive decreases for whatever reason, respiratory rate and depth decrease, become irregular or stop. The difference between adequate and inadequate respiration is not always clear. Vital signs are likely to be affected by whatever the nervous-system problem is, and therefore are not reliable indicators of whether or not the patient is getting enough oxygen. However, anyone with pale or blue skin, slowed or irregular breathing, and reduced level of consciousness should be considered to be in need of treatment for respiratory distress.

⊞ *Treatment for decreased nervous-system drive:*
1. Basic life support (see pages 194–207).
2. Generic treatment for respiratory distress (see page 217).
3. Evacuation. Correcting the nervous system problem is not something you are likely to do in the field.

Hyperventilation (increased nervous-system drive)

Increased respiratory drive normally occurs with altitude, exercise and other physiological demands. Abnormal increase in respiration occurs with acute stress reaction (see pages 193–4). The result can be an abnormal decrease in the carbon-dioxide concentration in the blood, with the pH increasing. This is blood chemistry out of balance, which can affect the nervous system, usually referred to as 'hyperventilation syndrome'.

Assessment of hyperventilation: Hyperventilation can occur with or without obvious fast and heavy breathing. It takes only a slight increase in depth and rate over time to cause changes in blood pH. The respiratory changes observed in your measurement of vital signs may be very subtle.

It can be difficult to distinguish between hyperventilation syndrome and serious respiratory- or nervous-system problems, especially if there is a positive mechanism for injury. As with other components of acute stress reaction, however, it gets significantly better with time and basic treatment.

There are some classic nervous-system effects of hyperventilation which are worth mentioning. Tingling of hands and feet occurs with most moderate and severe reactions. Tingling and numbness around the mouth is also common. The ability to move extremities voluntarily is unaffected.

⊞ *Treatment of hyperventilation:*
1. Generic treatment for respiratory distress (see page 217).
2. Specific treatment for hyperventilation syndrome.
   Reassurance is specific and effective. Patients generally feel better with an explanation of their symptoms, and can be 'coached' to breathe slower. When you are certain that hyperventilation is the only problem, breathing into a paper bag is occasionally used to increase artificially the concentration of carbon dioxide in the air inhaled. This seems to work, probably mostly by placebo effect.

The nervous system

Structure and function

The nervous system consists of the brain, spinal cord and peripheral nerves. In addition to being responsible for remembering where you left your torch, the brain controls all critical life functions. Its primary connection with the circulatory and respiratory systems is through the spinal cord. The brain and cord are encased in the bony structures of the skull and the spinal vertebrae.

From the gaps between vertebrae, peripheral nerves branch out from the spinal cord to all body tissues. Nerves controlling the most critical functions leave the cord at the base of the skull and in the neck. This is why spinal-cord injuries that occur in this area can cause extreme disability or death due to the loss of nervous-system control over vital body functions.

All nervous-system tissue is extremely sensitive to injury, especially oxygen deprivation. The most highly evolved functions of the brain, such as intellect and personality, are the most susceptible. For example, reduced perfusion due to shock will affect mental status before it affects the more primitive respiratory-drive centres of the brain. This is why changes in mental status are often the best first indicators of a developing life-threatening condition.

The nervous system consists of two major components:
1. The central nervous system – consists of the brain and spinal cord encased in the bony protection of the skull and spine.
2. The peripheral nervous system – composed of the unprotected nerves running between the central nervous system and the body tissues. These nerves typically run in bundles along with arteries and veins.

Normal nervous-system function requires:
1. Uninterrupted perfusion of the central nervous system with oxygenated blood.
2. Intact central and peripheral nerve pathways between the central nervous system and the body tissues.

Nervous-system problems

Increased intracranial pressure (ICP)
This condition is sometimes referred to by first aiders as 'brain compression'. Like other body tissues, the brain will swell from bleeding and oedema when injured, Unlike other tissues, however, the brain is confined within the rigid structure of the skull (cranium) where there simply is not much additional space to accommodate swelling. Therefore, injury to the brain or other intracranial tissues can produce a dangerous rise in intracranial pressure which can prevent adequate perfusion with oxygenated blood. Common causes include severe head injury, stroke and high-altitude cerebral oedema.

Assessment of increased ICP: Like shock, brain compression has a typical pattern and spectrum of severity, regardless of its cause or rate of onset.

Assessment of increased ICP:

- **History** – look for cause of injury to brain tissue such as trauma, suffocation or altitude.

- **Abnormal consciousness** – although other vital-sign changes occur, alteration of consciousness and mental status is the most sensitive early indicator of increased ICP. This is the peeling of the 'evolutionary onion' again. The patient may appear 'drunk' or become combative or restless early, with decrease on the AVPU scales as the condition progresses. It can be very difficult or even impossible to tell the difference between a patient who is intoxicated by alcohol or drugs, and someone with developing compression.

- **Vomiting** – persistent vomiting is also a relatively reliable early indicator of problems with ICP.

- **Headache** – severe headache is an early sign of increased ICP. However, it is easily confused with pain from an injured neck, scalp or skull.

- **Unequal pupils** – this sign is worthy of special mention because it is frequently cited as evidence of brain injury, even in patients showing no mental-status changes. However, this is a late sign in increased ICP. It occurs only with or after significant changes in consciousness. An alert, oriented person with unequal pupils either has an eye problem or is just built that way. Do not rely on this sign out of context.

- **Other signs** – paralysis, fits, irregular breathing or other signs of BIG 3 problems may also develop late in the progress of increased ICP. They may follow consciousness and mental-status changes by minutes, hours or days.

⊞ *Treatment of increased ICP:* Unfortunately, field treatment will have little effect on the patient's chances of recovery. Surgery is generally required to relieve pressure and stop intracranial bleeding. The rapid onset of severe swelling and compression from intracranial bleeding will probably be fatal in most wilderness settings.

However, early recognition of swelling which may be developing more slowly can save lives. As long as the patient remains alive, there are steps you can take to give the injured person a chance. The key is good basic life support and rapid evacuation, with special attention to protection of the cervical spine and the airway. As long as there is a heartbeat, there is a chance of at least partial recovery from severe head injury. Once the heart has stopped, however, there is little or no chance of recovery.

Concussion (minor head injury)

Minor head injury, usually referred to as 'concussion', occurs when the patient strikes their head while falling, or something falls on the patient's head. The event results in a temporary loss of some neurological function, indicating that the brain has suffered some degree of injury, although pressure within the skull is not increased.

Assessment of minor head injury: Typically, the patient experiences a brief loss of consciousness or lapse of memory for the event itself. ('What happened? How did I get here?'). They may feel dazed, sleepy or nauseated.

Assessment is directed at determining whether the injured brain tissue will swell enough in the next 24 hours to increase pressure on the brain. Will this minor concussion become a severe head injury?

This is one of the classic medical dilemmas: to evacuate now, or wait and watch.

There are no absolute rules, but there are some general guidelines. Minor head injuries associated with the danger signs listed overleaf are more likely to become serious problems.

⊞ *Treatment of minor head injury:* Concussion requires no specific field treatment. However, it is important to monitor the patient carefully for at least 24 hours to detect any onset of brain compression. Patients being monitored should not use narcotic or stimulant drugs, or drink alcohol. These would make the assessment of consciousness and mental-status changes very difficult.

Generally, in a remote wilderness setting it is best to begin the evacuation of patients with confirmed concussion, rather than wait

---

DANGER SIGNS – minor head injury:

● **Any decline in consciousness or mental status following an injury.**

● **The patient vomits or complains of severe headache.**

---

for the onset of brain compression. This is especially true of patients with the danger signs listed above. You must also remember to evaluate and treat as for cervical spine injury, which has the same cause of injury (see page 250).

In less remote settings, you might choose to camp closer to a road for a day. If you are on the water, you might want to alter course to sail closer inshore as you monitor your patient over the succeeding 24 hours.

Fits

Brain tissue has electrical properties much like heart tissue. Fits are caused by an unco-ordinated burst of electrical activity in the brain. They have a variety of causes.

Assessment of fits: The important consideration in assessment is the context in which the fit occurs. Fits can be part of the pattern of increased ICP in trauma patients, or a relatively expected occurrence in a patient with epilepsy. They can be related to drug use, or occur for no apparent reason in an otherwise healthy individual.

The classic 'grand mal' fit is characterized by generalized tensing of all body muscles and repetitive, purposeless movement. Although the eyes may be open, the patient will be unresponsive during the fit, and may be incontinent. There will usually be a period of drowsiness and disorientation after the fit has ended.

⊞ *Treatment of fits:* Protection from injury is the most important treatment that you can provide the patient during the fit. Most will resolve spontaneously in a short period of time. Protect the patient from injury when falling or thrashing. Common layman's 'treatments', such as chest compressions and trying to force objects between the teeth, are unnecessary and should be avoided.

Fitting patients will normally hold their breath for a short period of time and become cyanotic (blue). This is not a problem as long as it does not last more than a couple of minutes. Position the patient and ventilate if necessary after the seizure has resolved. Be prepared to open and clear the airway, if necessary, once the fit has ended.

The real worry, of course, is not the fit itself, but what has caused it. Unless the patient is a known epileptic who has frequent fits, the cause must be researched by a neurologist. Since the fit may be the first sign of a serious condition, evacuation is a good idea.

Spinal-cord trauma

The delicate tissue of the spinal cord, really an extension of the brain, is surrounded and protected by the bones of the spinal column. Unstable injuries of the spinal column, such as fractures or dislocation, can easily injure the cord. Spinal-cord injuries are usually permanent, but recovery is sometimes possible with careful treatment.

Field assessment and treatment of spinal-cord injury: This is essentially the same as that for spine fracture, which is covered on pages 249–54. Even if the cord is already injured, careful extrication, treatment and evacuation controls further damage and increases the chance of recovery.

Peripheral-nerve injury

The peripheral nervous system encompasses all nervous tissue outside of the brain and spinal cord. Peripheral nerves have the same cable-like structure as the spinal cord, but they are not enclosed in bony protection. They are damaged in the same manner as the cord by direct trauma from adjacent bones and joints which are unstable.

Peripheral nerves are also affected by pressure, which can deprive them of adequate perfusion by oxygenated blood. The gradual onset of tingling and numbness of the arms caused by pressure on the nerves under rucksack straps is a minor condition familiar to backpackers.

Assessment of peripheral-nerve injury: Loss of movement and sensation in the area beyond an injury site can indicate nerve damage, for which little can be done in the field. However, remember that this can be caused by ischaemia (loss of circulation), which is usually easily remedied.

⊞ *Treatment of peripheral-nerve injury:* In the field, the treatment of peripheral-nerve injury is the same as the treatment for loss of circulation. Both are managed by removing the source of pressure, such as by loosening a splint, realigning a fracture or dislocation, or reducing swelling of an injured extremity. This is part of the general management of fractures (see pages 235–43).

7

Bones, Joints and Soft Tissue

The musculoskeletal system

You will recall from the previous chapters that a life-or-limb-threatening emergency involves a major problem with the nervous, respiratory or circulatory systems. It is extremely important to recognize these problems when they occur. However, in a remote situation it can be just as important to recognize when they *don't*.

If you have taken a first aid course, you may recall a lot of concern over fractures of the femur (thigh bone), skull, spine, pelvis and ribs. It is important to appreciate that the real problems are not the fractured bones themselves, but the potential injury to the vital organs adjacent to them. Trauma patients do not die from fractures, sprains, strains and contusions. They die from airway obstruction, blood loss and brain injury.

With a fractured femur or pelvis, we actually worry more about lacerated arteries (major circulatory system injury). With the ribs, we are concerned with the lungs, liver or spleen (circulatory and respiratory systems). With the skull or spine fractures, it is the brain and spinal cord (nervous system) inside that is of real concern.

Therefore, an important first step in handling any musculoskeletal problem is ruling out a major injury to one of the BIG 3 body systems. Remember that your primary survey should always focus on Airway, Breathing, Circulation and Disability, not broken bones or dislocated joints. However, suspecting fractures in the pelvis, femur, spine and skull should serve to focus your attention on the potential for BIG 3 problems.

If your primary survey reveals no existing BIG 3 injury, you have given yourself the luxury of time: time to perform a secondary survey, think, treat and safely evacuate yourself or your patient to medical care hours or days later. This may require help from rescue teams, but rarely as a hurried or risky undertaking.

Structure and function

Arms, legs and fingers work on a system of cables, pulleys and levers. The components are called muscles and tendons, ligaments, cartilage and bones. The basic structure involves long bones connected by ligaments at joints which are padded by cartilage. Muscles and tendons work in balanced opposition across joints. The contraction of muscle on one side of the joint moves the bone one way; contraction on the other side moves it back. There are, of course, many types of bones and joints, but it is not necessary to know each one for effective field treatment.

The spine is best viewed as another long bone with the head and pelvis as joints on each end. The same basic parts and principles are at work. The major difference is the complexity and importance of the adjacent soft tissue.

Musculoskeletal-system problems

The familiar medical terminology used to describe musculoskeletal injury includes:

Contusions – bruising of soft tissue or bone.
Strains – stretch injuries to muscle or tendon.
Sprains – stretch injuries to ligaments.
Fractures – broken bones.
Dislocations – disruption of joints.

In the field, what we really want to know is whether the injury is *stable* or *unstable*. Since fractured bones are a good example of the kind of unstable injury we worry about, we can simplify our assessment to determine whether an injury is likely to involve fracture (unstable), or unlikely to involve fracture (stable).

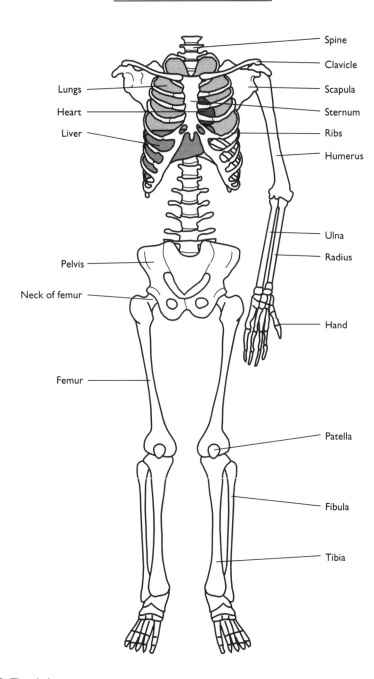

7.1 The skeleton.

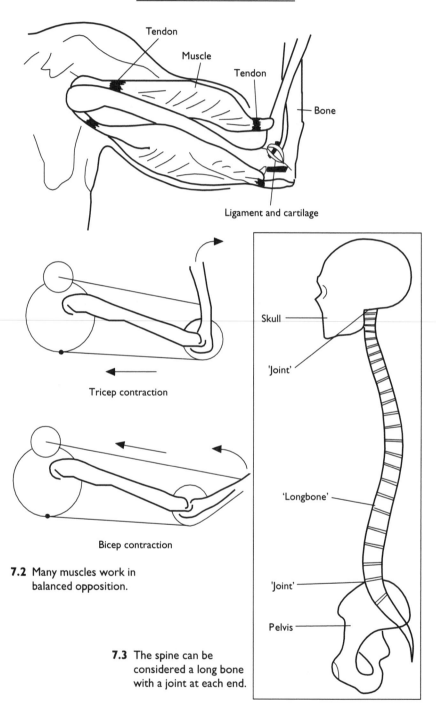

Tendon

Muscle

Tendon

Bone

Ligament and cartilage

Tricep contraction

Bicep contraction

7.2 Many muscles work in balanced opposition.

Skull

'Joint'

'Longbone'

'Joint'

Pelvis

7.3 The spine can be considered a long bone with a joint at each end.

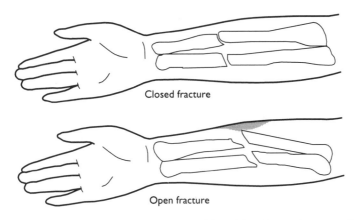

7.4 There are two main types of fracture, closed (simple) and open (compound).

Unstable injuries – fractures

Fractured bones result in unstable or potentially unstable fragments with very sharp ends. Fractures may be open (*compound*) or closed (*simple*). In an open fracture, the fracture site is exposed to the outside environment through a wound in the skin. This opening can be produced from inside by sharp bone ends, or from outside by the same object that caused the fracture.

Bones are living tissue. They are painful when injured and can bleed from their own rich blood supply. Unstable fragments can cause injury to adjacent nerves and blood vessels. It is important, therefore, to stabilize adequately any injury in which fracture is a possibility.

Since very few of us go backpacking or canoeing with an X-ray machine, it is often impossible to tell if a bone is actually broken. In the field, we use other assessment skills and rule of treatment. When an injury has the cause, signs and symptoms of fracture, we treat it as such. For our purposes in the field:

Possible fracture = Fracture

In talking about the assessment and treatment of fractures, we will consider three main groups:

1. *Extremity fractures* requiring the stabilization of an individual extremity such as an arm or ankle.
2. *Dislocations* which may require reduction (putting the dislocated bone back in place) as part of the stabilization.
3. *Spine, pelvis and femur fractures* requiring stabilization of the whole body.

Extremity fracture

Mechanism of injury: Fractures of extremities can be caused by a variety of mechanisms reflecting the different ways in which force can be applied to the bone. The injury may be caused by leverage, twisting, direct impact or a piece of bone being pulled away where the tendon or ligament attaches to it (avulsion fracture). For field purposes, however, defining the mechanism of injury can be generalized to the question: was there sufficient force to cause a fracture? It is difficult to define 'sufficient force', especially as individuals differ. Older people have more brittle bones and unfit people do not have the strong supporting muscles and ligaments of someone in good training. As an example:

Positive mechanism of injury = Sufficient force for fracture

Yes – a 2m (6ft) fall on to a ledge while rock climbing.

No – waking up sore all over after a night sleeping on a ledge while rock climbing.

Assessment of extremity fracture: To the vague definition of 'sufficient force', we add the not-so-vague signs and symptoms of fracture. Combined with the mechanism of injury, these provide a fairly clear guideline for identifying injuries that are likely to involve broken bones or other unstable components such as severe sprains.

Positive mechanism + Positive signs and symptoms = Fracture

Positive signs and symptoms:

The inability to move, use or bear weight within an hour of the injury.

The immediate development of severe pain, tenderness and swelling.

Feeling or hearing a 'snap or crack'.

Obvious deformity or angulation.

The sensation of bones grating against each other (crepitus) on movement.

The patient or examiner feels instability of bones or joints. For example: 'After the fall, I tried to ski but my knee gave out …'

⊞ *Treatment of extremity fracture:* An extremity fracture by itself is never an emergency. Our real concern is the potential for damage to the circulatory- and nervous-system tissues around the fracture site. The usual cause, and biggest worry, is extremity ischaemia (see page 192). However, treating the fracture correctly will often fix or prevent this problem.

The causes of extremity ischaemia should sound familiar – either too little perfusion pressure in the circulatory system, or too much pressure in the tissues to allow perfusion to occur. This can happen at the site of deformed fractures and dislocations where blood vessels are kinked or lacerated. Blood flow can also be stopped by splints or bandages which are tied too tightly.

As we have said, nervous-system tissue is the most sensitive to oxygen deprivation. With the loss of effective blood circulation, peripheral nerves stop functioning and the extremity goes numb. With further obstruction, circulation, sensation and movement are affected. You will have noticed this if you have slept on your arm, or left it draped over a cinema seat for too long. Circulation is impaired, it goes numb and you cannot move it. As circulation is restored, movement returns, then tingling, then full sensation.

Circulation is assessed by looking for evidence of blood flow in the injured extremity. Are you able to detect any pulses beyond ('distal' to) an area of injury? Is the skin normal in colour, or is the skin pale or blue? Is the skin colder than the same extremity on the other side?

Sensation is the most important assessment tool. Loss of sensation is the first sign of ischaemia. A normal patient will be able to feel the light touch of a finger or of a small object. In the early stages, the patient may complain of a tingling sensation, and then numbness.

Movement refers to the patient's ability to move the extremity on command. The loss of the ability to move, such as wiggling fingers or toes, develops later in ischaemia than the loss of sensation.

It is not unusual for an extremity to feel numb or cold immediately following injury, especially if the fracture results in deformity or the patient is having an acute stress reaction. However, your treatment will usually improve circulation and restore sensation and movement.

As a general rule, extremity tissue can survive up to two hours of ischaemia with minimal damage. Beyond this, the risk of permanent damage increases quickly with time. *If your treatment efforts do not succeed in restoring circulation, sensation and movement, you have a limb-threatening emergency. Immediate evacuation is indicated if conditions permit.*

Treatment of fractures
The generic treatment of fractures has three distinct phases:
1. Traction into position (TIP).
2. Hand stable.
3. Splint stable.

Traction into position: Injured bones and joints, and the soft tissues around them, are much more comfortable and much less likely to be damaged further if splinted in their normal anatomic position. While many injured extremities will remain in good position or return there on their own, some will require help from you. We know that the idea of manipulating fractures contradicts older first aid teaching, which states 'splint it where it lies', but remember that older first aid texts were not written from the perspective of the wilderness traveller.

To restore anatomic position of a fractured bone, we first apply traction. This separates bone ends and reduces pain. Then, while traction is maintained, position is restored. To understand how this works, picture moving a chain by holding the links under tension, rather than allowing them to rattle against each other.

Shaft fractures of long bones are brought into the line of normal bone axis, the 'in-line' position. This is where the effect of opposing muscles is most balanced, and the blood circulation to the extremity beyond the injury is best maintained.

Fractured joints, such as elbows, shoulders and knees, do not usually need to be repositioned. If your patient is conscious and mobile, they will already have found the most comfortable position for the injured joint and be holding it there by the time you come along. If not, gentle traction to a position in the mid-range of the joint's normal motion is the best approach for long-term care.

In severely deformed joints, such as dislocations, there is likely to be a loss of circulation, sensation and movement (CSM) beyond the injury site. Under these conditions, TIP with movement toward the mid-range position is used until circulation is re-established. In some specific cases, which are discussed later, TIP can be used to reduce dislocations (put the dislocated bone back in place) with significant improvement in both comfort and circulation.

Traction into position is a safe procedure if done properly. It generally decreases pain rather than increases it. However, to be successful it helps to have the co-operation and confidence of the injured person. If necessary, you and your assistants may want to practise on an uninjured limb first.

Occasionally it will be impossible to restore position comfortably and safely, even using TIP. *You should discontinue TIP and stabilize the injury in the position found if TIP causes a significant increase in pain, or if movement of the extremity is prevented by resistance.*

Hand stable: Once you have repositioned an extremity injury, stability must be maintained until the splint can take over. This may mean having someone hold gentle traction on the extremity while you collect materials (Fig 7.5). If you do not have an army of assistants you may have to use snow, rocks or pieces of equipment to hold things in place. Do not just let the foot, arm or whatever lie there unsupported now that you have it where you want it. Of course, if you were really thinking, you might have had your splint materials ready before you started the process.

7.5 Hand stable – prevents further damage from sharp bone fragments until splint can be applied.

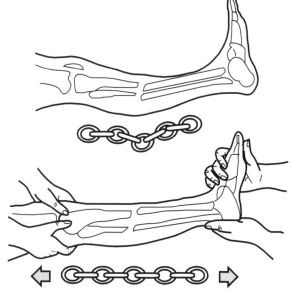

General principles of splinting:

- **Long bone fractures** – splint in the 'in-line' (looks normal) position.

- **Long bone fractures** – include the joint above and below the injury. For example, to splint a lower-leg fracture effectively, the ankle and knee must be immobilized.

- **Joint fractures** – splint in the position found, or in the mid-range position.

- **Joint fractures** – include the bones above and below. For example: to splint the elbow, the forearm and upper arm are included in the splint. There is no need to include adjacent joints in the splint. The shoulder and wrist may be left mobile.

- **Padding of splints** – good padding allows normal bone and joint contours to fit your splint material without pressure points or loose spots.

- **Multi-dimensional splints** – in these, splint material is applied on both sides of the injured part and generally provides the best stability and comfort.

- **Splints should be strong and snug** – this prevents movement of the injured parts.

- **Monitor splints frequently** – pain is a good indicator of movement. Bone fragments are adequately stabilized if the pain is well controlled. Check distal (beyond the injury) circulation, sensation and movement (CSM) before and after splinting. Continue to monitor CSM, especially during prolonged transport. This should be done every 15 minutes in the first few hours, then at least every hour thereafter. This is especially important during cold weather because extremity ischaemia can result in frostbite.

  The splint should allow easy access to fingertips or toes for monitoring. If ischaemia develops, you may need to loosen or rearrange the splint. Your splint should improve and preserve blood circulation and nerve function, not impair it. A good splint should provide decreased pain and intact CSM.

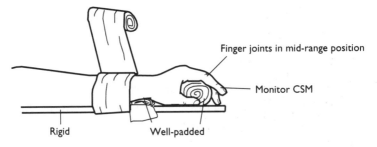

Finger joints in mid-range position

Monitor CSM

Rigid Well-padded

7.6 Hand, wrist and forearm splint.

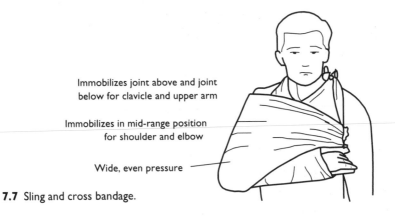

Immobilizes joint above and joint below for clavicle and upper arm

Immobilizes in mid-range position for shoulder and elbow

Wide, even pressure

7.7 Sling and cross bandage.

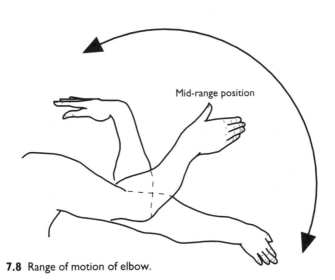

Mid-range position

7.8 Range of motion of elbow.

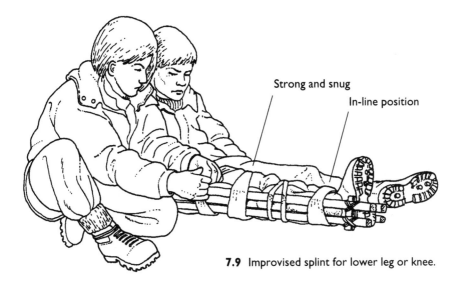

Strong and snug

In-line position

7.9 Improvised splint for lower leg or knee.

Splint stable: The best splints are simple, effective, and probably in your rucksack or canoe right now. Any splint will be good as long as it meets the general principles of splinting, no matter what its component parts are in real life.

Once the extremity is stabilized with your perfect splint, and you are satisfied that CSM is improving, treatment should include rest and elevation to reduce swelling and discomfort (see page 257). As long as distal CSM remains normal, or continues to improve, you can take your time planning a safe and comfortable evacuation.

Joint dislocations

The typical joint is a complex, mobile assembly of bones, ligaments, cartilage, tendon and muscle. A dislocation occurs when enough force is applied to the bone to tear the restraining ligaments and allow the joint to come apart.

By definition, dislocations have the mechanism of injury, signs and symptoms of fracture. We treat them by the same general principles as other joint fractures: stabilize in position and evacuate to treatment. There are, however, three specific dislocations which

243

deserve special attention because they are relatively easy and safe to treat in the field. These are simple dislocations of the shoulder, patella (knee cap) and digits (fingers and toes). This can save a lot of pain and trouble by transforming a gruesome, agonizing, medical emergency into a minor logistical problem.

Shoulder dislocations: Simple dislocations are caused by *indirect injury,* where force is applied at a distance from the joint and the dislocation is caused by leverage or torque. The usual mechanism is forced external rotation. This movement is similar to throwing a cricket ball, high bracing with a kayak paddle, or catching a fall on an outstretched arm while skiing. Fractures are uncommon, and generally do not interfere with treatment.

These injuries can be extremely uncomfortable and result in significant damage to the joint and surrounding soft tissue if untreated for more than a couple of hours. Fortunately, these dislocations can often be reduced using gentle traction into position, even by an inexperienced rescuer. This is best accomplished within an hour of the injury, before severe swelling and muscle spasm occur.

The more serious dislocation from *direct injury* is usually the

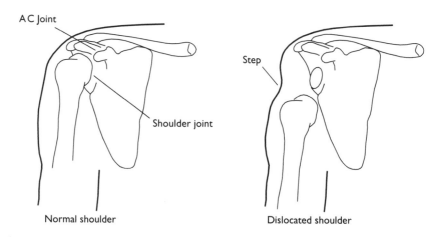

7.10 A dislocated shoulder loses its normal rounded contour.

result of a high-speed impact into a solid object. Distinguishing this mechanism from that of indirect force is usually not difficult. Sufficient force is applied directly to the joint area to force the bone ends apart. These injuries are almost always associated with other major injury, and probably will not be your primary focus of attention in those cases.

Assessment of shoulder dislocation: Assessment is directed towards identifying the simple dislocations caused by indirect force which may be fixed in the field. This is where careful attention to the mechanism of injury during your surveys can really pay off.

The patient will describe the classic mechanism of injury consistent with simple dislocation. He will frequently give a history of recurrent dislocation in the same extremity. On examination, you will notice right away that the person with a dislocated shoulder is in moderate to severe discomfort. There is often some degree of acute stress reaction. In about half the cases there is some CSM impairment of the arm and hand. The shoulder itself loses the rounded contour, becomes 'stepped' and has a hollow area where the shoulder is normally full and rounded (Fig 7.10). The patient will be unwilling to move the shoulder joint without help and coaching.

⊞ *Treatment of shoulder dislocation:* A simple dislocation of the shoulder should generally be treated in the field if the evacuation time to definitive care will be greater than two hours. It should also be considered if the evacuation will be exceptionally difficult or dangerous to perform while the shoulder remains displaced. These criteria probably apply to most wilderness and marine situations.

Several techniques are effective in reducing dislocated shoulders. Traction and external rotation, the most effective and easiest to perform in the field, require only a small patch of level ground and one rescuer. Before starting, remember to check and record distal CSM. You will want to be sure that your treatment has resulted in improvement.

To begin, the patient's arm is supported while they are moved to lie on their back. Gentle traction on the upper arm will help relieve pain during movement. The patient's co-operation and relaxation is essential. This will take some time; there is no reason to torture your patient with speed. Once the patient is lying on their back, the rescuer applies gentle traction to the arm and slowly swings it into a position about 90 degrees from the body, with the elbow bent.

The rescuer continues to hold TIP with one hand just above the elbow. Traction should be firm, but not enough to slide the patient across the ground. With the other hand on the patient's forearm, the rescuer gently and slowly externally rotates the arm until the 'throwing position' is reached. This looks just like it sounds (Fig 7.11). It is exactly the position in which the patient would have the arm if they were throwing a ball. The patient should be gently and repeatedly encouraged to relax. Within 5–10 minutes the muscles will fatigue, allowing the joint to slip back into place. *Remember to stop this process if pain or resistance is increased!*

You will know when the shoulder joint has been reduced by a dramatic relief of pain and return of mobility of the joint. You can

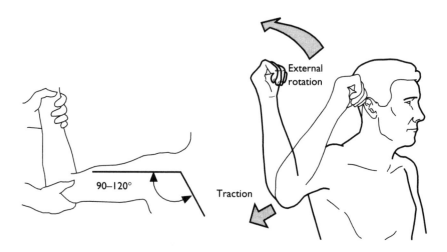

7.11 'Throwing position' for reducing a dislocated shoulder.

often feel and see a sudden shift of the upper arm as it relocates in the socket. If CSM impairment was present before reduction, it will improve rapidly afterwards. Remember to check and record CSM both before and after reduction.

After reduction, it is worth remembering that a joint dislocation has similarities to a fracture and should be treated as such. Inevitably, swelling will occur and pain will increase over time. The most effective splint is a simple sling-and-cross bandage or the equivalent.

An alternative reduction technique is simple hanging traction. This is accomplished by stabilizing the patient face down on the edge of a flat ledge or deck, where the dislocated arm can hang straight down. Pad the arm pit. 4.5–7kg (10–15lb) of weight can then be taped or tied to the arm to apply steady gravitational traction. As the muscles fatigue and then relax, the shoulder will slip back into its place. This technique may take up to 60 minutes to be successful.

Some shoulders will remain painful immediately after reduction. This is especially true of dislocations which are likely to include fractured bones. As long as distal circulation and sensation (CSM) are intact, however, this should not be a cause for alarm. You are treating for fracture anyway.

Dislocations which result from direct force on to the shoulder are generally more complicated, and usually not reduced in the field. Position the patient for safe evacuation. This usually also takes the form of a sling-and-cross bandage immobilization.

Patella dislocation: The patella (knee cap) is an isolated bone embedded as a kind of fulcrum in the quadriceps tendon. This large tendon transmits the powerful force of the quadriceps muscle in the front of the thigh to the front of the lower leg to allow you to extend the knee. This is the motion you would use to bring your foot forward to kick a ball.

The quadriceps tendon passes over and through a groove in the femur, like a cable through a pulley. In patella dislocation, the cable

247

– patella included – slips off the femur, making it impossible for the knee to function.

Like the shoulder, the patella can dislocate with a direct blow (rare) or indirect mechanism, typically a sudden extension of the knee. The patient often has a history of recurrent dislocation. The dislocation is always lateral (to the outside), leaving the patella pinned against the outside of the knee by the pull of the quadriceps. It is particularly common in young women.

Assessment of patella dislocation: Appearances can be deceptive. Shifting the patella laterally will make the bony prominence of the inside of the knee stand out and look like the missing patella. Do not be fooled by this. Feel for the patella laterally and you will find it.

Like the shoulder, these dislocations are extremely uncomfortable, and little or no motion of the joint is possible. Distal circulation and sensation is usually unaffected, but you should check it anyway. Damage to surrounding soft tissue will increase with time, as will the difficulty of reduction.

⊞ *Treatment of patella dislocation:* Like the shoulder, a dislocated patella should be reduced if the evacuation time will be greater than two hours, or the evacuation will be unreasonably difficult. Reducing a dislocated patella also reverses the mechanism of injury. Take the tension off the 'cable' by straightening the knee and flexing the hip (make the patient sit up) and then pop the patella back in place with your thumbs. Relief will result, but splint the knee for fracture anyway. These injuries are unstable, and will result in significant pain and swelling after several hours. Again, remember to check and record CSM status before and after reduction.

Digit dislocation – fingers and toes: Joints in the fingers usually dislocate due to an indirect force which levers the bone ends apart. The classic example is catching a falling ball the wrong way, but any outdoor activity can produce many opportunities for this injury. In any case, you end up with a finger pointing the wrong way at the distal or middle joint.

There is often an associated small chip fracture. Motion of the joint is usually impossible, and there will be some degree of CSM impairment. Damage will increase with time.

⊞ *Treatment of digit dislocation:* Reduction will be accomplished most easily immediately after the injury has occurred, before pain and swelling become significant.

After getting your patient's consent, simply grasp the end of the offending finger with one hand and the rest of the finger in the other. Pull the end of the finger in the direction it is pointing; then, while maintaining traction, swing it back in line. This is not as easy as it sounds, but it does work. You will probably need to wrap the end of your patient's finger in gauze or a handkerchief to help keep your grip.

After reduction, resist the temptation to play with it. Remember that fracture is very likely and it will need medical attention at some point, so splint it in the mid-range of the joint's motion and give it a rest. Again, do not forget to check CSM before and after reduction. Things should improve with your treatment.

Difficult dislocations: In remote areas, any dislocation which resists your efforts at reduction can become a serious problem. Pain may be severe, and the potential for soft-tissue damage increases with time. If CSM is significantly impaired, and cannot be restored by traction and repositioning, immediate evacuation to medical care is warranted. These are limb-threatening emergencies.

Spine, femur and pelvis fractures

In stabilizing musculoskeletal injuries to the spine, pelvis and femur, we apply the same assessment skills and splinting principles as in extremity fractures. However, to satisfy these principles the splint is usually a long backboard or stretcher which can secure the hips, back and neck. This pretty well eliminates walking your patient out of the woods.

The equipment necessary is brought to the scene by rescue teams or aircraft, and requires a carry-out or airlift evacuation. Your role will usually be limited to moving the patient to shelter, or shelter to the patient, and stabilizing in place until help arrives.

Spine fracture: The spine is fractured like any other bone, by both direct and indirect trauma. All spine injury is significant, but the most potentially devastating is the fracture or the dislocation of the cervical spine (the neck).

The delicate tissue of the spinal cord, really an extension of the brain, is surrounded and protected by the bones of the spinal column. Unstable injuries of the bony spinal column can easily injure the cord. Cord injury above the level of the third vertebrae in the neck will cause respiratory arrest. Below that level, injuries usually result in quadriplegia, that is, loss of function to all four extremities. These injuries are usually permanent, but recovery is sometimes possible with careful treatment.

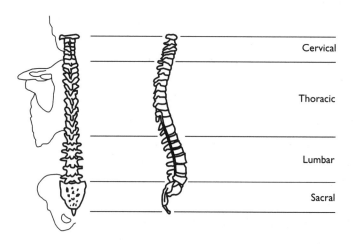

7.12 Anatomic divisions of the spine.

The neck is the most commonly injured area because it is the most mobile section of the spine, linking the heavy mass of the head with the body. As a result, it is very prone to injuries which snap the head back and forth like a ball on a string. It is also subject to damage when a force is applied to the top of the head, like being struck by a rockfall or diving into shallow water. The association between head injury and neck fracture is very common.

Injury to the spine at the thoracic (chest) level is much less common. Due to the added rigidity of the rib cage, this is the most stable area of the spine. In the wilderness setting, injury at this level is likely to be associated with other major trauma due to significant forces, such as a long fall or avalanche. Spinal-cord injury in the thorax causes paraplegia (loss of function of the lower extremities).

Below the thorax is the lumbar spine which, like the neck, is less protected and more mobile. Unstable injuries are more common here but, fortunately, cord injury is rare. Near the top of the lumbar spine the spinal cord separates into individual nerve roots, which are much more mobile and less likely to be injured.

Assessment of spine fracture: Assessment of spine fracture is similar to that of other fractures, but there are important differences, because the consequences of spinal-cord injury are so devastating. We tend to be much more conservative in our assessment and treatment.

In the urban setting, ambulance crews routinely immobilize any trauma patient with a positive mechanism of injury for spine fracture. This works fine in situations where the patient will arrive at the hospital within a few minutes, when the full assessment can be carried out in the controlled environment of the casualty department. In the wilds, however, we must recognize that committing a patient and rescuers to full spinal immobilization and evacuation can be impracticable, and even dangerous. Our field assessment must be more complete.

In the presence of a positive mechanism of injury, we look for the same signs and symptoms of fracture found in extremity injury. We apply the same principle: Possible fracture = Fracture. But, since the brain and spinal cord may be involved, we must consider the possibility that normal body reactions, such as feeling pain, may be absent. This is especially true when spinal injury is accompanied by head injury. Therefore, a critical part of your assessment has to do with the reliability of your own examination.

In cases where the patient is not alert, is intoxicated or is altered in mental status, your examination for signs of spine fracture will be unreliable. You must assume that the spine is fractured and treat it as such, even when your examination is negative. You can evaluate again later when your patient may have cleared their head, calmed down or sobered up. In the wilds this could happen before you leave camp to get help, or at any time during the evacuation.

If, however, you can determine that your patient is calm, co-operative, sober and alert, your examination can be considered reliable. If there are no signs and symptoms of fracture, you can be comfortable in your assessment of 'no spine fracture'. There is no need for spinal immobilization.

⊞ *Treatment of spine fracture:* For field purposes, the spine is treated as a long bone with a joint at each end. The positioning and treatment principles are the same. The techniques will vary depending on the equipment available, the terrain to be crossed and the people doing it.

Unless the first aider has considerable experience in handling spinal injuries, gentle and conservative treatment is appropriate, with a view to stabilizing the injury and the arrival of specialist treatment, such as backboard or vacuum splints.

Allowing a patient with suspected spinal injuries to walk is an absolute last resort.

For short moves, or stabilization while waiting for help, you can use a combination of improvised collar and short backboard. A section of closed-cell foam sleeping pad or rolled bivvy sheet can be an effective cervical collar. A pack frame can double as a short backboard. As with extremity injuries, snow, rocks or equipment can be placed around a supine patient to prevent movement.

If the patient must be moved, the following principles apply:

- If possible, use three or four co-ordinated people as lifters.
- Move the head and trunk as a unit.
- Avoid rotation of the spine.
- Avoid any flexion of the spine.
- Gentle extension of the spine is permissible to restore normal anatomic position.
- Carry in the supine position.

The long-term care of the spine-injured patient is difficult, especially outdoors. The patient will be unable to exercise and generate body heat, so you must be careful to keep them warm. They will need help with everything. Care and evacuation is something you will

---

⊞ **Field assessment of spine fractures**

In the presence of a positive or uncertain mechanism of injury:
- Positive signs and symptoms = Spine fracture.
- Unreliable examination = Spine fracture.
- Reliable examination + Negative signs and symptoms= No spine fracture.

Positive signs and symptoms:
- Pain in the spine.
- Tenderness of the spine when palpated.
- Abnormal motor or sensory function of the extremities.

need lots of help with, so if the criteria for spine injury are met, send for help. Proper care, not urgent evacuation, is the priority.

Femur fracture: The femur (long bone in the thigh) is part of the lower extremity and structurally is similar to the other long bones in the leg and arm. We group femur fractures with trunk injuries because, unlike the other extremities, they require whole-body stabilization. The hip and pelvis form the joint above the injury, requiring a stretcher or backboard to secure. The powerful thigh muscles are easily thrown into spasm by any movement.

Femur fractures also deserve separate consideration due to the possibility of volume shock from a lacerated femoral artery (circulatory system injury). It is not easy to fracture a femur: massive direct force is required.

Assessment of femur fracture: Of the signs and symptoms of fracture, the one most typical of the femur is severe pain. Unless there is pain masking from another injury or intoxication, these patients will be very uncomfortable. They do not smile, laugh or ask questions. They hurt. Movement is difficult, and weight bearing is impossible. If the injured person (without pain masking) looks at all comfortable, you have reason to doubt that the femur is fractured.

Suspected femur fracture should lead you to observe for signs of volume shock from major circulatory-system injury. Even in a closed fracture of the femur, considerable blood can be lost into the thigh. Massive swelling will often be evident (Fig 7.13). The *primary* problem may be a fractured femur, but the more serious *anticipated problem* is volume shock.

⊞ *Treatment of femur fracture:* Firm traction into position reduces pain and spasm, the chance of injury to arteries and the space available inside the thigh for blood loss. TIP should be applied as soon as possible whenever femur fracture is diagnosed, and maintained throughout the splinting process.

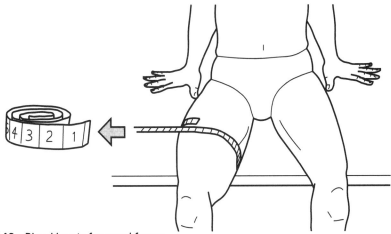

7.13 Blood loss in fractured femur.

The ideal femur splint would maintain traction all the way to the hospital, and there are several types of specialized traction splint made for this purpose. They require training and experience to use and, even when properly applied, can impair circulation. This quickly becomes a problem in the long-term care situation.

Improvised traction splints for field use employing ski poles, canoe paddles etc, are usually more architecturally interesting than medically useful. The simplest, safest and most universal splint is firm immobilization on a long board or stretcher without traction.

Pelvic fracture: Like the femur, it takes a significant force to fracture the pelvis. This is usually the injury of long falls, high-speed ski accidents and avalanches. There are, however, rare instances when the pelvis can be fractured by an apparently mild event. Also, as with the femur, a major concern is the possibility of severe bleeding from arteries and veins adjacent to the fracture site.

Assessment of pelvic fracture: Pelvic fractures are a little tricky. They are usually quite painful, but not always. They can also be difficult to distinguish from hip or lower lumbar-spine fractures. There is no single outstanding sign or symptom. In the presence of a positive mechanism, pelvic pain and tenderness, and an inability to bear weight, you have little choice but to treat for fracture.

⊞ *Treatment of pelvic fracture:* Pelvic fractures also require immobilization of the trunk to meet the principles of splinting. Because of danger to adjacent blood vessels, possible pelvic fractures also deserve long board or litter stabilization. Volume shock should be in your anticipated problem list, if it is not already present. As with the femur, it will often be best to stabilize in place and call for help with evacuation.

Stable injuries

Assessment of stable injuries: Typical signs and symptoms of a stable injury (which includes contusions, strains and sprains) include a positive mechanism and pain, but none of the specific signs and symptoms of fracture (see page 237). The patient is able to use, move or bear weight in the area more or less normally within the first hour following injury. There is no history of a 'snap, crack or pop'. There is no deformity, crepitus (grating sound) or sense of instability.

Swelling is common, but develops slowly over several hours from the accumulation of oedema fluid, rather than rapidly from bleeding. It is not unusual for the patient to experience considerable pain and immobility the next day as this swelling reaches its peak. This is especially true if they continued to use the injured part for a while after the injury.

With the exception of blisters, sprained ankles are the most common walking injuries. They are mostly caused by the patient 'going over' on their ankle with the foot bending inwards under them. This stretches the outer ligament (bundle or band of fibrous tissues joining the foot bone to the leg bone) to such an extent that it partially tears or ruptures. A complete rupture would cause so much pain and crippling that walking would be out of the question except as a matter of life or death. Partial tears cause immediate pain and tenderness.

A less common strain is caused by a fall or stumble with the foot bending outwards, resulting in damage to the medial ligament.

⊞ *Treatment of stable injuries:* The early treatment of stable injuries is essentially the same as for fracture. This conservative treatment prevents the development of disability from excessive pain and swelling.

Rest − local rest, splinted or limited use.

Ice − cold packs. Use as tolerated for the first 24 hours.

Compression (elasticated bandage) − use only on distal
    extremity (Fig 7.14).

Elevation − raise the injury above heart level.

Pain-free activity − after the first 24 hours, or when most of
    the pain and swelling has resolved, the injured person
    may perform whatever activity is possible as long as
    additional pain is not caused. This may include skiing, or
    it may require very limited activity around camp for
    several days.

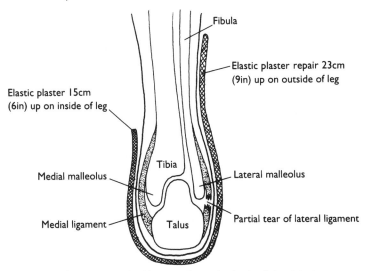

7.14 Treatment for a sprained ankle, seen from the back of the right leg.

Medication – anti-inflammatory medication, such as aspirin or ibuprofen, can help reduce swelling and discomfort.

Most of the swelling will occur over the first six hours. Over the next 18 hours, the rate of swelling tapers off. Generally, little swelling occurs after that. Elevation and rest are the most important elements of treatment, and are most useful early on when the swelling is likely to be worst. Ice is also very helpful, if available. Even in the summer, you can achieve some cooling by evaporation by wrapping the injury in a water-soaked bandage.

Following these treatment guidelines, all stable injuries should show steady improvement. If not, your patient is being too active, or your assessment may be wrong. Never be afraid to reassess the situation and change your mind. Medical people do it all the time.

Case study 1

Subjective: a 23-year-old female instructor glissading a snow field in the Cairngorms caught her heel in the snow, causing a tumbling fall. She felt a pop and a brief burning pain in her left knee. On attempting to stand, the knee 'gave way'. She did not hit her head, and has no neck pain. She has full recollection of the event. She has an allergy to codeine, takes ibuprofen for headaches, has never injured the knee before, and has no significant past medical history. Her last meal was 20 minutes ago. The glissade was at the end of a 3-day mountain journey, with only a half a mile to go.

Objective: The instructor was found sitting upright in a stable position with the left knee flexed. She was fully alert, and warm and reasonably dry. She had no neck tenderness. The left knee was tender, but not swollen, deformed, or discoloured. She was able to flex and extend the knee fully with little discomfort. Distal CSM was intact. There was no other obvious injury. Vital signs at 13.20 were normal.

Assessment: Fracture of the left knee.

Plan: The knee was splinted with taped and padded tent poles, and an improvised stretcher was fashioned from a closed-cell foam sleeping mat and nylon webbing. The woman was carried the last half mile to the road. Distal CSM was monitored by asking if she could feel and wiggle her toes inside her boots.

Discussion: Although the temptation to limp the last half mile was very strong, the patient agreed to the appropriate treatment. This injury fits the criteria for fracture because of the history of a 'pop' during injury, and the instability experienced afterwards. This story is typical of a ligament rupture, which is every bit as unstable as a fracture.

Case study 2

Subjective: A 17-year-old girl caught her right index finger between loose rocks during a descent of a scree slope 16km (10 miles) from the road. She was able to dislodge herself, but complained of immediate pain. Shortly afterwards she became dizzy and nauseated. The group leader climbed back up the slope to examine the girl. Witnesses told him that she did not fall, and that she was not struck by anything. She has no allergies, is not on medication, has no significant past medical history, and is up to date on tetanus vaccination. She had breakfasted 2 hours previously. She had been walking without difficulty prior to the accident, and she was well rested and hydrated. The rock was stable, but the weather was cool and windy.

Objective: The patient was found lying against a large rock. She was disoriented, pale and sweaty. The tip of the right index finger was swollen and very tender, with a superficial abrasion. There was no other injury. Her vital signs at 11.30 were – BP: unknown P: 64; C: V on AVPU with confusion and disorientation; T: feels cool; S: pale, cool, moist.

259

Assessment:

1. Fracture to tip of right index finger.
2. Abrasion of right index finger.
3. Acute stress reaction.

Anticipated problems: Infection of abrasion on the right index finger.

Plan: The finger was immersed in clean, cold water to irrigate the abrasion and relieve the pain. She was encouraged to lie in a sleeping bag and calm down. The finger was splinted by taping it to the third finger with a gauze pad and antiseptic ointment between the fingers.

The girl was instructed to keep the finger elevated as much as possible, and use cool soaks for swelling and pain relief during the rest stops. The wound was to be irrigated, and the dressing changed daily. She was cautioned about the signs and symptoms of infection, and instructed to check circulation and sensation at the fingertip frequently. She would be referred to medical care when the group reached the road, but no urgent adjustment of their plans was considered necessary.

Discussion: Although this patient was displaying very frightening signs and symptoms immediately after the injury, there was no mechanism to explain it, except acute stress reaction. The changes in level of consciousness and mental status rapidly resolved with rest, reassurance and pain relief, leaving only an unhappy girl with a sore finger.

Skin and soft tissue

The equipment to deal with minor lacerations is basic indeed – fresh water, soap and clean gauze dressings. The primary goal is to assist the body's own defensive and healing mechanisms. Definitive care, like suturing (stitches), can be performed hours or days later if necessary.

Structure and function

The skin is the largest of the body's organs. It performs the remarkable function of separating the flora and the fauna of the outside environment from the sterile, temperature- and chemical-sensitive internal organs. Most of the time it does a pretty good job, considering it is only about 6mm (¼in) thick.

Soft tissue – the tissues between the skin and underlying bone, joints and organs – includes fat, muscle and connective tissue, as well as the small vessels and nerves found in these layers. Problems begin when the protective outer layer of skin is damaged, and the tissue beneath is exposed. This permits fungi, bacteria and other creatures to invade unprotected tissue, as well as allowing vital body fluids to escape.

Skin and soft-tissue problems

Wounds

A wound is any injury that disrupts the skin. It can be superficial or deep. It can also involve structures other than soft tissue, such as bone, major nerves and vessels, and internal organs. Wounds come in a fascinating variety of types, but for field purposes we will put them into four manageable groups:

1. *Laceration and avulsion* – the skin is divided (laceration) or sliced or torn away (avulsion). The wound may be superficial or deep. There may be an 'avulsion flap' still attached. The wound may also include some crushed and dead tissue. A deep cut from a broken bottle would be a typical deep laceration.

2. *Amputation* – a complete segment of an extremity is lost, such as a finger or arm. Bleeding may be severe. The amputated part may sometimes be re-attached several hours after injury.

3. *Shallow wounds* – superficial burns and abrasions which disrupt the skin, but do not penetrate the soft tissue. A graze or a rope burn would be examples.

4. *Puncture wounds* – skin disruption is minimal, but the injury extends into the soft tissue. The object which causes the puncture drags bacteria and other foreign material into the wound, almost invariably causing some degree of infection. Standing on a protruding nail in bare feet or a stab wound are examples.

All wounds damage blood vessels and cause bleeding. The body can stop this blood loss by automatically constricting blood vessels at the injury site to reduce flow. A clot then begins to form and, if left undisturbed, can bring bleeding to a halt within 15 minutes. Serious bleeding problems can develop when injured vessels are numerous or very large. Severe blood loss (a BIG 3 circulatory-system problem) can occur before the clotting mechanism seals the wound.

After the blood loss has been stopped, the slower process of wound repair begins. The initial stages of natural wound cleansing occur over a period of several days. The clot surface dries, forming a natural bandage in the form of a scab. Underlying tissue is further protected by the process of inflammation, which forms a protective barrier below.

Any contamination, such as dirt and bacteria, is moved to the surface as the wound drains. By the third or fourth day, the protective barriers are established and cleansing is well under way. The signs of normal inflammation – redness, warmth, swelling and pain – begin to subside as the protective barrier continues to grow stronger.

After six to eight days the wound is very resistant to new outside contamination. As inflammation subsides, wound edges migrate together and form a scar where they meet. Re-injury or excessive movement of the wound area during the early stages can disrupt the barrier effect, fostering infection and delaying the healing process.

If the inflammatory process is overwhelmed, and the wound is not internally sealed or externally drained, invading bacteria may pass through the protective barrier into the surrounding tissues. If the body's immune system is unable to control them, bacteria can reproduce rapidly, causing an infection. In an attempt to re-establish the barrier, the body increases local inflammation. Pus develops as the cellular debris and oedema fluid accumulates. This combination of processes produces the early signs and the symptoms of an infection.

If the infection spreads, it will ultimately enter the general circulation and cause a systemic infection, sometimes called 'blood poisoning'. The body responds with systemic inflammation, producing generalized redness, fever and pain. Patients with systemic infection are extremely ill. Fortunately, this complication of skin wounds is rare in healthy individuals.

Some wounds are more prone to infection than others. These we label as 'high risk' wounds because they require more care and earlier medical attention. This category includes puncture wounds and wounds involving joints and other complex structures. It also includes wounds which are dirty or which involve crushed or dead tissue.

Assessment of wounds: Although wounds, like fractures, are sometimes obvious and dramatic, they are rarely life-threatening in themselves. Assessment is directed initially towards finding and treating associated BIG 3 problems. The wound itself is then evaluated for evidence of 'high risk' factors.

⊞ *Treatment of soft-tissue wounds:* Treat the BIG 3 problems first! Your riding partner goes over the handlebars on a steep descent, and you find them sitting on the track with their face covered in blood

High-risk wounds

Dirty wounds
Injuries with embedded foreign materials such as gravel, sawdust, or clothing fibres, harbour bacteria which are difficult to dislodge.

Ragged wounds
Wounds in which there is crushed, shredded or dead tissue that provides a good growth medium for bacteria.

Underlying injury
Wounds which involve injuries to joints, tendons and bones (open fractures) are difficult to clean adequately and are prone to serious infection.

Bite wounds
Mouths harbour a wide variety of virulent bugs. Human bites are among the worst. Cats are pretty bad, too. Any wound exposed to human or animal saliva constitutes a bite wound, and has a very high infection rate.

Puncture wounds
Small openings in the skin with a wound track that extends through several layers of tissue, depositing bacteria in areas that are unable to drain properly. These have a way of looking minor at first, but becoming a big problem later. This is especially true of 'nail through the shoe into the bottom of the foot' injuries.

from a small scalp laceration. Your first instinct is to wipe the blood away and help them up because you hate the sight of blood and want everything to look normal again. This is a perfectly natural reaction, but quite wrong. Do not forget that this is the mechanism for an unstable cervical spine injury. Stabilize the neck until you are certain there is no spine injury or other BIG 3 problem, then worry about the laceration.

Once your surveys are complete, and any more serious conditions are dealt with, you are ready to treat a soft-tissue wound. There are several steps to follow. These apply to all wounds: big and small, clean and dirty, superficial and deep, and head to toe.

Stop external bleeding – *direct pressure* stops most bleeding. You need to see clearly where the blood is coming from so you may need to cut away clothes, remove equipment, cut hair or whatever else is necessary. If pressure is well aimed, most bleeding stops within 15 minutes as clotting is activated.

If bleeding persists, it is usually because the pressure applied was too light, or was poorly aimed. Remove the bandage, find the bleeding site and try again. Once bleeding has stopped, the clot will keep it stopped unless disturbed.

Elevation helps reduce bleeding by reducing the blood pressure in the affected extremity.

Splinting helps reduce bleeding by preventing disruption of the clot by movement.

Ice, if available, will help constrict blood vessels in the area of the injury.

Tourniquets are used ONLY with amputations – loss of a finger, hand etc – if severe bleeding does not stop with direct pressure. Pressure points are rarely useful in the field setting.

Prevent infection – long-term management (anything over two hours) requires early wound cleaning to help prevent infection. Cleansing a wound usually restarts some bleeding by disturbing the clot. If severe bleeding is a problem, leave the pressure dressing in place until bleeding has definitely stopped. Do not attempt to clean wounds associated with life-threatening bleeding.

Wash around the wound with soap and water and/or disinfectant. Clean a wide area of skin, being careful not to allow soap or disinfectant into the wound itself. The exceptions are shallow wounds, like small burns and abrasions, which can be washed with soap and water applied directly to the wound surface.

Irrigate the wound with any clean water suitable for drinking. Rinse the wound by pouring water directly into the opening, allowing it to run out by gravity. The greater the volume of water, the better. You are flushing out debris and reducing the bacteria to levels which can be managed by the body's own defences.

Sea water contains bacteria and can be irritating to tissues, but can be used for initial irrigation if fresh water sources are unavailable. Perform the final rinse with drinkable fresh water. It is unnecessary, and can be harmful, to irrigate a wound with full-strength (typically 10 per cent) iodine preparations. Iodine kills both bacteria and body cells, leaving a partially sterilized wound lined with dead tissue. This can actually increase rather than decrease the chances of later infection.

Remove any embedded debris from the wound. Anything which was not flushed out by irrigation should be removed manually. Brush out the obvious junk with a toothbrush or other clean tool. A pair of tweezers is useful for removing pieces of gravel or clothing that resist gentle persuasion. If a wound is very dirty, make yourself comfortable and plan to spend quite a bit of time doing this. Also remove any torn pieces of tissue in the wound that are no longer receiving blood flow. These are the pieces of skin and fat that are 'hanging by a thread' or have turned blue or black.

Cover the wound with sterile dressings to prevent outside contamination. Keep the dressings as clean and dry as possible. Sterile dressings can be covered with non-sterile bandages. Recleanse the wound and change the dressings regularly. This is usually daily, but can be more frequent in wet or dirty conditions.

Allowing the wound to drain is important. Do not close the wound with tape (butterflies or steristrips) or try to suture it with dental floss. A closed wound has a much greater chance of getting infected than an open one. It is much easier to allow the wound to heal cleanly and naturally, and have a surgeon fix the scar later if necessary.

Splint the extremity if conditions and travel allow, or if the wound is over a joint or in another area of skin which is mobile. This will minimize the breakdown of the protective barrier.

Medical care – *high-risk wounds* should receive early medical attention whenever possible, especially where open fracture is suspected. Infection generally takes a day or two to get going, so your ideal evacuation plan would have your patient out of the wilds within 48 hours. During your walk out, the wound should receive the same careful attention as any other. This is especially true for the removal of debris and irrigation. If your treatment is particularly effective, infection may never start.

Sutures (stitches) are used mainly for cosmetic purposes, to connect deep structures and to close gaping wounds to reduce healing time. Closing a wound with sutures requires training, experience and a scrupulously clean environment, and should usually be done within six to eight hours following the injury. In most cases, suturing is neither a necessary nor an appropriate field treatment. While early suturing may be desirable for certain wounds, it can usually be delayed safely for three to five days if early treatment is not possible.

Tetanus prophylaxis is an injectable vaccine given to anyone with an open wound who has not had a vaccination within 10 years, or five years in the case of particularly dirty wounds. This is best done within 24 hours of injury. You can prevent this from becoming a problem by ensuring routine tetanus vaccinations are up to date.

Infection is a possibility in any wound, at any time during the healing process. In normal wound healing, pain, redness and inflammation decrease with time. If the wound becomes infected, these signs and symptoms will begin to increase. Pus – an opaque white to yellow substance – may be noted in the wound and may be accompanied by a foul smell.

Almost any wound that is becoming infected earns the status of 'high risk' and should receive medical care. It should continue to be treated by cleansing and with dressing changes. If the infected wound has been closed with tape or sutures, it should be opened and allowed to drain. Irrigate with water to remove pus. Do not squeeze the wound, or you will simply drive bacteria through the protective barrier into healthy tissues.

Warm soaks will increase circulation to the area to help the body fight the infection locally. Use only as much heat as you can stand comfortably against normal skin. Apply for 30 minutes at a time, as often as five or six times a day.

Monitor for signs of infection whether or not you choose to evacuate. You should also monitor the circulation, sensation and movement distal to the injury, as you would with a musculoskeletal problem. Bandages, splints and swelling can create the same ischaemia (lack of perfusion) as well.

Impaled objects

Impaled objects are foreign bodies that extend through the skin into underlying tissues. These are best removed by a surgeon in hospital. If possible, stabilize impaled objects in place, and transport the patient to medical care.

In many wilderness cases, however, transporting the patient with the object in place will cause more tissue damage than pulling it out: the impaled pick of an ice axe, for example, can do a lot of damage if the shaft bumps into a tree or rock wall. In cases such as this, removal of the object should be considered.

Remove impaled objects if:

- The object prevents the application of necessary dressings or safe transport.
- The object is safe and easy to remove.

Abrasions (shallow wounds)

Abrasions are shallow wounds in which only the superficial layers of skin are scraped away. Because the skin is not divided, healing can occur from the bottom up and is usually fairly rapid. Wound-care principles are the same: stop bleeding and prevent infection.

Assessment of abrasions: No soft tissue below the skin is visible. There is usually some ground-in dirt and there may be thin flaps of skin hanging on at the wound margins. The biggest problem with abrasions is the potential for infection, and they always seem to happen in a place that is difficult to bandage.

⊞ *Treatment of abrasions:* As with lacerations, brush or pick out the foreign material, then irrigate with clean water. Any hanging and dead skin should be trimmed away. Abrasions can be covered with antiseptic ointment and dressed with sterile gauze.

Long-term care is similar to that for lacerations. Clean at least daily and re-dress with sterile dressing. Generally, after about three or four days the abrasion will have healed enough to allow it to dry and scab over. If this is successful, keep it covered with dry dressings until it has healed completely.

Burns

All burns are caused by heat. Damaging heat can be encountered in the form of hot gases or objects, or be produced by a chemical reaction between the skin and a caustic substance. Burns can involve internal structures, such as the respiratory system, as well as the outside skin.

Assessment of burns: For field management, you need to know the depth and extent of burns, as well as the location. The extent is described in terms of body surface area and is estimated using the 'rule of nines':

Head and neck	9%	Front of torso	18%
Each arm	9%	Back of torso	18%
Each leg	18%	Genitalia	1%

Estimates of irregular burns can be made using the size of one surface of the patient's hand, which is about one per cent of the body surface area.

269

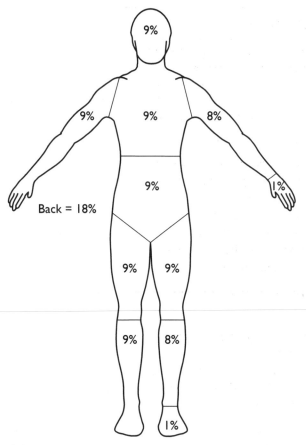

7.15 Rule of nines

The depth of burn can be difficult to estimate, particularly where different areas are burned to various degrees. Here is a rough guide to the different depths of burns:

1. *First-degree burns* – the skin integrity is not disrupted. Capillaries and nerves are intact. Inflammation occurs normally with redness, pain and warmth. This is the typical sunburn.

2. *Second-degree burns* – the skin surface is damaged, but the injury is limited to the outer layers. Capillaries are damaged, but the deeper skin blood vessels and nerves are intact, allowing

High-risk burns

1. Any respiratory involvement

Burned respiratory passages will have the same problems with inflammation, blisters and leaking fluid that normal skin would have. Respiratory burns should be suspected in cases where the face and lips have been singed, or the patient was trapped in a closed space, such as a burning house or tent.

Respiratory distress will develop as pulmonary fluid builds up in the lungs. Swelling of the upper and lower airways can develop, producing airway constriction and obstruction (see pages 218–20). Like any other swelling, it can develop over a period of 24 hours. Respiratory distress should be an anticipated problem in any case where hot gases have been inhaled, even if the patient seems to be breathing well immediately after injury.

2. Second- or third-degree burns of the face, genitalia, hands or feet

3. Burns of any degree greater than 30 per cent body surface area

These burns have the potential to cause volume shock. The capillaries in burned skin are no longer able to contain the fluid components of the blood.

4. Third-degree burns greater than 10 per cent body surface area

5. Chemical burns

It can be difficult to arrest the burning process fully as some chemicals react with the skin. Damage can continue for hours afterwards.

6. Electrical burns

Skin damage may be minor, but electrical current can cause extensive injury to internal organs and tissue.

7. Burns associated with other serious injury

8. Burns of very young or old patients

inflammation to produce blisters. There is fluid loss, redness, warmth and pain.

3. *Third-degree burns* – the full thickness of the skin is damaged. Capillaries, blood vessels and nerves are destroyed. Normal inflammation cannot occur, and as a result blisters do not develop. The burned area may appear charred black, or grey. The area may not be painful, due to loss of nerves. Small third-degree burns may appear to be less serious because of this.

As with other injuries, the assessment of burns is directed first towards identifying potentially life-threatening problems. These will usually come in the form of volume shock and/or respiratory distress. Secondary assessment considers burns which are likely to involve significant anticipated problems due to the potential for pain, infection or scar formation. These all come under the classification of 'high-risk burns'.

⊞ *Treatment of burns:* Stop the burning process. The first step in the management of burns is to remove the heat immediately. The fastest way to do this is to immerse the patient or injured part in water. Fortunately, this is almost instinctive, as it serves to relieve pain as well. Be careful, as it is possible with larger burns to make your patient hypothermic as a side effect of your good intentions. If the burn is greater than about 10 per cent of body surface area, limit your cooling to just a few minutes.

In chemical burns, continued irrigation with water will not only cool the area but help remove the chemical itself. Irrigation should continue for at least 30 minutes.

Treat the life-threatening injuries – if burns have the potential to cause life-threatening BIG 3 problems, use basic life support techniques (see pages 194–207) and request emergency evacuation.

Cleanse the burn – if the burn is not a life-threatening emergency, clean and dress it with antiseptic dressings as you would for a minor abrasion. This can be done along with the application of cool soaks for pain relief. Continue to treat as any open wound. If the burn falls under the category of 'high risk', plan to get the patient to medical care as soon as possible.

Blisters

Blisters, such as the kind you get on your feet while hiking, are really burns caused by the heat generated by friction. Your boots and socks rub against your skin, and the damage results in leaky capillaries and swelling. You not only have a skin injury to treat, but a transportation problem as well.

Assessment of blisters: Blisters progress through three stages. They begin with 'hot spots', progress to blisters filled with sterile fluid, and then break to become contaminated superficial wounds. The stage at which you confront them, and your logistical situation, will determine your treatment. Generally, they act just like other 'shallow wounds'.

⊞ *Treatment of blisters:* Hot spots are when you begin to feel discomfort. You know something is wrong in your left boot, but as you are only 10 minutes into the walk you do not want to stop yet. But, stop you must. Outward Bound instructors routinely stop their group early in their first walk to do a foot check and talk on blister prevention.

Stop the friction *now* and you can prevent a blister from forming. Change your sock, fiddle with your laces or cover the sore area with smooth surface tape, gel dressings or moleskin. You can also apply petroleum jelly, antiseptic ointment or even sun cream to lubricate the area and reduce friction. Whatever time it takes to cool the hot spot will be well worth it in the long run and save you from blisters.

The important fact to remember early on is that a blister is a sterile wound until it breaks. Like an abrasion, the deeper layers of

273

the skin are still intact, making quick healing from below a possibility. Whenever you can, you should try to keep it that way. Small blisters can be covered with gel dressing. Larger ones will usually cause some degree of disability unless you can take the pressure off.

If the blister has formed in a bad spot, like the back of your heel, you may have to drain it in order to be able to walk. You will then be converting a closed and sterile wound into an open one. You can minimize the risk of infection by treating the wound before this happens.

As with other wounds, clean the skin around and over the blister with soap and water. Sterilize a needle or sharp knife blade by flame or alcohol. Make a tiny hole in the blister at the lower margin and allow the fluid to drain out. Leave the skin over the blister intact: it acts as its own sterile dressing. Cover the area with antiseptic ointment and dress it as you might a 'hot spot'. Like any open wound, it must be cleaned and dressed daily, and monitored for signs of infection.

Open blisters occur when a blister has broken into a non-sterile environment. They should be treated like abrasions. Remove dead skin and debris, and cover with antiseptic ointment and sterile dressing. Remove the source of friction. Clean daily and monitor for infection.

Sunburn

First-degree sunburn is reddening of the skin, which may be treated by lotions. Second-degree burning involves blistering and should be treated initially with cold water for long enough to let the pain subside, say 30 minutes, and subsequently with sterile dressings, preferably sterile plastic, such as the inside of an unused polythene bag. In all cases, further exposure to the sun should be avoided.

8

Toxins and Allergies

Toxic substances can produce systemic effects, local effects, or both. Systemic effects would be typified by the ingestion of poisonous mushrooms and by carbon monoxide poisoning; local effects by simple insect bites or nettle stings.

Toxins, like trauma, can cause simultaneous involvement of more than one body system. This is most spectacularly seen in the intense reaction of anaphylactic shock. This involves both a local reaction (say, to a wasp sting) and an overwhelming systemic reaction. The cause-and-effect relationship may be fairly obvious, or quite confusing. Fortunately, the generic treatments can be applied successfully without knowing exactly which toxin you are dealing with.

The major concern is to determine how the body is reacting to the toxin, and what you can do to lessen symptoms and prevent serious injury.

General principles

In Britain, naturally occurring toxins are not the widespread problem that they are in countries with more exotic flora and fauna. Some of the toxins that might be encountered during wild country journeys are listed below.

Toxins that may be encountered:

- Carbon monoxide poisoning (faulty stove/poor ventilation).
- Snakebite (adder).
- Insect stings.
- Poisonous mushrooms.
- Giant hogweed (*Heracleum mantegazzianum*).
- Jellyfish stings.
- Alcohol/drug/solvent abuse.
- Poisonous plants.

A number of these would be self-inflicted by the patient. Poisonous plants such as deadly nightshade (*Atropa belladonna*) are most commonly eaten by children, but adults sometimes mistake harmful mushrooms for their edible relatives. The most notorious species in this respect is *Amanita phalloides* – the Death Cap.

The generic approach to treatment is summarized in the tables below.

⊞ General treatment for toxin exposure

Remove and dilute:

Ingested toxins
Induce vomiting. This is best done within the first hour, but may be effective up to eight hours post ingestion. Give 1–2 tablespoons (15–30cc) syrup of ipecac orally. Give 2 cups of water to dilute the toxin. The patient will vomit within 20 minutes. Be sure that the patient is positioned to prevent airway obstruction. Do not induce vomiting in any patient who is unable to protect their airway, or when the ingested substance is corrosive or a petroleum product.

Inhaled toxins
Move the patient to clean air. Provide the generic treatment for respiratory distress (see page 217).

Skin and soft-tissue toxins
Clean the area as for a skin wound. Irrigate copiously with water.

⊞ Field treatment summary for toxins

Remove and dilute toxin.

Antidote.

Basic life support.

Specific treatments.

Basic life support

Most toxins are excreted or metabolized by the body over time. Treatment is largely aimed at supporting body systems and treating problems as they develop, until the toxin is removed or can be neutralized by an antidote. This generic approach is also effective when toxins are mixed or unknown. It is helpful to be able to identify or take a sample of toxin to assist subsequent medical treatment, but this is not essential for field treatment.

Specific toxins

Snakebite

In Britain, the adder is the only poisonous species. Bites are rare and hardly ever fatal, but patients are likely to be very anxious and suffering from acute stress reaction. In other countries, snakebite is a more widespread problem and the following principles should be followed.

Assessment of snakebite: Identification of the snake may be helpful, but is not required for treatment. If venom has been injected (envenomation) there will be immediate swelling and pain. If no venom was injected, the pain will be only what you would expect from small puncture wounds, and will not get any worse.

⊞ *Treatment of snakebite:* In addition to basic life support, the following procedures are advised.

Antivenin – this is the specific treatment. Its use is usually restricted to the hospital because in rare cases it can cause allergic reactions. It is most effective during the first four hours, but can be given up to several days following the bite and still have some benefit.

Transport – move the patient as quickly as possible to a source of antivenin (antidote). Although local discomfort may be severe, systemic signs and symptoms can be delayed for two to six hours following the bite. Walking your patient out is reasonably safe unless severe systemic signs and symptoms occur. It is also significantly faster than trying to carry them. Splint the affected part if possible.

Expect swelling – remove constricting items such as rings, bracelets and clothing from the bitten extremity.

Do not delay – immediately following the bite of a snake thought to be poisonous, evacuation should be started. It can always be slowed down or cancelled if it becomes obvious that envenomation did not occur, or the snake was not poisonous.

Most medical experts agree that traditional field treatments, such as tourniquets, pressure dressing, ice packs and 'cut and suck' snakebite kits, are generally ineffective and possibly dangerous. Poisonous snakebite is one of those conditions that you cannot treat in the field. Do not waste valuable time trying.

Insect and arachnid toxins

Tick bite: Although not toxic in its effect or mechanism, the bite of ticks can transmit Lyme's disease. People suffering unresolved flu-like symptoms and aching joints should inform their general practitioner if they have been bitten by ticks. The condition is readily treatable when identified. In the field, the advice is simply to check for ticks and to remove any that have taken hold. It appears to take several hours for transmission of infection to occur.

⊞ *Treatment of insect and arachnid toxins:* Local reactions – treat for comfort. Use cool soaks, elevation and rest. Aspirin or other mild pain relievers will help. There are also a number of over-the-counter medications for insect-sting discomfort.

Systemic reaction – anaphylaxis (see opposite) is a true medical emergency. Medication, specifically epinephrine (adrenaline) and antihistamines, can be life-saving.

Anaphylaxis

Anaphylaxis is a severe, systemic (whole body), allergic reaction to a foreign material that enters the circulating blood. It can be caused by substances which are absorbed through the intestine from food, inhaled and absorbed through the lungs, or injected into the skin (eg bee venom). The reaction to substances eaten with food may be delayed due to the time it takes to digest them. Reaction to inhaled or injected material is usually immediate (within 5–15 minutes).

Assessment of anaphylaxis: The signs and symptoms are caused by widespread blood-vessel dilation and tissue swelling of all body surfaces. This can produce life-threatening volume shock and airway constriction. In severe reactions, death can occur in a matter of minutes. Most patients have a history of known allergy to the suspected substance, but this is not always the case. Past reactions may have been more or less severe than the present one.

In true anaphylaxis, the patient may complain of hot, burning, itchy skin. There may be nausea, vomiting and even diarrhoea. There will be some degree of respiratory distress. The patient may feel weakness and disorientation with the onset of shock. Vital signs are consistent with shock due to widespread blood-vessel dilation and respiratory distress due to lower airway constriction (see pages 208–12).

Vital signs in anaphylaxis:

BP Decreased if severe.

P Increased.

R Increased with distress/wheezing if severe.

C Anxious/confused; V, P or U if severe.

T Unchanged.

S Flushed with weals, general swelling.

Survey will reveal generalized swelling of the face, eyes, tongue and skin. Do not confuse anaphylaxis with a severe local reaction, such as a swollen arm after a bee sting. The anaphylactic patient will almost always have altered mental status, and may not be responsive. It is easy to mistake anaphylaxis for seizure or acute stress reaction.

Treatment of anaphylaxis: Provide basic life support as you would for any patient with shock and respiratory distress. However, specific treatment with drugs is generally required to reverse severe reactions. This works best if done in the field, before the reaction has progressed to a critical condition.

The drug most frequently used is injectable and reverses the effects of severe reactions by causing systemic constriction of blood vessels. People with a known allergy to insects would be advised to carry a 'pre-loaded' syringe of this drug. 0.5–1ml of 1:1000 adrenaline is given by intramuscular injection. In addition, chlorpheniramine may be given.

Be aware that adrenaline does not remove or neutralize the foreign material which caused the reaction. It is possible to see a 'rebound reaction', with reappearance of symptoms minutes or hours later when the adrenaline wears off. Multiple doses may be necessary.

Antihistamines are also used in the treatment of anaphylaxis. These drugs do not reverse blood-vessel dilation or vascular shock, but can help prevent further reactions to histamine and rebound effect. Any antihistamine is helpful, even the stuff in your over-the-counter cold medication.

Since the effects of adrenaline are temporary, evacuation should be instituted at once. If the patient has recovered from the event, it need not be an emergency. Careful monitoring for rebound reaction is crucial. Also, be aware that a second exposure to the same foreign material can cause an even more severe reaction.

9

Environmental Medicine

Problems with body-core temperature

The core of the human body operates most efficiently at or very near a temperature of 37.2°C (98.5°F). Even a small change in either direction can adversely affect the normal chemical reactions that are part of all body processes. Fortunately, a healthy body can control its internal temperature by balancing heat loss and heat production against the challenges of environmental conditions.

You are usually a willing participant. You put on or shed clothing, seek the shade when you are hot, or lie in the sun like a lizard when you're cold. You curl up to preserve heat, or spread yourself out to get rid of it. Your intelligence and freedom of movement are two of the factors used in striking the balance.

Much of the process is unconscious. You do not have to think about it. The body's compensatory mechanisms constrict blood vessels in the skin to keep heat in the core, or dilate them to radiate excess heat. Sweat glands release fluid to enhance cooling by evaporation. Shivering is the body's attempt to produce heat by involuntary exercise. While you can watch them work, these mechanisms are not under your direct control.

Problems with temperature regulation develop when the compensatory mechanisms fail due to injury, illness, accident or ignorance. As you should have guessed, one of the first signs of abnormal core temperature is a change in consciousness and mental status. You rapidly lose your judgement and common sense, and from there the problems only get worse.

Hyperthermia and hypothermia are systemic problems involving too much or too little heat in the body core. We can define three distinct stages with each. The first stage is the body's normal and healthy response to the environmental challenge. The second marks the failure of the compensatory mechanisms and mild changes in core temperature. The third stage represents a severe, life-threatening condition with complete loss of temperature regulation.

The core temperature depends upon the body balancing its own temperature control against the sometimes overwhelming environmental challenges of heat and cold. If the balance of the see-saw tips either way, problems ensue.

Hyperthermia (elevated body temperature)

Heat challenge v. passive heat loss + active heat loss: Factors in the heat challenge are both internal and external. The internal contribution is the body's production of heat through metabolism and exercise. The external factors include the temperature of the surrounding environment, air movement (wind) and humidity.

The body attempts to balance these effects by passive and active heat-loss mechanisms. Passive heat loss relies on the ability of the body to radiate heat. Skin blood vessels can be dilated to bring heat to the surface, where it can be lost to the environment. We consciously assist this mechanism by removing insulating clothing and spreading our extremities to the wind.

Active heat loss is accomplished by sweating. Water absorbs heat from the skin as it evaporates, so the body constantly sacrifices fluid to maintain normal temperature in hot environments. The effectiveness of sweating is limited by the volume of fluid available to produce sweat.

Water will evaporate very quickly into air that is dry, and slowly or not at all into air that is already saturated with water. Sweating is a much more efficient method of heat loss in very dry environments. In fact, sweat can evaporate so quickly in dry climates that profuse sweating may go unnoticed until fluid loss is severe. In high humidity the amount of fluid lost to sweat will be much more obvious, as it runs into your eyes and drips off your nose because it cannot evaporate. The low rate of evaporation also prevents efficient cooling.

Heat response
Here we see the body's passive and active heat-loss mechanisms at work. The blood vessels in the body shell (the skin) are dilated, and sweat is being produced. Fluid is being sacrificed at a prodigiously fast rate.

Assessment of heat response: The mechanisms for shedding heat are working, and the body temperature is near-normal. Level of consciousness and mental status are still normal. The person (note: not yet a patient) is responding appropriately to the heat challenge by reducing exercise, removing clothing, seeking shade, replacing fluid and so on, as needed to maintain normal body temperature. Common sense is intact.

⊞ *Treatment of heat response:* No specific treatment is required. Common sense should tell you that keeping the balance between heat challenge and heat loss is critical. Pushing yourself or others out of balance is asking for trouble. When the signs of heat response are present, pay attention to fluid replacement, maximizing heat losses and minimizing heat challenge.

While you are thinking about this, it is important to recognize that being thirsty is a relatively late sign of fluid depletion. By the time you feel thirst, your tank is already getting low. In the face of heat challenge, drink before you become thirsty!

A better sign of fluid status is your urine output. You will know that you are getting enough water if you are producing light yellow urine at your normal and healthy rate. If your urine is darker (that means it is more concentrated) and less frequent than you are used to, you will know that your body is trying hard to conserve water.

Heat exhaustion

This is the beginning of trouble. Heat exhaustion is really early volume shock caused by dehydration (sweating losses exceeding fluid intake). The term is a little misleading, however, because core temperature is not yet significantly elevated.

Assessment of heat exhaustion: You will recognize the vital sign pattern as mild compensated volume shock (see pages 210–13), including the shell/core effect. In the wilds, heat exhaustion is a serious problem which requires immediate treatment.

Vital signs in heat exhaustion:

BP Normal or decreased.

P Increased.

R Increased.

C Usually alert with normal mental status.

S Variable, may be flushed or clammy and sweaty.

T Normal or slightly elevated (below 40.6°C/105°F).

Urine output Decreased, as body seeks to preserve
fluid balance.

General condition Weak, thirsty and nauseated. Vomiting
is common.

⊞ *Treatment of heat exhaustion:* Reduce the heat challenge – move the patient into the shade. Stop physical exertion, fan the patient with air and assist evaporative cooling with water. The object is to stop the progression of volume shock by stopping fluid loss through sweating. Radical cooling, such as immersion in iced water, is not necessary.

Fluid replacement – this should begin immediately. Oral intake is usually adequate, but intravenous fluid is faster if available. Oral replacement is still possible even if the patient is vomiting, by giving fluid frequently in small amounts. Look for urine production as an indication of the return of normal fluid volume.

Replacing salt is a good idea following heavy sweating, but is not necessary for emergency treatment. Salt, if you are worried about it, is provided by most processed foods. Do not use salt tablets, which cause stomach irritation and vomiting.

Heat stroke

This is a true medical emergency. The active and passive heat-loss mechanisms are overwhelmed by the heat challenge, and the body's core temperature rises out of control to critical levels (greater than 40.6°C/105°F). The patient's fluid-volume status depends on the rate of rise in temperature. Contrary to what is described in some first aid texts, it is possible to have heat stroke and still be sweating.

In a state of fluid depletion, heat exhaustion results in loss of effective sweating (sweating absent) and precedes a rise in core temperature. This could occur after walking all day in a warm environment with limited water intake. In the presence of an extreme heat challenge, a critical rise in core temperature can occur before fluid stores are depleted (sweating still present). This can be caused by forced exercise in a hot environment. It can also be caused by staying in the sauna too long.

Vital signs in heat stroke:

BP Variable to decreased.

P Increased.

R Increased.

C Changes in consciousness preceded by mental-status changes (hallucinating, agitated etc); may also have a fit.

T Severely elevated above 40.6°C (105°F).

S Variable, may be flushed or clammy, dry or sweaty.

Assessment of heat stroke: Regardless of how quick the onset, these people are very sick. There are unmistakable changes in level of consciousness. Severe mental-status changes will rapidly lead to a drop on the AVPU scale. The skin may have the classic hot, red and dry appearance, but this is not a reliable sign. If the fluid volume is intact, it may be wet with sweat or clammy due to shock. The key indicators are a positive mechanism for hyperthermia, a high core temperature and any changes in level of consciousness.

⊞ *Treatment of heat stroke:* This is a life-threatening emergency requiring immediate field treatment. There is no time for delay. Once hyperthermia has reached this point, the chances of survival are not good.

Radical cooling – the best method is immediate immersion in cold water. If this method is used, you must monitor core temperature to prevent hypothermia. If no thermometer is available, look for an improvement in consciousness and mental status to determine the return of more normal temperature. If no pond, river or ocean is available, pour whatever water you have on to the skin and fan vigorously.

Fluid replacement – this is critical. Normal cooling requires normal volume. Oral fluid replacement is too slow and is impossible in the unresponsive patient. Intravenous replacement is clearly the treatment of choice, but not in everybody's rucksack.

Basic life support – institute to preserve vital functions while cooling. The recovery of a heat-stroke patient is dependent on quick, radical field treatment. It is rarely a problem that reaches hospital.

Evacuation – this is necessary even if you succeed in reducing the core temperature in time to save the patient. These people have suffered a severe injury, and require treatment and observation in a hospital. Brain injury and/or shock are common, so emergency evacuation is certainly justified.

Field treatment summary for hyperthermia

Heat response – maintain balance: replace fluids, reduce exercise, increase heat loss.

Heat exhaustion – immediately reduce heat challenge, replace fluid volume.

Heat stroke – radical cooling.

Case study – hyperthermia
Subjective: John, an 18-year-old student on the final day of a three-day mountain journey in the Lake District in very hot weather, suffered sunburn and then began to complain of the cold and started shivering. His group were in upper Eskdale just a mile from the road when he collapsed. Two people immediately ran and fetched expert help, leaving John in the care of three others.

Objective: Patient seriously ill, delirious, shivering. P:110 feeble; R:30 shallow; V: responsive to verbal stimuli but very confused, T/S: skin feels hot.

Assessment: Heat stroke.

Plan: Patient was radically cooled with several buckets of cold water. Within minutes, his condition improved dramatically. He was kept under observation and encouraged to take fluids.

A serious problem was narrowly avoided. Immediate radical cooling by his companions would have been preferable.

Hypothermia (reduced body temperature)
Outward Bound staff spend more than enough time in cold and uncomfortable environments. Over the years they have learnt to take control of their own thermal equilibrium and are able to use this experience to look after their groups in harsh conditions in small boats and on high mountains.

When we work hard, we generate heat and can take clothing off; when we slow down, we cool down. If we do not eat, our ability to generate heat to stay warm is reduced.

If it is cold and windy we lose more heat, especially if our clothing is wet. If we start to get very cold our co-ordination, morale and judgement are affected.

The experienced person recognizes the signs and reacts by putting on more clothing, by eating, by increasing their work rate or by getting more shelter. Less experienced people are inclined to do nothing and therefore lose control of their thermal equilibrium. They become victims of their environment and can rapidly become victims of hypothermia as well.

Cold response

This is the body's heat-retention and heat-production mechanisms at work. The shell/core effect reduces blood flow to the skin, reducing heat loss to the environment. There may be shivering as the body attempts to produce heat from muscular exercise.

Assessment of cold response: Since the compensation mechanisms are working, the core temperature is normal. Level of consciousness and mental status are normal. The skin will be pale and cool with the person (note: not yet a patient) feeling uncomfortably cold. Shivering may be slight, or very obvious.

⊞ *Treatment of cold response:* No specific treatment is required. However, the cold response indicates that the body is already using compensatory mechanisms to maintain core temperature. Further changes in the environment, or a limited food and fluid supply, may overwhelm compensation, resulting in hypothermia.

Now is the time to maintain the balance of thermal regulation by reducing the cold challenge and increasing heat retention and production. Beware of trying to produce heat without calories to burn. *Living outside in a cold environment can require more than 6000 calories a day. This is no time to be on a diet, and no time to be lying passively in cold bilge water. Get into dry clothing, eat and exercise.*

In cold, dry climates, cold diuresis, and the logistics involved in obtaining fresh water in an extreme environment, can lead to fluid volume depletion. Normal volume is necessary for normal heat production. Make the additional effort to keep yourself well hydrated in this situation.

The onset of hypothermia is insidious more often than dramatic. Any idiot can diagnose hypothermia in someone who has been overboard in the North Sea for 20 minutes. The usual case, however, creeps up on you, because you allow yourself or someone else to be just a little cold for a long time. Awareness of the potential for the problem must be coupled with action to prevent it before your common sense and judgement are affected.

Mild hypothermia

Passive heat retention and active heat production are overwhelmed by the cold challenge, and the body-core temperature falls below 35°C (95°F). This can occur rapidly, as during cold-water immersion, or slowly over hours or days. Hypothermia can often co-exist with other problems and is exacerbated by exhaustion. It can be a complication of trauma, intoxication, altitude sickness or any other condition which reduces a person's resistance to the cold challenge.

Hypothermia can contribute to injury or death from other mechanisms. Most drowning, for example, occurs because the extremities become uncoordinated as the body shell cools by exposure to cold water. Hypothermia can lead to errors in judgement, resulting in falls while rock climbing or working on a slippery deck offshore. It must always be suspected in any problem occurring in a cool setting.

Assessment of mild hypothermia: In rapid-onset cases, such as immersion, the body's fuel stores of available calories have not been used up. There is often a radical difference in temperature between the body shell (skin) and the body core. In slow-onset cases, such as during an arduous mountain journey, fuel stores are often depleted. The temperature difference between shell and core is not as dramatic. The gradual appearance of symptoms may be difficult for the patient and rescuer to recognize.

The most obvious outward signs of mild hypothermia are mild to moderate mental-status changes and shivering. The patient may become lethargic and withdrawn, irritable, and lose problem-solving ability and judgement. The skin will be pale and cool, and there may be some loss of dexterity in extremities as the shell/core effect reduces blood flow. Shivering can be mild to severe as the body forces muscles to exercise to generate heat.

Vital signs in mild hypothermia:

BP Normal.

P Normal.

R Normal.

C A on AVPU, mild to moderate mental-status changes.

T 32.2–35.6°C (90–96°F).

S Shell/core effect.

Temperature readings are unlikely to be helpful. Firstly, a special low-reading thermometer is required and, secondly, obtaining the more accurate rectal temperature presents difficulties in a hostile climate.

⊞ *Treatment of mild hypothermia:* Mild hypothermia is an urgent field problem. Unless positive changes occur in the temperature of the outside environment, the body's heat retention or the body's heat production, severe hypothermia will soon follow. Field rewarming must be an immediate priority to prevent further problems. Any field rewarming technique is generally safe. The several options available allow you to choose a procedure to fit the conditions.

Field rewarming techniques:

- **Reduce the cold challenge** – sheltering the patient from the wind and wet. Remove wet and cold clothing. Add heat to the environment. Build a fire, lie the patient in the sun, or surround him/her with warm bodies. The addition of heat to insulating materials helps prevent further cooling, but does not generally cause significant rewarming. Avoid placing anything hot directly on the skin, as the patient may not be able to feel a developing burn.

- **Heat retention** – clothe or wrap the patient in dry insulation, paying special attention to the head and face. A vapour barrier over your insulation, such as a plastic or foil blanket, will reduce evaporative cooling and the effect of wind, and aid in heat retention. Be sure to insulate from the cold ground as well.

- **Heat production** – produce body heat by providing quick calories, fluids and exercise. The fastest way to make calories available for heat production is to feed the patient foods containing lots of simple sugars. This means chocolate, glucose and hot sweet tea. This simple energy will be absorbed quickly and burn fast, which is exactly what is needed.

- **As a last resort** – survival bags are infinitely better than nothing. A survival bag is a large, heavyweight plastic bag. To use it as an emergency shelter, cut out a small hole for your face and pull it over your head. Tuck it in neatly around you and sit on it, using your sleeping mat or sack liner to insulate you from the ground. Pull your rucksack up over your legs. If the bag is large enough for two people, the warmth factor increases considerably.

Once the patient has warmed up a bit, and the digestive system is working again, fuel stores can be replenished with the more complex carbohydrates, fats and proteins of a square meal.

This is really just the same concept that you use to start a campfire. First comes the kindling, which lights with a match and burns rapidly. Once the heat is available, you add the sticks and logs. If you are successful, you have a nice, even-burning, night-long source of heat. Let it die, and you have to start again with the kindling.

Exercise is an excellent way of warming a well-fed cold person, if it can be done without increasing exposure to the cold challenge. Shivering is an involuntary form of exercise, which produces a significant amount of heat while burning a lot of calories. Do not try to prevent shivering: just be sure to provide plenty of fuel.

Severe hypothermia

Severe body-core cooling results in a hibernation-like state. This phenomenon can be protective, because the demand for oxygen in the tissues is reduced along with the ability of the body to perfuse them. The gradual slowing of the circulatory, respiratory and nervous systems results in a 'metabolic icebox' in which life can be preserved for a considerable period of time. As cooling and time progresses, however, the systems will ultimately cease to function, and death will occur. It is quite possible to mistake severe hypothermia for death. The layman should assume that life continues until qualified medical opinion is available.

Assessment of severe hypothermia: The distinction between mild and severe hypothermia is critically important for field treatment. Accurate measurement of core temperature by rectal thermometer can be very helpful when you are trying to decide how to treat.

As the core temperature falls below 32.2°C (90°F), mental-status changes will be severe, leading to a decreasing level of consciousness. The severe hypothermic may exhibit bizarre personality changes, hallucinations and confusion, followed by a drop to V, P or U on the AVPU scale. This is quite different from the lethargic but responsive mild hypothermic. Shivering will stop as shell cooling and lack of calories to burn de-activate muscles.

Vital signs in severe hypothermia:

BP Decreased; may be unobtainable.

P Decreased; may be as slow as one beat per minute.

R Decreased; may not be observable.

C Severe mental-status changes leading to decreased level of consciousness.

T Below 32.2°C (90°F).

S Cold, pale.

⊞ *Treatment of severe hypothermia:* Field rewarming can be dangerous and is usually ineffective. Severely hypothermic patients should be transported as quickly as possible to controlled rewarming in a hospital. The 'metabolic icebox' effect is protective, but only for a limited time. During evacuation, the following steps should be taken as the situation allows:

Transport – do this gently, because cold heart muscle is extremely irritable. Jostling or other rough handling can cause ventricular fibrillation. Do not exercise the patient. Ventilation may be performed if respiration is deemed inadequate.

Lay the patient flat – the blood vessels in the body shell have lost their ability to constrict, and will allow blood to escape the core if the patient is held upright. If the patient must be lowered down a cliff, or hoisted into a helicopter, do it only with the patient positioned horizontally in a stretcher.

Apply mild heat only – external heat sources, such as heat packs, help prevent further heat loss and can be used safely. However, active rewarming, such as a hot bath, is difficult to control and dangerous.

Wrap the patient – use dry insulation, such as a sleeping bag, and a vapour barrier, such as a tent fly or bivvy bag, to prevent further heat loss. Remember that prevention and early walking out of a patient with mild hypothermia is far preferable to the life-endangered stretcher case that will ensue if deterioration continues.

Field treatment summary for hypothermia

Cold response – maintain balance between cold challenge and heat productions and retention; eat, drink, exercise.

Mild hypothermia – field rewarming.

Severe hypothermia – evacuate to controlled rewarming.

Case study – hypothermia

Subjective: A 17-year-old male student was removed from the bow of a cutter after being on watch without relief for three hours during a cold and wet sail to windward. He had been asked repeatedly if he was cold, or would like something to eat, and each time replied 'OK'. He responded in the same way when asked if he saw anything ahead. Since no one else was particularly enamoured with the prospect of replacing him, he remained at his post. Eventually, someone noticed that his wool hat had rolled down over his eyes. After some debate among the students, this was brought to the instructor's attention.

The student had no known allergies, he was not on medication, he had no history of significant medical problems, and his last meal was over four hours before. There was no reason to suspect trauma.

Objective: on examination, the student was lethargic but responsive to verbal stimuli. He could open his eyes and sit up on command. His foul-weather gear was open in front and he was soaked to the waist. Vital signs at 16.15 were – BP: 110/70; P: 60; R: 12; C: V on AVPU; T: felt cool; S: pale.

Assessment: Mild hypothermia.

Anticipated problems: Severe hypothermia.

Plan: Sail was reduced and the boat was turned downwind. One student was detailed to start the stove, and another to replace the patient on watch. Other students removed the patient's soaked gear. He was clothed in dry thermals, placed in a doubled sleeping bag, and wrapped in a plastic bivvy bag. He was given a couple of cups of warm thick cocoa to drink.

Discussion: Although this problem could have been avoided, it was handled appropriately once discovered. The instructor's plan stabilized the scene, reduced the cold challenge and increased heat retention and production.

This fellow showed almost immediate improvement in level of consciousness and mental status. Evacuation was not initiated, but the instructor chose to continue downwind to an anchorage several miles away. The expedition continued in the same messy and cold easterly wind the following day, but the entire crew was warm, well fed and hydrated.

Cold injury

Exposure to temperatures below 0°C (32°F) can freeze body tissues. Any factors which reduce the circulation of warm blood to tissues allow freezing to occur more readily. In people who are already a little chilled, the cold response with shell/core effect reduces perfusion to the extremities to maintain core temperature. Constricting clothing, such as ski boots or a splint tied too tightly, can reduce blood flow as well. Cigarette smoking can be an additional factor, infusing the body tissues with nicotine, which is a powerful vasoconstrictor that shuts down the blood flow to the extremities.

Although relatively rare in Britain, frostbite is by no means unknown. In arctic and alpine countries it is a significant hazard which must be taken seriously, both in prevention and cure. Anyone stranded on a ski-lift in a winter gale will be aware of how quickly the extremities can cool.

Certainly, well-insulated and fitted boots, gloves and a face mask can go a long way towards preventing frostbite in extreme conditions. But equally important is maintaining an active and warm body core. This will ensure a good supply of warm blood to the extremities. That is why you eat a decent breakfast and wear a hat to keep your feet warm!

At some time when you are not paying attention, or you are a little hypothermic and not thinking clearly enough to prevent it, tissues will begin to freeze. You will not feel it happening. Remember that nerve tissue is the most sensitive to oxygen deprivation, so when circulation stops, the affected part goes numb. Ice crystals form, doing the same kind of damage ice can do anywhere. The same forces which can crack the granite cliffs that you are climbing are at work damaging the cells in your skin and soft tissues.

The very early stage of freezing is called 'frostnip'. This occurs when there is a loss of local tissue perfusion with the beginning of ice-crystal formation. Only the outer layers of skin are affected and damage is minimal. Prompt rewarming at this stage usually causes no disability or tissue loss.

Severe damage can result with prolonged or very deep freezing (frostbite). Much of the damage occurs during and after rewarming. Rewarmed tissue is very sensitive to further injury, even from normal use, and refreezing is devastating.

Assessment of cold injury: Frostnip – this is the loss of circulation due to early freezing of the superficial layers of the skin. The area will appear waxy white or grey (pink or red in dark-skinned people) and feel cold and stiff to the touch. However, it will remain pliable enough to allow movement over unfrozen deeper layers, joints and tendons. The typical discomfort of early cooling will be replaced by numbness. It is commonly seen on exposed ears, noses or cheeks in cold and windy weather conditions, and is most readily spotted by your companions.

Frostnip responds rapidly to rewarming. There will be pain during treatment, with only mild inflammation following. The rewarmed skin will be mildly tender, red and slightly swollen. Blistering generally does not occur. No specific long-term care is required, although the affected skin will be more susceptible to further cold injury.

Frostbite – in frostbite, the skin and underlying tissues are frozen solid. The area is white or bluish and firm to touch. Skin does not move over the joints or underlying tissues. Ice crystals are usually visible on the skin surface. There is a complete loss of sensation. The digit or extremity feels like a club.

Rewarming is extremely painful and can cause further damage if not done properly. The rewarmed tissues do not look or feel normal. There will be signs of mild to severe inflammation with blisters, swelling and redness. There may be some death of tissue, which will appear dark blue or black.

⊞ *Treatment of cold injury:* Frostnip – rewarm immediately at the first sign of numbness. Left frozen, frostnip can easily progress to frostbite. Like early hypothermia, frostnip is a case for stopping whatever you are doing and making the time and effort to warm up. Any method which does not cause tissue damage is fine. Usually just sheltering or covering the area better will do it. Remember to warm the whole body as well as the affected part. Reverse the shell/core effect. Put a hat on, eat something, and exercise to produce heat. The people who get into trouble with frostbite are the ones who ignore the first signs of frostnip.

Frostbite – rewarm under controlled conditions. The chances of further damage from trauma and infection occurring are high. Pain will be severe. Usually this means the patient should be in a hospital. Keeping tissue in the frozen state for several hours during an evacuation is generally a better plan than attempting uncontrolled field rewarming. This is especially true of frozen feet and hands, which will be impossible for the patient to use once rewarmed.

Field treatment summary for cold injury

Extremity cooling – reverse shell/core effect: eat, exercise, drink, insulate.

Frostnip – immediate field rewarming.

Frostbite – evacuate to controlled rewarming; protect any rewarmed parts from trauma and refreezing.

Occasionally, deep frostbite rewarms spontaneously as the shell/core effect is reversed by exercise or insulation during the walk out. There is no safe way to prevent this rewarming (do not pack frozen extremities in snow, for example). It is vital to prevent trauma to the rewarmed part. This generally means no use of the digit or extremity.

On no account allow the part to refreeze. Consider rewarmed frostbite to be a high-risk wound. Bandages and splinting are required. If we are talking about rewarmed frostbitten feet, a carry-out evacuation is required.

Be sure to keep the patient warm, dry, well fed and hydrated. Monitor distal circulation, sensation and movement frequently to ensure that splints or bandages do not constrict circulation as swelling develops. If possible, keep the part elevated. Early medical follow-up is essential.

Near-drowning

Drowning refers to death by respiratory failure because liquid gets in the way of gas exchange in the lungs. The liquid is usually water, and it usually comes from outside the body. This generally occurs when the patient inhales part of the lake, ocean or river in which they are submerged.

The most common cause of drowning is loss of muscular co-ordination due to the rapid shell cooling that occurs in cold-water immersion. No longer able to swim, the patient sinks below the surface and inhales water. Even the strongest swimmer can drown in this way.

Drowning can also happen almost instantly with the involuntary gasp that sometimes comes with the surprise of sudden immersion. This can affect kayakers rolled by a wave, or fishermen pulled out of the boat by their nets.

They are immediately deprived of any reserve air and will not remain conscious for more than a few seconds. Most of the time, water fills the lungs all the way to the alveoli. In about 15 per cent of cases the larynx goes into spasm, closing off the lungs and resulting in a 'dry drowning'.

In either case, a water-filled respiratory system is unhealthy, but not always fatal. The term 'near-drowning' indicates at least temporary survival of water inhalation. This occurs in very cold water where the rapid onset of hypothermia offers temporary protection to the brain deprived of oxygen. In rare cases in the civilized setting, patients have been resuscitated after up to an hour under cold water with little or no long-term brain damage. What is meant by 'cold' is controversial. Generally, though, any water below about 21°C (70°F) can be considered cold enough to have the desired effect. The degree of protection offered by the onset of hypothermia probably increases considerably as water temperature goes down.

Assessment of near-drowning: This is a primary survey problem. You are looking at the Airway, Breathing, Circulation and Disability.

Evaluation includes determining how long the patient was submerged, how cold the water is, and how soon advanced life support can be reached.

⊞ *Treatment of near-drowning:* Respiratory failure is a BIG 3 problem, and is treated immediately with artificial ventilation (see pages 199–200). There is no need to drain water from the lungs, and there is no difference in field treatment between salt and fresh water. Confirmed lack of pulse (cardiac arrest) is treated with chest compressions.

When hypothermia is a factor, the pulse can be very difficult to find. While continuing ventilation, be absolutely certain about the absence of a pulse before beginning chest compressions; this may take as long as two minutes, but it reduces the chance of damaging a functioning heart that has been slowed by hypothermia.

Most of the people who survive drowning *have* functional heart activity, and respond to ventilation within the first 20 minutes while you are still feeling for a pulse. These people have suffered a serious injury and are still at risk from respiratory distress. Water is an irritant to lung tissue, and will cause the later development of pulmonary oedema (fluid in the lungs). Even though they may appear to be recovering, patients should be evacuated quickly to medical care. Anyone who has been recovered from a near-drowning MUST go to hospital as soon as possible. Further complications can occur even up to 72 hours after the original incident.

Those who are in cardiac arrest when they are pulled from the water have a much lower survival rate. In the urban setting, basic life support with cardio-pulmonary resuscitation begins immediately. Rapid transport to a hospital with well-controlled resuscitation and rewarming follows close behind. There have been a few dramatic resuscitations performed in this way.

In a wilderness environment, success with those who do not respond quickly to basic life support is less likely. The question of further treatment is controversial. Some authorities suggest that these patients should be treated as severe hypothermics, wrapped up to prevent heat loss, and transported gently to controlled rewarming in a hospital.

Acute mountain sickness (altitude sickness)

Mountaineers in Britain might regret the absence of high, glaciated mountains, but at least altitude sickness is not a problem they have to face. However, trekkers or climbers in places such as Mount Kenya, the Andes or the Himalayas can be at very high risk.

An increase in altitude, whether travelling by foot, car, plane or hot-air balloon, changes the atmospheric environment that is around you. The higher you go, the less oxygen there is. At about 5500m (18 000ft) above sea level, air pressure is reduced by 50 per cent. This is accentuated at higher latitudes because the earth's atmosphere is thicker at the equator and thinner at the poles. Thus, the effects of altitude on the summit of Denali (Mt McKinley) in Alaska are about 15 per cent greater than at the same altitude in the Himalayas.

At a constant altitude, the amount of oxygen in the air is constant. It does not fluctuate significantly with the temperature, time of day, season or any other routine environmental changes. Your BIG 3 body systems become accustomed to this. Your rate of respiration, the number of red blood cells in your circulation and other physiological parameters are in balance with your environment, whether you are a trawlerman or a mountain guide.

There are compensatory mechanisms which allow you to change altitude, within limits, without getting out of balance. You can move from sea level to about 2400m (8000ft) with minimal effect. In the short term, there will be an increase in respiratory rate with associated chemical changes (elevated pH) in the blood. If you stay several days, your kidneys will rebalance the pH of the blood, resetting your system to your new environment.

If you were to continue even higher, your body would compensate and rebalance again. Over the course of weeks, you would undergo further physiological changes, such as producing more red cells. Ultimately, you would reach the limit of your body's ability to compensate.

This ability of the body to adapt to altitude, and the speed with which it happens, varies widely from person to person. It appears to have no relationship to physical fitness or gender. Some people adapt to altitude better than others. However, everyone's ability to adapt to higher altitudes is reduced by dehydration, alcohol and depressant drugs, and over-exertion.

The best way to adapt is to take your time, maintain hydration, stay away from depressants and take it easy. Allow your normal compensatory mechanisms the time necessary to work by ascending in stages. Climb no faster than your body can adapt. Do not over-exert on the first day at the new altitude, and plan to remain for two to three days before proceeding higher. If you pay attention to what your body is trying to tell you, you should be able to avoid the more severe forms of altitude sickness.

Severe altitude sickness develops when the reduced oxygen results in capillary leakage and generalized body-tissue swelling. The organs most seriously affected by this are the brain and lungs, producing the symptoms of acute mountain sickness (AMS). The two major components are high-altitude pulmonary oedema and high-altitude cerebral oedema.

Assessment of acute mountain sickness: In the early stages, symptoms are attributable to the chemical effects of having less oxygen per breath, and the work the body has to do to make up for it. Later, more serious symptoms appear as oedema develops throughout the body. Its effects are first noticed in the lungs and brain. Severe altitude sickness includes the effects of pulmonary fluid and increased intracranial pressure (see pages 221 and 226).

Mild AMS − characterized by mild headache, easily relieved by aspirin or ibuprofen, and slight nausea with little or no vomiting.

The patient may experience slight dizziness, loss of appetite and mild fatigue. There is usually some degree of insomnia and increased shortness of breath on exertion.

Moderate AMS – this produces severe headaches, which are not relieved by aspirin or ibuprofen, and persistent vomiting. The patient will complain of moderate fatigue.

Severe AMS (high-altitude pulmonary and cerebral oedema) – a life-threatening emergency in which the patient will show changes in consciousness and mental status. They may become ataxic (unable to walk straight), severely fatigued and short of breath even at rest. The examiner may note a cough, possibly with gurgling respirations due to the accumulation of fluid in the lungs. The patient may appear cyanotic (blue or pale) and much weaker than others in the group.

The symptoms of severe AMS can be confused or mixed with those of other problems, such as hypoglycaemia (low blood sugar), dehydration, hypothermia and exercise exhaustion. All of these problems can cause a decrease in muscular performance and efficiency, and all can cause changes in level of consciousness and mental status.

Under most field conditions, the most practical approach is to regard all five problems as possible causes until proven otherwise.

⊞ *Treatment of AMS*: This is where two days of prevention is worth 1200m (4000ft) of cure. The key is to recognize the mild form of altitude sickness and allow your body time to adapt.

Mild AMS – give mild pain relievers, such as aspirin, ibuprofen or paracetamol. The patient should avoid sedatives, such as alcohol or narcotic drugs, which can depress respiration. This is the time to rest at the present altitude, or descend to a lower altitude until the body adapts. Acetazolamide, available by prescription, is occasionally used to increase the rate of respiration by changing blood pH. (Consult a physician about its use.)

Moderate AMS – this is treated with pain medication, rest and avoidance of sedatives. In addition, an immediate descent of 300–600m (1000–2000ft) is recommended, if possible. The patient should be observed closely for increasing severity of symptoms. Be prepared for an emergency descent if symptoms worsen. Supplementary oxygen and steroids (by prescription) may be helpful if available.

Severe AMS – use all the techniques covered under the mild and moderate forms, plus an immediate descent of 600–1200m (2000–4000ft). The generic treatment for respiratory distress (see page 217) should be followed. Exertion should be minimized, but there should be no delay in descent.

Field treatment summary for altitude sickness

Mild AMS – rest until adapted, pain medication.

Moderate AMS – descend 300–600m (1000–2000ft).

Severe AMS – descend 600–1200m (2000–400ft).

10

Common Medical Problems

Abdominal pain

The word 'abdomen' is derived from the Latin word for 'hidden', and rightly so. Everything that goes on inside the abdomen is well hidden from our eyes and can become the subject of a lot of conjecture and consternation. How do you know if your crew member's tummy ache is from a developing appendicitis, or simply a comment on your cooking? Should you call a passing ship for a lift to the nearest port, or stick it out until the passage is complete?

Few symptoms can cause as much unnecessary grief as abdominal pain. Even experienced surgeons, using a variety of diagnostic tests and tools, have a difficult time ascertaining what is going on inside a sore abdomen. Do not feel too bad if you cannot work it out either. Focus instead on the question: is this pain likely to be caused by a serious problem?

For our purposes, we can consider the abdomen to be hiding three major components: hollow organs, such as the stomach and intestines; solid organs, such as the liver and spleen; and the abdominal lining, called the 'peritoneum'. Hollow organs contain digestive fluids and have muscular walls which contract rhythmically to move these fluids along the digestive system. Solid organs have a variety of functions and associated diseases, but in the field we worry mostly about their potential for traumatic rupture and severe bleeding.

The peritoneum is a membrane that lines all the organs and the abdominal wall inside the body cavity, normally isolated from digestive enzymes and bacteria. It is exquisitely sensitive to irritation from things such as blood, bacteria and digestive fluids that have entered the cavity through injury or illness. The peritoneum also

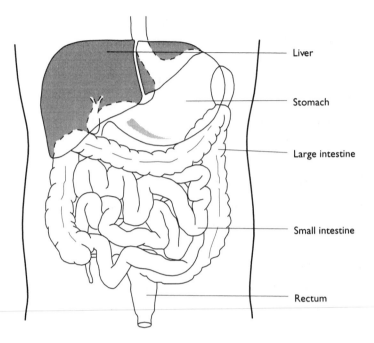

10.1 The digestive system.

represents a large surface area which, when irritated, can leak a large volume of fluid in a short period of time. Shock can develop rapidly.

Assessment of abdominal pain: Most abdominal pain is caused by the stretching of the hollow organs of the digestive system. This occurs when they are distended by gas or food while attempting their normal, rhythmic muscular contractions. This produces the crampy pain which precedes a bout of diarrhoea or flatulence, after which you feel much better. The problem is well contained within the intestine and, when relieved, the system returns to normal.

Another source of benign abdominal discomfort is abdominal wall pain. This is associated with the musculature of the abdomen rather than any internal organs. It can usually be attributed to exertion. This type of pain will be relieved by rest, and made worse by movement.

Real problems begin when whatever is happening in the abdomen begins to affect the circulatory system. This usually comes in the form of severe fluid loss from continued vomiting or diarrhoea. Even more devastating is perforation of a hollow organ, which releases its contents into the abdominal cavity. This will inflame the peritoneum, with subsequent severe pain, volume shock and death.

A non-penetrating blow to the abdomen can cause severe bleeding from a ruptured solid organ, leading to shock. This should be anticipated in cases of persistent abdominal pain following injury. It can develop almost immediately, or become evident only after the peritoneum becomes irritated by free blood in the abdominal cavity.

Symptoms of peritoneal irritation from whatever cause are to be considered serious. These symptoms are included in the danger signs of abdominal pain.

Danger signs – abdominal injury:

- Fever.
- Blood by mouth or rectum.
- Persistent vomiting or diarrhoea.
- Pain persisting more than 12 hours.
- Tenderness (to the touch).
- Signs of volume shock.
- Pain becoming worse following trauma.

The presence of danger signs in abdominal pain does not always guarantee serious problems. It just means that the chances are high enough to warrant an evacuation.

⊞ *Treatment of abdominal pain:* Treat the cause. This usually means that you cannot fix it in the field. Whether you are a surgeon or a woodcutter, Danger signs = Evacuation. You should continue to monitor the patient during transport and note any changes in condition. In the long-term care setting, abdominal pain or the accompanying danger signs may resolve, revealing the problem to be less serious. It is always better to cancel or slow down an evacuation in progress, rather than start one too late.

Chest pain

Anyone who enters a hospital emergency department and uses the words 'chest' and 'pain' in the same sentence will be treated as if they are having a heart attack. It happens even though doctors know that there are many causes of chest pain that have nothing to do with the heart. They recognize that the risk and expense involved in testing for heart attack is much lower than the risk and expense involved in failing to detect one. For the hospital, the choice is easy and the policy is clear. Unfortunately, this does not translate very well into the remote environment. We need a much better indication of the real potential for a heart problem to balance against the hazards of evacuation.

Summary of heart attack symptoms:

- Crushing pain in middle of chest.
- Shortness of breath.
- Sweating.
- Signs of shock.
- Irregular heartbeat.

Assessment of chest pain: Just like the hospital, we look for a reasonable explanation for the pain. This may include heart problems. More often, however, it will be attributable to one of a number of other possibilities.

The most common cause of chest pain in the wilderness setting is muscle or rib pain from exercise or injury. This type of pain can usually be reproduced by movement. There is often a tender area in the same spot where the patient complains of pain. It is usually relieved by rest and aspirin or ibuprofen. The patient does not generally appear otherwise ill, or short of breath.

Chest pain from respiratory infection or lung injury will usually have a pretty clear history of preceding illness or injury. It may be accompanied by a cough, fever and a sore throat. It is usually made worse by coughing and by deep breathing. The patient is usually somewhat ill in his or her appearance. This pain may be part of a serious respiratory-system problem, but it is not an indication of a heart attack.

The pain associated with indigestion is usually accompanied by burping, heartburn and nausea. Unlike the pain of heart attack, it is relieved by antacids. The patient will often give a long-standing history of similar episodes associated with certain foods or stress.

The chest pain of a heart attack is caused by ischaemia (inadequate perfusion) of the heart muscle. It is typically described as being in the middle of the chest radiating to the jaw and left arm. The pain is often referred to as 'crushing or constricting'. There may be shortness of breath and sweating. Vital signs may show an irregular heartbeat and the signs of shock (see page 210).

At least, this is what the textbook says. Unfortunately, the classic pattern does not occur in all cases of heart attack. It can be mistaken for indigestion, respiratory infection or chest-wall pain. In fact, the patient will be trying very hard to mistake it for anything but a heart attack. If there is no other obvious cause, we must assume that chest pain represents a serious medical problem, especially when associated with danger signs.

This does not mean that a slim, relaxed, non-smoking, athletic, 20-year-old woman cannot have heart problems. It just means that it is very unlikely. But if your chest-pain patient is an overweight, 20-a-day, 45-year-old male stockbroker, then anticipate the worst. This does not mean he is having a heart attack, but the likelihood is high enough to justify evacuation.

Danger signs – possible heart attack:

- Non-traumatic chest pain with no other obvious cause.

- Risk factors for heart disease.

- Smoking.

- Overweight.

- Sedentary lifestyle.

- Past history of heart attack.

- History of high blood cholesterol.

- Male over 40 years of age.

- Female after menopause.

⊞ *Treatment of suspected heart attack:*

Basic life support.

Rest and reassurance.

Oxygen – give if available.

Evacuation – this should be quick, but not stressful.

Medication – if the patient has medication, assist him/her in taking it according to his/her directions.

Aspirin – if the patient takes one tablet with a small amount of water it can considerably reduce dangerous blood clotting.

Nausea and vomiting

Like diarrhoea, vomiting can be the result of a problem with the gastro-intestinal system, or be a symptom of other problems, such as motion sickness, toxin ingestion, head injury or infection. Finding and treating the primary cause is the priority. However, you must consider the additional problems that can be caused by severe fluid loss as well.

Danger signs – vomiting:

- Fluid losses cannot be replaced by drinking.
- Associated with danger signs for abdominal pain.
- Persistent, more than 24 hours.

⊞ *Treatment of vomiting:*
   Replace fluid losses – as for diarrhoea.
   Protect airway – vomiting can cause airway obstruction or
      pulmonary oedema if inhaled. Position the patient to
      allow drainage.
   Evacuate – if vomiting is potentially serious.

Nosebleed

It does not take much trauma to rupture the blood vessels in the nose. The most easily injured ones are near the front. Blood from here will drain out if the patient is positioned upright with the head forward.

Assessment of nosebleed: The problem here is to distinguish a simple nosebleed from something more significant. If the bleeding started spontaneously, or while blowing or picking your nose, you can be pretty sure it is not complicated. However, if the bleeding is the result of trauma, you must consider the possibility of facial bone fracture and head injury.

⊞ *Treatment of nosebleed:* First, sit your patient down, and position them to allow for drainage out of the nose. Then get them to blow out any clots. This sounds scary, but it will not cause the bleeding to get worse. Now, you or the patient should pinch the nostrils together and hold firmly for 15 minutes while sitting erect. This applies simple direct pressure to the most likely bleeding source. Remember, to stop the bleeding it is essential to hold enough

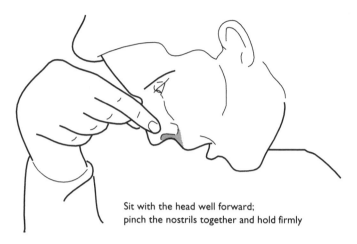

Sit with the head well forward;
pinch the nostrils together and hold firmly

10.2 Treatment of nosebleed.

pressure for a long enough time. This should stop most nosebleeds. Bleeding might return over the next few hours, but the treatment simply needs to be repeated.

If you encounter the rare, persistent nosebleed in the field, your best response is the same as for any other bleeding which you are unable to control. Make the patient as comfortable and quiet as possible and send for help. Control the airway by positioning the patient face down, or on their side, with the chest and head supported to allow for drainage from the nose and mouth. Prepare for a carry-out evacuation.

Respiratory infections

The 'common cold', with its stuffy nose, sore throat, runny eyes and cough has been harassing people since people began. There is no reason to believe that it will not pick on you, expedition or no expedition. You should be ready to deal with it.

The mild respiratory infections that we label 'colds' or 'flu' are caused by viruses. They produce a multiplicity of symptoms which conspire to keep us miserable until our body's immune system identifies the bug, produces specific antibodies and eradicates it.

Problems develop when the virus is particularly virulent or the viral infection opens the way for a secondary bacterial infection to take hold. This is how people who start with a cold can end up with pneumonia, bronchitis or strep throat.

Assessment of upper respiratory infection: Mild upper respiratory infection is characterized by runny nose, mild headache, sneezing, coughing, weeping eyes, mild sore throat, muscular aches and low-grade fever (below 38.9°C/102°F). Other than being slightly annoyed and uncomfortable, the patient is not usually significantly impaired in their ability to perform normal tasks.

Significant respiratory disease may have been preceded by the above symptoms, or develops independently. In serious respiratory infections, coughing typically becomes productive of thick yellow, green or brown sputum ('coughing in colours'). The patient may experience fevers and chills, shortness of breath, and chest pain on respiration.

✚ *Treatment of upper respiratory infection:* The treatment of mild upper respiratory infection involves making the patient more comfortable while the body works to defeat the virus. Use whatever over-the-counter medications make the patient feel better, while not interfering with their ability to function. Local decongestants such as nasal sprays, systemic decongestants and non-narcotic cough medications are very helpful. So is aspirin.

Equally important is maintaining fluid balance, eating well, staying warm and getting enough rest. This reduces the number of threats that the body has to deal with. The system will then be free to focus on fighting the virus and preventing a secondary bacterial invasion. The patient who is 'coughing in colours' generally requires antibiotics and further medical care.

Eye problems

The common term 'red eye' refers to inflammation of the thin, membranous lining of the eye and the inside of the eyelids (conjunctiva). The cause of the inflammation may be infection, sunburn, sand in the eye, trauma, chemical irritation or even fatigue. It can also represent one of the symptoms of a more serious condition, such as glaucoma. The patient will complain of an itching or burning sensation, tearing and discomfort caused by bright lights. Vision will be unaffected except for transient blurring caused by tears or yellow exudate. Normal eye movements will be uncomfortable, but fully intact.

In more severe cases there may be clouding of the cornea, persistent visual disturbances and severe headache. Causes include:

Foreign body – sand or other debris which gets on to the conjunctiva will cause immediate irritation, redness and watering.

Corneal abrasion – the clear centre structure of the eye can be scratched by a foreign body, branch, fingernail or wind-blown ice crystals. It is exquisitely sensitive and will cause considerable pain and inflammation.

Snow blindness – this condition, caused by sunburn of the eye, can be extremely painful and complete blindness can ensue for several days. It can occur very quickly, even in mist, especially at high altitudes. The sunglasses that you wear for, say, driving are not necessarily effective against the strong ultraviolet (UV) rays encountered on mountains. Goggles or side-screened glasses should be worn and spares carried.

Infection – this is what is meant by the term 'conjunctivitis'. Bacteria invade the conjunctiva, causing the typical signs and symptoms of infection. The patient may notice yellow oozing, which can stick the eyelids together during sleep. The eyelids themselves may appear slightly puffy and reddened.

Chemical irritation – soap, dirty contact lenses, stove fuel and other irritants can cause chemical conjunctivitis.

⊞ *Treatment of red eye:* Mild inflammation is usually easily treated in the field. If the cause is known, correct and/or protect it, and allow it to heal.

Foreign body – the easiest and least traumatic way to remove something from the eye is by irrigation with water. The simplest way to accomplish this is to have the patient immerse their face in clean water and blink the eyes. If there is no lake or stream handy, irrigate with your water bottle. Position the patient on their side with the affected eye up. Pour water gently on the side of the eye and let it run across towards the nose. Holding the lids open is not necessary if the patient can continue to blink during irrigation.

This technique will remove almost any object that lands in the eye. If the patient continues to have the sensation of something in there, you will have to go looking for it. Gently pull the lids away from the eye one at a time while the patient looks in all directions. Look on the eye itself as well as on the conjunctival surface of the inside of the eyelids. A torch will help.

If you find something, use a wet cotton swab or corner of a gauze pad to lift it off the membrane. If the object is embedded in the conjunctiva or cornea and resists your efforts to remove it, leave it alone. Embedded foreign bodies require medical attention. Patch the eye, if safe to do so, and plan to walk out. Beware, however, of using a patch in situations where impaired vision could be dangerous. Depth perception is lost when one eye is patched. Be careful when walking anyone whose vision is impaired.

Corneal abrasion – if the foreign body sensation persists but you are unable to find anything, the problem may be a corneal abrasion or scratch on the conjunctiva left by the dislodged foreign body. Sometimes the abrasion will be visible on careful examination. This will usually resolve itself over the course of 24 hours. A patch should be used if it makes the patient more comfortable and the reduction of vision can be tolerated safely.

Snow blindness – most inflammation from UV exposure is mild and self-limiting. However, if the damage is severe enough to cause cloudiness of the cornea or snow blindness, the eyes must be rested and allowed to heal. Fortunately UV rays do not penetrate deeply, so damage is usually superficial.

Treatment involves patching both eyes (as in the treatment for corneal abrasion), keeping the patient rested and quiet, and giving pain medication as necessary. Symptoms should resolve within 24–48 hours. This is the time to bivouac, not stumble blindly down a glacier to find a helicopter.

Infection – as with any infected tissue, allow the eyes to drain. Do not use a patch because this will prevent drainage of bacteria. Some relief may be obtained using frequent rinsing and warm soaks. Treatment with antibiotics is usually necessary, especially if symptoms appear to become progressively worse. Note also that a conjunctival infection can be quite contagious. Avoid sharing towels, goggles or face masks.

Chemical irritation – the treatment for chemical exposure is irrigation, and lots of it (30 minutes minimum). Expect mild redness following prolonged irrigation, but it should begin to resolve within a few hours following treatment. If it gets worse, the chemical may still be present. Irrigation should be repeated and evacuation plans made.

11

Rescue

'Going for help' or 'Evacuating to civilization' may sound simple but can be extremely difficult. If the casualty is unconscious and needs airway management, the problems are formidable. If the injured person is one of a group which is out of its depth, the situation is a nightmare. Some people call for external rescue at the first sign of difficulties, but most would prefer in the first instance to draw upon their own capabilities. After all, this self-sufficiency is one of the great satisfactions of travelling in wild places in small parties.

Preparation

The traditional view holds that 'The best preparation for medical emergencies is not to have them in the first place'. There are other books in this series on walking, backpacking, rock climbing, sailing and canoeing to help you do it right. Read them.

Taking the statement a step further: 'The best time to have a medical emergency is when you are ready for it'. Being ready means having the right attitude, knowledge, equipment and margin of safety for the expedition you are planning. Many of these aspects have been covered in Part I, but it is worth looking at some of them again.

Attitude, in this context, is the way you relate to the forces of the natural world. It is so much more peaceful to flow with natural trends than to push against them. However, it is not always possible to go downriver, downhill, downwind or with the tide. We tend to have timetables, destinations and personal goals that put us in confrontation with nature.

Of course, challenging the elements can be great fun and an exhilarating experience. However, you must beware of developing an adverse relationship with nature. This is a forewarning of serious trouble. When it starts raining on you, or the wind shifts just to make you angry, or the snow starts just because it knows you are almost at the summit, your attitude has become dangerous. In an emergency situation, a bad attitude is big trouble. It contributes to irrational behaviour, poor judgement and despair. When you feel the 'attitude', it is time to change your plans and re-establish harmony with your surroundings.

Knowing how to handle medical emergencies is a product of both information and experience. Only by combining the two can you gain real competence in the art of wilderness medicine. The information is readily available in this book, but the experience is more difficult to come by. You may indeed 'get the examination first and the lesson afterwards'.

Knowing what to expect of the environment you are entering is important too. What are the weather and terrain like? How far will you be from help, if needed? What kind of help is available? Whom do you contact? Where can you find shelters, telephones, roads and so forth?

Equipment for wilderness emergency care is surprisingly simple. The real first aid kit is your knowledge and experience. The bandages, ointments and other items in your pack (see Appendix I) are just tools for minor maintenance and repair.

How much first aid equipment you carry is a function of how you carry it, how many people you are responsible for, where you are going and what you know. There is no point in taking anything you do not know how to use. If you are carrying it on your back, there is no reason to take anything which can be improvised from something else. As a result, the average backpacker's first aid kit is very small and simple. Larger groups, or people travelling by vehicle, boat or horse, have the luxury of carrying more complete supplies.

The margin of safety in wilderness travel is the most important factor of all. If there is, say, a suspected broken leg in your party but you are dryish, warm and well fed, with a dry tent and sleeping bags, and enough food, water and fuel, you will be prepared to spend another night out if necessary. If you allow yourselves to get wet, chilled and low on food, the situation is entirely different. Breaking a leg at that point could easily be fatal. This is so often the case near the end of an expedition, when fatigue has set in, supplies are low and common sense flies to the moon.

When you are in the mountains, out at sea or on the river, you should frequently ask yourself 'What would I do if something went wrong?' This is a great exercise for the traveller new to the wilds. If your answers don't come up clear and reasonable, you are beyond your margin of safety.

As you gain experience, your awareness of your own margin of safety becomes part of you. You feel comfortable within it, and uneasy outside it. Pushing your own limits then becomes a matter of choice, rather than accident.

Communication

When you have stabilized a medical problem as best you can, and have decided that outside help will be required, your communication skill becomes critical. Presenting a clear picture of the situation allows rescuers to apply best their own local knowledge, experience and resources to helping you solve your problem. This is where your response summary really becomes valuable. Not only has it helped you organize your thoughts, it can now provide the basis for organizing an evacuation. This it true whether you communicate by radio, telephone, carrier pigeon, or by sending a runner with a note.

Your note should also include information about the scene. Describe the general condition of the group, weather and terrain conditions, and the availability of shelter and any specialist equipment. Remember the most vital information is your location – use every method to give an unambiguous description.

Essential rescue information:

- Grid reference (get it right!).
- Marked map.
- Name of climb, anchorage or rapid.
- Bearings to prominent objects.

If you are passing on the message in person, you will have to remain available to provide additional information for the rescue personnel. Try to stick to facts as much as possible. Avoid value judgements like 'Oh my God, it's really bad, come quickly!' These provide no useful information and only distract people from a good planning process. A proforma may be useful (Fig 11.1).

If you are unable to send for help, you must try to attract attention. The International Distress Signal is given below.

International Distress Signal:

- Whistle, shout, flash a light or make any other signal six times in a minute.
- Then pause for a minute's silence.
- Signal for a further minute and to continue alternating minutes of signal and silence.
- Do not stop signalling until you are absolutely certain your position has been fixed.

Recognize that any good rescue team is trained to perform their own assessment of the scene and the patient's condition. Their assessment may differ from yours. Work with them, pointing out elements of your assessment that will help form a reasonable plan. This is no time for arguing. In all but the most unusual cases, when you have asked for rescue the rescuers are in charge.

PATIENT OBSERVATION FORM

Time
Pulse rate per minute
Temperature
Respiration rate per minute
Pallor/flush/cyanosis/greyness
Degree of coma
Reaction of pupils to light

It is suggested that observations are made every 15 minutes

RESCUE MESSAGE FORM

Name and age of casualty
Nature of injuries

Degree of consciousness
Time of accident
Location of telephone
Name of caller
Phone number
Grid reference of casualty location
Description of location

Number and condition of rest of party

What first aid has been done

Weather at casualty location
Number of rescuers required
Is stretcher required
Is helicopter evacuation suggested
Degree of urgency
(e.g., head injury, shock, abdominal injuries, diabetic coma, heart attack, breathing difficulties, hypothermia, bad weather)

11.1 Patient observation form and rescue message form.

Evacuation

Response to a medical emergency can happen either by bringing the medical resources to the patient, or the patient to the medicine. Usually, it is a combination of the two. For example, rescue teams may bring intravenous fluids and oxygen to assist in stabilizing a patient during the carry-out. For the most part, though, the patient needs to return to civilization for definitive care.

The urgency with which this happens is a consequence of the patient's condition, and the resources and skills available. It also hinges on your ability to distinguish real emergencies from logistical dilemmas. Very few wilderness situations really justify an all-out rapid evacuation. Only those injuries which involve a BIG 3 system in a big way deserve a big evacuation. Anything else can be more controlled, less desperate, and less trouble.

Water rescue

Sailing

Capsize recovery

Getting wet is definitely a part of dinghy sailing and capsizing should be considered an integral part of your training. In conditions it is sensible to start off in you might capsize accidentally, so you may need to make sure that you can make it happen on purpose. It is important that you feel able to recover the boat with confidence and it is essential that you gain that confidence in conditions where it is a good bit of fun. Therefore it is best to practise when things are well in control and you have the cover of a safety boat. You do not want to be trying this for the first time in a force 4 or more when you might be sailing at the limit of your early ability. It should not be necessary to remind you to check the buoyancy, but you will find out soon enough if there is a problem with it! Buoyancy bags should be full of air and strongly secured. Built-in buoyancy tanks should be empty of water and often have a drain plug to check this.

Once the capsize has happened, the first consideration is to stay with the boat. This should continue to be your priority even if for some reason you cannot right it. It has a large amount of buoyancy in it and will provide considerable support if necessary. It also presents a large target to spot and someone is likely to notice if you are in trouble. Read the section on indicating *distress* on pages 325–7, but if you just need a bit of a hand from the safety boat then a simple wave or whistle would be more appropriate.

A boat full of water will be quite unstable so will have to be balanced carefully at this point. If the water level is near the top of the centreboard case, then it is worth the crew doing a stint of bailing before bringing the helmsman aboard. Modern dinghies, however, tend to ship little water and will self-bail once you get going again.

The crew helps the helmsman aboard at the windward shroud. This place is important as the wind will blow the mainsail to the leeward side, keeping the mainsheet out of the way and helping to balance the boat. If the helmsman is further aft then they will act as a drogue and the boat may blow around to head downwind. If this happened, the sails would fill and off it would go and the helmsman would be dragged along, left behind or the boat would gybe accidently, which might cause it to capsize again.

Once you are all aboard, sort out the mess, bail out if necessary and sail off when you are ready. Do not forget to keep an eye on your surroundings. Once you are upright, and the more empty you are, the quicker you will be drifting downwind. Do not waste time emptying the boat out completely, as the self-bailers will drain the last of the water once you get moving quickly.

Windward capsize
If the boat capsizes to windward then the sail will end up lying in the water to windward. If the above procedure is followed, then the wind is likely to get under the mainsail as soon as it lifts, and as the

boat rapidly rights itself with the crew weight on the leeward side, a swift repeat capsize is extremely likely. To avoid this, it is necessary to get the boat approximately head to wind before attempting to right it. This is best done by holding on to the bow and letting the hull swing downwind of you. Righting can then proceed as has been outlined above.

Full inversion

Sometimes the boat will turn fully upside down. This will take longer to sort out but is not usually too great a problem. The helmsman climbs on to the hull holding the leeward jib sheet and pulls the centreboard up into the fully lowered position. The crew can help by climbing on to the stern to break the suction. The helmsman, with back to the wind, leans back, pulling on jib sheet or centreboard. This should bring the boat into the semi-inverted position, when you can proceed as before.

If this has not worked, try moving weight around the hull to break the seal. If the mast is stuck on the bottom you will need to get the safety boat to help you out.

Recovering a single-hander

With a capsize to leeward in a single-hander, you can often avoid going into the water by climbing up the high side of the boat as it goes over and swinging a leg over on to the daggerboard. You can then right the boat again by leaning to windward and climb back in as it comes upright.

Man overboard recovery

This is a skill worth practising, as not only would it be essential if the helmsman or crew were to fall overboard, but it also brings together a lot of basic sailing skills and judgement. Practise it frequently and do not stop doing so once you start doing it well, particularly if you are sailing a different boat, as handling characteristics vary tremendously. For practice, find an area with plenty of unobstructed water and use something which floats low in the water that will drift as a person would. A bucket with a fender attached is popular, but do not chuck out your only bailing bucket. Another option is a large and nearly full water container.

A fine reach is the most controllable point of sailing for manoeuvring, and this exercise is an important and typical example. Your aim, if you have lost someone over the side, is to get the boat under control as quickly as possible, keep sight of the person in the water and sail back to them on a fine reach with speed well under control, so that you can stop when you get there. It is no good charging back and running over the person in the water at 4 knots; better to take your time, stay calm and keep in control.

Coastal safety

Distress signals

Once you extend your sailing to the coast, particularly if you are sailing away from the cover of a safety boat, then if you get into trouble that is life-threatening you need to know how to attract attention to summon help. There are a large number of internationally recognized distress signals you could learn but only those relevant to this situation are described here.

Firstly, if you do get into difficulty then stay with the boat. This is the most important thing to remember, which you ignore at your peril. The boat will have a large amount of buoyancy to help support you in the water and furthermore presents a much bigger target if someone is looking for you. If you should become separated from the boat, just your head visible in the water will be difficult to spot. Distances at sea are difficult to judge and where you might feel quite happy swimming 1km (½ mile) in the swimming pool it is a different matter swimming in cold, deep water with the restrictions of clothes or wetsuit and buoyancy aid.

Man overboard step by step:

1. As soon as possible, regain control of the dinghy, sheeting out everything and lying to for a few seconds if necessary to sort things out. Then head off on a beam reach. If your boat will manoeuvre well under mainsail alone, then just leave the jib flying free – it is one less thing to worry about. Similarly, have the centreboard about three-quarters down and leave that too.

2. Tack when you have enough distance to give plenty of room on the way back to manoeuvre on to the right line. This comes with practice, as you do not want to go so far that you lose contact with the person in the water. In a dinghy, try about 50m (55yd) to start off with. Head back on a beam reach initially.

3. Bear away on to a broad reach in order to get downwind a bit. Remember that you are aiming to be able to approach your person in the water on a fine reach. If you go too far downwind at this stage you will end up beating back to them; not far enough downwind, and you will still be on a beam reach and have trouble slowing down.

4. Approach on a fine reach, controlling your speed by spilling or filling your mainsail. If you have misjudged the angle of approach or are travelling too fast, then sail past and return on the other tack for another attempt.

5. Stop the boat with the person in the water at the windward shroud. If you give the tiller a nudge up to windward at this stage you are less likely to end up tacking the boat round on top of them. You will now have stopped in the water with the sails flapping away and the boat lying to. Help the person aboard at the windward shroud (the above section on capsize explains why). If you have trouble with this, use a loop of the windward job sheet or a bowline tied in the end of it for them to step up on.

The standard distress signal that is applicable even on inland waters is slowly to raise and lower both arms outstretched. This is one that everyone on the water knows and will respond to. You can help draw attention to yourself by combining it with the audible signal of a whistle blast of SOS in Morse code (three short blasts followed by three long, then three short). Obviously these rely on your being seen or heard, so it is not wise to depend on them in a coastal situation, where your problem might be exactly that you are unable to return to the proximity of the shore, and other people and boats.

For this reason, it is essential that any boat operating away from safety cover on coastal waters should carry flares. The basic minimum would be a couple of hand-held smoke flares, not buried deep in a locker but ideally in a waterproof container attched to the boat. The usual type of smoke flares burn for 50 seconds and give off a large cloud of orange smoke. They are expiry dated and last for three years, but even after this there is a fair chance they will still work. For this reason, as well as two in-date smoke flares it is a good idea to keep a couple of recently expired ones as well. If you are in trouble, then the more chance you have of attracting attention the better. These orange handsmokes are only of use in daylight and within a maximum of 5km (3 miles) from where you hope to be seen. Further offshore and in more remote situations parachute flares are necessary, as they can be seen from a much greater distance. Therefore if you extend your cruising you will need to extend your flare supply as well.

Being rescued is something to avoid, but if it happens you should do everything possible to stabilize your situation, make it easier for rescuers to locate you and, when they arrive, to be of assistance to them. The greatest help is to listen carefully to instructions and avoid doing anything unpredictable. Fortunately, with proper training and preparation, many difficulties can be resolved without drawing on external assistance.

Helping a boat in distress

Should you see another boat in distress, then you have a responsibility to make sure that help is despatched as quickly as possible.

You should only consider going to a boat in trouble yourself if it is within the usual limits of your area sailing and if you do not put yourself and your companions at risk by doing so. You also have to consider whether as a small engineless sailing boat you will be more effective by raising the alarm than by going to help, when you will have limited space aboard to take people off and little power to tow. If you are the only people who have spotted the casualty and you sail off to help, only to discover you cannot do so, then you will have delayed effective rescue by quite some time. Also bear in mind your own skill level and whether you may cause more problems than you can solve. As a general guide, it is recommended that as an inshore dinghy sailor you should only go to a boat in trouble if you can see it and you know you can help. Only if it is close to you will you be able to tell the size of it, its position and likely problem, and then you may be in a position to make a judgement as to whether or not you can help.

If the boat is some distance away and perhaps all you see is a smoke flare, then your priority must be to call the coastguard. Remember the approximate position of the vessel and get ashore to the nearest house or phone to call the coastguard. If you are sailing in the vicinity of larger boats such as a yacht or motor cruiser, fishing boat or work boat, then sail across to raise their attention. They probably have a VHF radio and will be able to call the coastguard direct and possibly provide assistance themselves.

The primary role of the coastguard is to co-ordinate marine search and rescue and they will take over the responsibility of directing the help available. They decide whether to call a helicopter or lifeboat or to use the other vessels in the area. If the phone is your method of contacting them, then do not hesitate to call. They would rather have ten reported sightings than none at all, because everyone thinks someone else will call. They might even build up a better idea of the location of the casualty if they have several sightings to go on. The other main distress signals you may come across are red, hand-held, burning flares and red parachute flares used for inshore distress at night and distress offshore respectively.

Canoeing

Canoeing is a safe sport. There are very few fatalities, but there are correlations between accidents and inexperienced paddlers. Ignorance is not an excuse but a potential death trap. Safety is an attitude that you should have towards the water, based on a respect for what can happen if things go wrong. The rescues covered will give beginners a good grounding from which to progress, with some information specifically related to white water.

The type of rescue, when needed, will be determined by the situation, the number and experience of people available, and where you are. Assuming that you are paddling in a group of three or more, then there should be people to help. Rescue methods should always be practised and you should be confident of getting into and out of your canoe in all kinds of situations, so that when it happens for real it becomes an incident rather than an emergency. Make sure you are in safe water (such as a swimming pool) when you practise these rescues, so that you do not become an emergency yourself or passers-by do not think you need help.

Rescue priorities

Good practice is to work on the assumption that you will rescue yourself. Never assume someone else will do it for you. Giving help to someone else, however, should be done in an order of priority.

This does not mean that you physically go through this order, but that there are different ways of tackling rescues, some methods

Order of priority when helping others:

1. Reach.

2. Throw.

3. Tow/Row.

4. Go yourself.

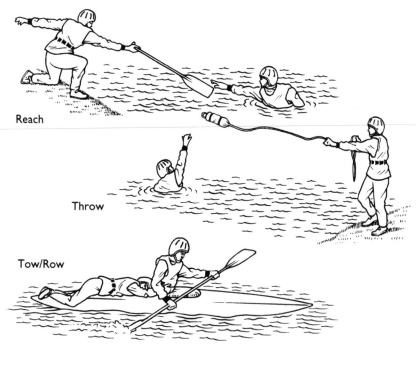

Reach

Throw

Tow/Row

Go yourself

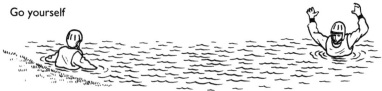

11.2 The sequence of Reach, Throw, Tow/Row and Go yourself is the basic priority of any water rescue.

being simpler or more appropriate than others, but this depends on the circumstances.

What to do after a capsize

If you capsize and come out of your canoe, it is better to hang on to it as it is buoyant, will give you support and help you to be seen by others. You should only abandon your canoe if there is a hazard that makes it more dangerous to stay with it, and this is really only likely to be in white water. So take a breath and work out what you should do. If the water is cold it will drain your energy fast, so you need to decide quickly.

If you are separated from your canoe

If you become separated from your canoe, but you have made it to the shore, then one of your party could push your canoe to the shore with the nose of their canoe. If you are in the water, then you are more important than your canoe and should be helped by one of your party first. That could also mean being pushed, towed or helped to shore on the end of their canoe.

There are many different methods of towing which on still, calm water are relatively simple to do. A rope from the paddler doing the towing is clipped on to the grab handle of the canoe that needs assistance, then the tow commences. Having a quick-release system on the body of the paddler doing the towing is important, as they need to be able to escape from it if anything goes wrong. The paddler who is being towed can help by paddling as well.

Capsize and swimming

This next section on capsizing and what to do afterwards is not intended to put you off paddling more gentle beginner's white water, but to inform you of what you need to be able to do to be safe in all grades of white water. The responses you need to make have to become totally instinctive and second nature, which only happens with training and practice. Experienced paddlers who rarely fall out of their canoes are often the least experienced at swimming in an unexpected capsize, as they rarely get the practice. Practise in safe white water first so that when it happens for real you are trained to respond automatically.

After a capsize in white water – keep your feet up, lie on your back and keep your feet downstream.

After a capsize:

- Keep your feet and hips up and very close to the surface.

- Go to the *upstream* end of your boat so that you are not caught between the boat and an obstruction. If you are in a rapid and cannot get upstream of the boat, push it away from you and leave it.

- Lie on your back, with your feet downstream of your body.

- Decide which bank to go for and *swim aggressively* towards it.

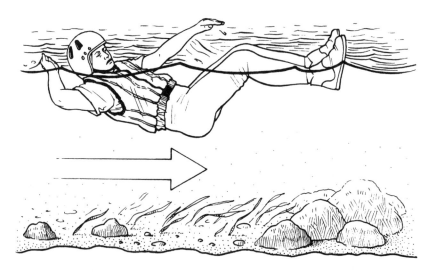

11.3 After a capsize in white water keep your feet up, lie on your back and keep your feet downstream. This is the safest way to swim in moving water.

These actions cannot be stressed enough. What you are avoiding is entrapment, which is getting your feet trapped in the river or you caught between your boat and an obstruction. With your feet up and downstream of your body, you can use them to fend yourself off rocks as you drift down.

Only stand up if your bottom is scraping on the ground. Do not stand up in white water when the water depth is above your knees – *anybody* will be knocked over very fast. If you are in water above your knees or close to your knee height and your feet get caught in the river, you can be knocked over instantaneously by the current and could possibly be held down with your head underwater.

The throw bag

The throw bag is a device that is designed to be an easy way of throwing a rope to someone quickly and accurately, with a minimum of practice. It is one of the most useful items of river safety and rescue equipment. At some point you may need to throw one to help someone else get out of trouble or be thrown one yourself, so you need to know what it is and how to use one.

The throw bag is usually some form of lightweight but durable bag which contains the rope. A loop of the rope is secured to the outside of one end of the bag, and the rest of rope is prevented from escaping out of the other by a quick-release system. The rope contained in the throw bag should be a buoyant one made of a soft material, about 15–25m (50–80ft) long with a minimum diameter of 9mm (⅓in).

At the bottom of the bag there should be a fixed piece of buoyant closed-cell foam, which will keep the bag afloat once it has been thrown into the water. Below are listed the various methods of using a throw bag.

Throwing: The rope must be able to run freely from the bag, snaking its way out without coming out all at once. Release the securing system at the top, take some rope out and hold the end of the rope

Open the throw bag. Take out some rope then
shout and signal to attract the swimmer

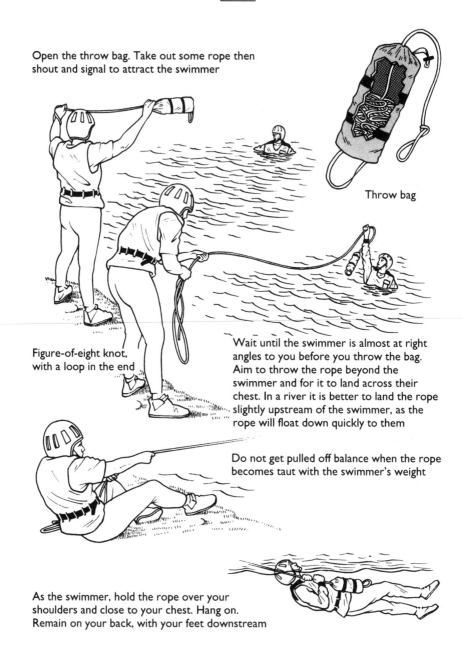

Throw bag

Figure-of-eight knot,
with a loop in the end

Wait until the swimmer is almost at right
angles to you before you throw the bag.
Aim to throw the rope beyond the
swimmer and for it to land across their
chest. In a river it is better to land the rope
slightly upstream of the swimmer, as the
rope will float down quickly to them

Do not get pulled off balance when the rope
becomes taut with the swimmer's weight

As the swimmer, hold the rope over your
shoulders and close to your chest. Hang on.
Remain on your back, with your feet downstream

11.4 The throw bag.

in one hand and the throw bag in the other. Throw the bag itself – underarm for short throwing distances and overarm for longer distances (over about 15m/50ft).

Aiming: Wait until the swimmer is at right angles to you or just upstream, as this will be the shortest distance to throw. Shout loudly to them before you throw the bag to attract their attention. Throw the bag beyond them, but aiming to land the rope across their chest. It is better to aim slightly upstream of their body for two reasons: the rope will float faster and catch up with them, and when they reach for the rope they can still keep their feet up. Reaching forwards lowers the feet and risks entrapment.

If you miss your target first time, pull the rope back in and either quickly recoil it or fill the bag with water and throw that. It will not travel as far but is worth a go.

After the rope is caught: As the thrower, you need to be ready to do one of two things: take the strain that will come on to the rope and allow the swimmer to swing in towards the bank; or, if they look as if they are being held under the current for too long because it is strong, move quickly but carefully down the bank while still holding the rope to swing them in lower down.

Receiving: The thrower should shout loudly to the swimmer to attract their attention. As a swimmer, watch for the rescuer if you can. When you catch the throw rope, hold it on your chest over your shoulder with your arms bent. You might initially be submerged for a moment, but hang on. Stay on your back, looking downstream, and allow yourself to be swung sideways, in towards the bank.

If you are holding a canoe as well, try to hold both the throw rope and the canoe's grab line in the same hand so that you do not get pulled apart, but do not let go of the throw rope in order to do this.

White water towing

Using any form of attachment in white water from canoe to canoe or paddler to canoe can be life-threatening and needs to be treated with extreme caution.

Towing in white water should only be done by experienced paddlers in the calmer, longer stretches of water, below any rapids. As a beginner, though, you may be helped by someone else who is more experienced. They may use a two-person 'raft', which is a short, quick and simple tow. The paddler having difficulties faces the rescuer, leans across the rescuer's canoe and holds on to both canoes, keeping them close together, while the rescuer paddles to a suitable place. The paddler who is being towed can help steer by pivoting their canoe slightly to one side or the other at the rescuer's request.

Flat water rescues

Swimmer-to-kayak rescue

The swimmer-to-kayak rescue can be used when a paddler has capsized and for some reason stayed in their canoe. The swimmer, having reached the upside-down kayak, leans over the centre of the upturned hull, grabs the cockpit on the far side – if possible grabbing the paddler's wrist or clothing as well – and, using body weight, leans backwards, pulling the kayak upright. Remember to stabilize the kayak before letting it go.

Eskimo rescue

In reality, this only happens if you are seen to go over by someone and both of you know what to do. However, to be rescued this way you need the confidence to hold your breath and keep yourself in your kayak by gripping tightly with your knees. Attract the attention of a rescuer by banging loudly on the bottom of your kayak. Keep your hands out of the water and be ready to grab hold of the bow of a canoe or a paddle.

The rescuer paddles towards your hands quickly, but in

control, so that neither you nor your canoe are damaged. You then grab the bow and right yourself with a hip flick. The rescuer needs to paddle gently towards your hands to prevent being pushed away.

If the rescuer is using a paddle instead of the bow of their kayak, they move alongside your kayak and place the paddle across both boats. Your hand nearest to the rescuer is placed, by them, on to the shaft of the paddle so that you can pull yourself upright. This method is safer than using the bow, as there is less chance of damage and the rescuer is also in a position to help you if you are hurt or tired. It is important that your hands are on the paddle between the canoes, otherwise you will have difficulty in righting yourself.

The swimmer grabs the cockpit rim and paddler's wrist and clothing

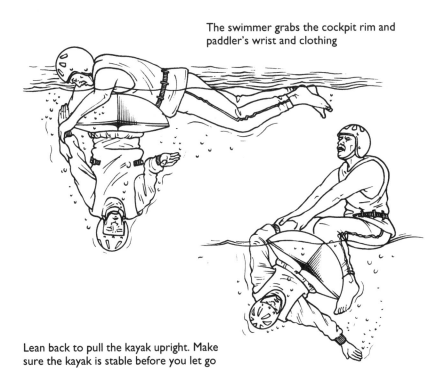

Lean back to pull the kayak upright. Make sure the kayak is stable before you let go

11.5 Swimmer-to-kayak rescue.

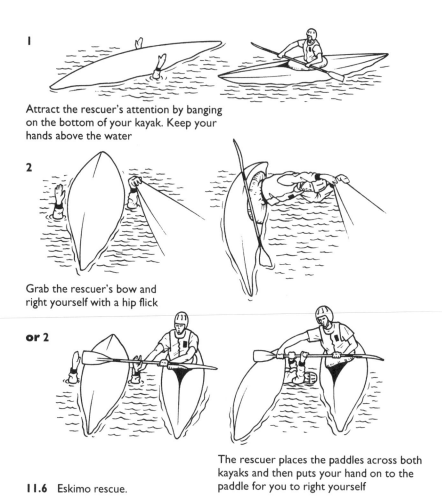

Attract the rescuer's attention by banging
on the bottom of your kayak. Keep your
hands above the water

Grab the rescuer's bow and
right yourself with a hip flick

The rescuer places the paddles across both
kayaks and then puts your hand on to the
paddle for you to right yourself

11.6   Eskimo rescue.

X-rescue

This can be performed by one person in a kayak or open canoe alike
and, if several people capsize, they can do this over each other's
capsized canoes. This is an 'all-in' capsize. If practised in safe water,
this type of capsize is good fun and good training.

The rescuer paddles to one end of the capsized canoe, reaches for
this end while the canoe is upside down, and carefully pulls it up
and over the side of his canoe. Keeping the canoes at right angles to

Open canoe

Kayak

Pull the boat across
to empty it

Lift the boat up

Turn the boat over and slide it back into the water

Swimmer backs in

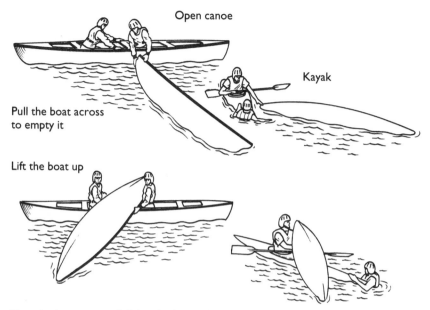

11.7 X-rescue.

each other will help make this easier. Then pull the canoe all the way across the deck using the decklines (or gunwales in open canoes), so that you can rock it empty. When it is empty, place it back in the water beside you so that the swimmer can climb back in.

Things to remember:

- As a rescuer, if you are in an open canoe and the other paddlers are cold, help them into your canoe before rescuing theirs.

- As a rescuer, if you are in a kayak, you should hold your paddle close to you because you will need it later on and do not want it to drift away.

- The swimmer should go to the bow of the rescuer's canoe so that they can be seen easily.

- As a rescuer, if you find doing the X-rescue difficult then the swimmer can help by going to the side of your canoe opposite to the capsized canoe and holding on to the side of the cockpit or gunwale. This provides some stability by counterbalancing the weight of the rescuer, who is leaning the other way.

There are many different ways to empty canoes which are swamped and awkward, as well as different ways to get back into them, which further reading and asking other, more experienced paddlers will reveal.

Getting back into the canoe and kayak
Place the kayaks so they face each other. Depending on the ability of the swimmer, they can enter in a variety of ways.

Rafted X-rescue
The X-rescue can also be done with two canoes rafted together for extra stability. This is effective at times when a straightforward X-rescue may not be, such as in bad weather, but it does require

co-ordinating another canoe to help. The principles are the same as for the X-rescue, except that another canoe is rafted alongside the rescue boat to give additional support and help.

Getting back into the boat:

- The standard way is from between both kayaks, getting the feet in first while leaning the body back in the water. The rescuer holds the paddles across both kayaks, braced for stability, with hands holding each side of the cockpit.

- The swimmer gets into the canoe from the far side to the rescuer. In a kayak, the paddles are put across both kayaks again and are used for stability. It is easy for the rescuer to help stabilize the nearest side of the kayak or open canoe for the swimmer when they enter at the middle of an open canoe and the cockpit of a kayak.

Hi rescue
The hi rescue is used in similar circumstances to the rafted X-rescue and is probably more stable. It needs two rescuers. Each rescuer positions their kayak facing the same way, on either side of the capsized kayak. The paddles are used to make a bridge between the rescuers' kayaks. The two rescuers lift one end of the capsized kayak up and over the paddles, which are held firmly and close to the bodies of the rescuers. The kayak can now be rocked empty over the paddles, then turned the right way up and put back in the water for the swimmer to climb back in. An alternative way of getting back into the kayak is for the swimmer to get on to the back deck of their own canoe and edge their way along to the cockpit. The paddles are used for stability in the same way as in the other methods of entry.

If you have the presence of mind to lift the bow over the paddles first this will make emptying the kayak easier, as there should be less

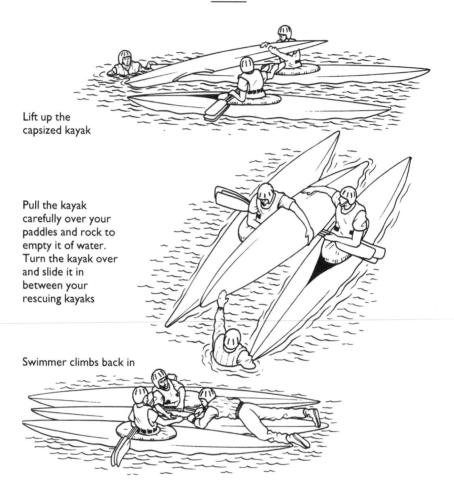

Lift up the
capsized kayak

Pull the kayak
carefully over your
paddles and rock to
empty it of water.
Turn the kayak over
and slide it in
between your
rescuing kayaks

Swimmer climbs back in

11.8 Hi rescue.

water to empty out of the stern because there is more buoyancy
there than in the bow.

There are many variations of these rescues and the limit for ideas
is really determined only by your creativity and improvisation.

Appendix I

Personal first aid kit – suggested contents:

Materials:

6	alcohol swabs
1	roll 2.5cm (1in) tape
4	10 × 10cm (4 × 4in) gauze pads
1	20 × 19cm (8 × 7½in) bulk dressing
1	7cm (3in) gauze roll
1	10cm (4in) elastic bandage
10	sticking plasters
1	8 × 15cm (3 × 6in) blister pad or moleskin
1	pair examination gloves
2	cotton-tipped applicators
6	blanket pins
1	scalpel blade or razor blade
1	pair fine tweezers
1	emergency torch
1	lighter or waterproof matches
1	knife
1	small container of soap
1	container of 2% tincture of iodine
1	tube of antiseptic

Medication (non-prescription):

Small bottle of aspirin, ibuprofen, or paracetamol
Small bottle of dental analgesic
Laxatives: pills or suppositories
Package of tablets containing loperamide
Package of antacid tablets
Cough and cold preparations as desired

Appendix II

Water purification:

There are three acceptable methods:

1. Boil: 10 minutes. Add one minute for each 30m (100ft) above sea level.

2. Chemicals:

(a) Iodine tincture (2%): use 5 drops of tincture per quart of water and let it stand for 30 minutes. Double the time if the water is cold. Double the dose if the water is cloudy.

(b) Iodine tablets: one tablet per quart of water and let it stand for 30 minutes. Double the time if the water is cold. Double the dose if the water is cloudy.

3. Filters: to prevent clogging, pre-filter the water through a cloth to remove large sediment. *Note:* The typical 0.2-micron filter does not remove viruses and hepatitis agents.

Glossary of Medical Terms

Common abbreviations:

ALS	Advanced life support
AMS	Acute mountain sickness
ASR	Acute stress reaction
AVPU	Alert
	Verbal stimulus response
	Painful stimulus response
	Unresponsive
BLS	Basic life support
C	Level of consciousness
CNS	Central nervous system
CPR	Cardio-pulmonary resuscitation
CSM	Circulation, sensation, movement
HACE	High-altitude cerebral edema (oedema)
HAPE	High-altitude pulmonary edema (oedema)
ICP	Intracranial pressure
TIP	Traction into position
VS	Vital signs (with time recorded):

	BP	Blood pressure
	P	Pulse
	R	Respiratory rate
	C	Level of consciousness (mental status if alert)
	T	Core temperature
	S	Skin

Terms:

Abrasion: Superficial wound which damages only the outermost layers of skin or cornea.

Abscess: An infection which has been isolated from the rest of the body by inflammation.

Acute stress reaction (ASR): Autonomic nervous system controlled response to stress which can cause severe, but temporary and reversible changes in vital signs. ASR can be sympathetic or parasympathetic.

Airway: The passage for air movement from the nose and mouth through the throat to the lungs.

Airway, lower: Trachea, bronchi, alveoli.

Airway, upper: Mouth, nose, throat (larynx).

Altitude sickness: Also known as acute mountain sickness (AMS). The combined effects of oxygen deprivation at high elevations. Can be mild, moderate or severe.

Alveoli: Membranous air sacs in the lungs where gas is exchanged with the blood.

Anaphylaxis: Systemic allergic reaction involving generalized oedema of all body surfaces and vascular shock.

'Anticipated problems': Problems which may develop over time as a result of injury, illness or the environment.

Aspiration: Inhaling foreign liquid or other material into the lungs.

Basic life support (BLS): The generic process of supporting the functions of the circulatory, respiratory and nervous systems using artificial ventilation, chest compressions, bleeding control and manual spinal immobilization.

Cardiac arrest: Loss of effective heart activity.

Cardiogenic shock: Shock due to inadequate pumping action of the heart.

Cardio-pulmonary resuscitation (CPR): A technique for artificially circulating oxygenated blood in the absence of effective heart activity. Includes artificial respiration and chest compressions.

Capillaries: The smallest blood vessels in body tissues where gases and nutrients are exchanged between tissue cells and the circulating blood.

Cartilage: Connective tissue on the ends of bones at joints which provide a smooth gliding surface.

Carotid pulse: The pulse felt on the side of the neck at the site of the carotid artery.

Central nervous system: The brain and spinal cord.

Cervical spine: The section of the spine in the neck between the base of the skull and the top of the thorax.

Cold challenge: The combined cooling influence of wind, humidity and ambient temperature.

Cold response: The normal body response, including the shell/core effect of shivering, to the cold challenge.

Compensation: Involuntary changes in body function designed to maintain perfusion of vital body tissue in the presence of injury or illness.

Conjunctiva: The membrane covering the white of the eye and the inner surfaces of the eyelids.

Conjunctivitis: Inflammation of the conjunctiva due to irritation, infection or injury. Also known as 'red eye'.

Consciousness, level of: Describes the level of brain function in terms of responsiveness to specific stimuli (the AVPU scale): A = Alert, V = Responsive to verbal stimulus, P = Responsive to painful stimulus, U = Unresponsive to any stimulus.

Cornea: The clear part of the eye over the iris and the pupil.

Dental abscess: Infection at the base of a tooth.

Diagnosis: The specific identification of an illness or injury by name.

Diaphragm: Muscle at the lower end of the chest cavity which, when contracting, creates a vacuum which draws air into the lungs. The diaphragm works with muscles of the chest wall, shoulders and neck to perform ventilation.

Disability: In the primary survey, loss or partial loss of central nervous-system function due to brain or spinal-cord injury.

Discharge: Fluid escaping from the site of the infections of inflammation.

Dislocation: Disruption of normal joint anatomy.

Distal: An anatomical direction; away from the body centre.

Drowning, near-: At least temporary survival of water inhalation. Usually associated with the protective effects of hypothermia in cold water.

Evacuation: Removing a patient from the scene of injury or illness, usually *en route* to medical care.

Extension: Movement which is the opposite of flexion.

Exudate: Discharge.

Femoral artery: Large artery which travels along the femur in the thigh.

Femur: Long bone of the thigh.

Fits: Uncoordinated electrical activity in the brain.

Flail chest: The loss of rigidity of the chest wall due to injury involving multiple fractured ribs.

Flexion: Movement of a joint that brings the extremity closer to the body.

Fracture: Broken bone or cartilage.

Frostbite: Frozen tissue.

Frostnip: Loss of circulation due to the vasoconstriction of blood vessels in the skin during the early stages of tissue freezing.

Glaucoma: Disease or condition causing increased pressure within the globe of the eye.

Haemothorax: Free blood in the chest cavity; usually from injury.

Heart attack: An episode of ischaemia of heart muscle caused by a blood clot or spasm of the coronary arteries.

Heat challenge: Combined warming effects of humidity, ambient temperature and exercise.

Heat response: The normal body response, including sweating and vasodilation of the shell, to the heat challenge.

Heat stroke: Severe elevation of body temperature (over 40.6°C/105°F).

High-altitude cerebral oedema/edema (HACE): Swelling of the brain due to oxygen deprivation at high altitude.

Hyperextension: To extend a joint beyond its normal range of motion.

Hyperventilation syndrome: The symptoms caused by reduced carbon dioxide in the blood due to excessive ventilation, usually associated with acute stress reaction.

Hypothermia: Below normal body-core temperature (below 35.6°C/96°F). Can be mild (below 35.6°C/96°F) or severe (below 32.2°C/90°F).

Infection: Invasion of body tissues by bacteria, virus or other micro-organisms.

Intoxicated: Altered nervous-system function due to the influence of chemicals such as drugs, alcohol and inhaled gases.

Intracranial: Inside the skull (cranium).

Intravenous (IV) fluids: Fluids infused directly into the circulatory system through a hypodermic needle inserted into a vein, usually used to increase temporarily the volume of circulating blood.

Ischaemia: Lack of local perfusion to body tissues.

Ligaments: Tough connective tissue joining bone to bone across joints.

Local effects: Effects which are restricted to the immediate area of injury or infection.

Long bones: Bones which have a long structural axis, such as leg and arm bones, as opposed to flat bones like ribs and shoulder blade.

Lumbar spine: The lower section of the spine between the thorax and the pelvis.

Mechanism of injury: The cause of injury, or the description of the forces involved.

Mental status: Describes the level of brain function in an alert patient (A on AVPU) in terms of memory, level of anxiety and behaviour.

Mid-range position: Position in a joint's range of motion between full extension and full flexion.

Monitor: Regularly repeated patient assessment for the purpose of revising assessments and plans as the situation changes.

Neutral position: The position approximately halfway between flexion and extension.

Oedema: Swelling due to leaking of serum from capillaries.

Open fracture: Fracture with an associated break in the skin.

Oxygenation: To saturate blood with oxygen. Oxygenation of the blood takes place in the lungs.

Patella: Knee cap.

Patient assessment: A system of surveys including scene survey, primary survey and secondary survey, designed to gather information about an injured or ill patient and the environment in which they are found.

Penicillin: An antibiotic drug.

Perfusion: The passage of blood through capillary beds in body tissues.

Peripheral nerves: The nerves running between body tissues and the central nervous system.

Pneumonia: Infection of lung tissue.

Pneumothorax: Free air in the chest cavity, usually from a punctured lung or chest wall (thorax). Usually associated with haemothorax.

Primary survey: The first examination of the injured patient, which includes assessment of airway, breathing, circulation and disability.

Pulmonary oedema: Swelling of lung tissue resulting in fluid in the alveoli.

Reduction: Restoring a dislocated joint to normal position. Also restoring a displaced fracture to normal anatomic position.

Scene survey: The stage of patient assessment during which you look for dangers to the rescuer and patient, numbers of people injured and the mechanism of injury.

Secondary survey: The stage of patient assessment which includes examination of the whole body, history and vital signs.

Serum: The liquid portion of the blood, as distinguished from blood cells and platelets.

Shell/core effect: A compensation mechanism seen in shock and cold response which reduces blood flow to the body shell in order to preserve perfusion and warmth in the vital organs of the core.

Shock: Inadequate perfusion pressure affecting the whole of the body.

Signs: Response elicited by examination, eg pain when the examiner touches an injured area (tenderness).

Spasm: Involuntary contraction of muscle.

Spinal cord: The cord-like extension of the central nervous system encased within the bones of the spinal column, running from the base of the brain to the mid-lumbar spine.

Spine: The column of body vertebrae extending from the base of the skull to the pelvis.

351

Stethoscope: An instrument used to transmit body sounds directly to the ears of the examiner via rubber tubes.

Survey: A systematic examination.

Swelling: Increase in fluid in body tissues from bleeding and oedema.

Symptoms: Condition described by the patient, eg pain on swallowing.

Systemic: Involving the entire body.

Tetanus: A disease caused by toxins released by *Clostridium tetani* bacteria which may infect wounds (also called 'lockjaw').

Thorax: The region of the body between the base of the neck and the top of the abdomen.

Tourniquet: A constricting band used to prevent or restrict the flow of blood to an extremity.

Toxins: Chemicals which have a damaging effect on body tissues or the function of the nervous system.

Traction: Tension applied along the long axis of an extremity.

Traction splint: A splint device designed to maintain traction on an extremity, used for femur fractures.

Trauma: Injury.

Vapour barrier: A wrap or covering which prevents passage of water vapour, reducing the effect of cooling by evaporation.

Vascular bundles: A nerve, artery and vein following the same pathway.

Vascular shock: Shock due to dilation of blood vessels.

Ventilation: The movement of air in and out of the lungs.

Vertebrae: The bones of the spine.

Vital signs: Measurements of body function including blood pressure, pulse, respiration, consciousness, skin colour and body-core temperature.

Index

abdominal pains 305–8
Aberdovey 127
abnormal consciousness 207
abrasions (shallow wounds) 262,
    268–9
ABS (acrylonitrile-butadiene-styrene)
    canoes 169
access restrictions 22–3
acetazolamide 303
acrylonitrile-butadiene-styrene (ABS)
    canoes 169
acute mountain sickness 301–4
acute stress reaction (ASR) 193–4,
    213–15
adders 277
Admiralty Charts 44
adrenaline 193, 278, 280
adventures 9, 10
aiming off 112–13
airway obstructions 196–8, 218–19
allergies 279, 280
almanacs 129
altitude sickness 301–4
aluminium canoes 169–70
amputations 261
anaphylaxis 279–80
Angel's Peak 30
Anglesey 32
anti-inflammatory medication 258
antihistamines 278, 280
antivenin 277
arachnid toxins 278
aspiration 220
aspirin 258
ASR (acute stress reaction) 193–4,
    213–15
asthma 146
athletes' chalk 91

atmospheric pressure 153
attack points 113
AVPU scale 182–3, 207
avulsions 261

balaclavas 62
barometric watches 152
basic life support 180, 194–5, 277
BCU (British Canoe Union) 45, 46
Bealach Dubh 135
bearings from two landmarks 104–5
Beinn a'Chaorainn 106, 107–8
Ben Alder 109
Ben Nevis 32, 109–11
bite wounds 264
black flies 141
bleeding 205–6, 262, 264–5
    nosebleeds 311–12
blisters 145–6, 273–7
blood pressure 182, 189
body heat loss 151
body-core temperature 281–2
bones see dislocations; fractures
boots 58–61, 81–5, 100–1
    and frostbite protection 145
boxing the corrie 107
breathing problems 198–200
British Canoe Union (BCU) 45, 46
British Mountaineering Council 34
British Waterways 46, 48
Brittany 33
broaching 161–2
bronchitis 313
buoyancy aids 93–4, 97
buoys 124
burns 269–73

cagoules 100
Cairngorms 30, 109
campsites 80–1
canals 48
canoe rescues 329–42
    X-rescue 338–40
    capsizes 164, 331–3
    Eskimo rescue 336–8
    hi rescue 341–2
    rafted X-rescue 340–1
    rescue priorities 329–31
    swimmer-to-kayak rescue 336,
        337
    swimming 332
    throw bags 333–5
    towing 331, 336
canoeing 45–53
    at sea 48–53
        coastguards 52–3
        firing ranges 51
        harbours 51
        information sources 50
        sea access 50
        surfing beaches 50–1
        weather conditions 49–50
        see also sailing
    clothing
        cagoules 100
        footwear 100–1
        paddle mitts 101
        wetsuits 100
    equipment
        buoyancy aids 97
        care of 164–5
        helmets 98
        packing 166–7
        safety equipment 165
        waterproof containers 166,
            167
    inland waters 45–8
        British Waterways licence 48
        canals 48
        code of conduct 48, 49
        guidebooks 46
        lakes 47

navigation rights 45–6
        reservoirs 47
        river grading systems 46–7
        repairing canoes 168–70
        safety checklist 163–4
capsizes 157, 162, 164, 322–4,
        331–3
cardiac arrest 201
cardio-pulmonary resuscitation
        (CPR) 201–3
carpet tape 168
cartilage 232
chalk bags 91
Chamonix 17
chart datum 122–3
charts 44–5, 119–25
    buoys 124
    chart datum 122–3
    danger symbols 123–5
    scale and distance 120–2
    soundings 123
    synoptic charts 18–20
    transits 124–5
check features 113–14
chemical burns 271, 272
chemical irritation of eyes 314, 316
chest
    compressions 201–2
    open wounds 222
    pains 308–10
    trauma 221–2
circulatory system 176, 208–15
    and abdominal pains 307
    acute stress reaction (ASR)
        193–4, 213–15
    bleeding problems 205–6, 262,
        264–5
    cardio-pulmonary resuscitation
        (CPR) 201–3
    perfusion 189, 192
    primary surveys 179
    pulse 182, 201–5
    shock 208–13
    and treatment of fractures 237–8
clegs (horse-flies) 141
closed (simple) fractures 235

clothing
    balaclavas   62
    boots   58–61
    canoeing   98–101
        cagoules   100
        footwear   100–1
        paddle mitts   101
        wetsuits   100
    choosing   54, 56–7
    Double-P system   56
    and frostbite protection   145
    gaiters   61
    gloves   62, 145
    hats   57, 62
    hot climate   57
    insulating properties   98–9
    layer system   55–6
    long johns   55
    for midge protection   141
    rock climbing   90–1
        boots   81–5
    sailing
        drysuits   97
        footwear   92, 96
        gloves   96–7
        hats   94
        inner layers   92
        long johns   96
        mid-layers   92
        waterproofs   92–3, 95
        wetsuits   95–6
    salopettes   55, 95
    shoes   58
    socks   60
    trousers   55, 57
    waterproofs   56
    see also equipment
coastal safety   325–9
coastguards   52–3, 328
cold injuries   295–8
cold packs   257, 258
cold response   288–9
colds   312
collision avoidance   159–91
communication with rescuers
    319–20

compensation mechanism   190
compound fractures   235
concussion   227–8
conjunctivitis   314
consciousness   182–3, 192
    abnormal consciousness   207
contusions   232, 256–8
corneal abrasions   314, 315
cornices   107–8, 140
Cornwall   32
Corrieyairack Pass   22
CPR (cardio-pulmonary
    resuscitation)   201–3
crevasses   140
cross-country routes   29–31

danger symbols on charts   123–5
deadly nightshade   276
decision-making   12
decompensation   192
dehydration   147
Devil's Point   30
Devon   32
diabetes   146
diarrhoea   310
digit dislocations   248–9
digit fractures   259–60
diseases   142
dislocations   243–9
    digit   248–9
    patella (knee cap)   247–8
    shoulder   244–7
    traction into position   239
    see also fractures
distance calculations   27
distress signals   117, 320, 325, 327
dog attacks   140
dome tents   74, 75
Double-P clothing system   56
drowning   220, 299–301
drysuits   97
Duct tape   168

earthquakes   153
electrical burns   271

emergencies
  communication 319–20
  equipment 67, 69
  International Distress Signal 320
  preparation for 188–9, 317–19
  see also patient assessment; rescue
emergency shelters 291
equipment 14
  canoeing 97–8
    buoyancy aids 97
    care of 164–5
    helmets 98
    packing 166–7
    safety equipment 165
    waterproof containers 166, 167
  emergency equipment 67, 69
  first aid kits 69, 148, 318
  flasks 68
  fuel 21, 66
  group gear 68–9
  knives 68, 148
  rock climbing 81–90
    boots 81–5
    chalk bags 91
    harnesses 85–8
    helmets 88–90
    sit-harnesses 85–7
  rucksacks 62–6
  sailing 91–7
    buoyancy aids 93–4
    helmets 94
    knives 97
    spares 94
    upgrading 95
  sleeping bags 79–80
  sleeping mats 80
  smoke flares 327, 328
  spades 68–9
  spares 68
  stoves 21, 66, 70
  torches 66–7
  water bottles 68
  weight efficiency 69–70
  whistles 67
  see also clothing; tents

escape routes 26
Eskimo rescue 336–8
evacuation 322
examining patients 180–1
external bleeding 205–6, 264
extremity fractures 236–43
eye problems 313–16

fax weather forecasts 43
Fell and Rock Climbing Club 35
femur fractures 254–5
fibreglass canoes 169
field rewarming techniques 291
finger dislocations 248–9
firing ranges 22, 51
first aid kits 69, 148, 318
First Aid Manual 195
first-degree burns 270
fitness 24
fits 228–9
'flail chest' 221
flares 327, 328
flasks 68
floods 137–9
flu 312
fluid replacement 283, 284–5
fly sheets 70
food 21, 68, 142
footwear 92, 96, 100–1
  and frostbite protection 145
  see also boots
forcing an ascent 150–1
fractures
  assessment 236–7
  and the circulatory system 237–8
  closed (simple) 235
  digit 259–60
  extremity fractures 236–43
  femur 254–5
  knee fractures 258–9
  open (compound) 235
  pelvic 255–6
  spine 250–4
  treatment 237–43
    hand stable 240

splinting   241–3, 249–50, 255
   traction into position   239–40
   and vital organ injuries   231, 235
   see also dislocations
friction boots   83
frostbite   144–5, 295–8
frostnip   144–5, 295–8
fuel   21, 66

gaiters   61
geodesic tents   74, 76, 77
Glen Etive   150
Glen Spean   106
Global Positioning System (GPS)   26
gloves   62, 96–7, 145
Gorge du Verdon   33
grading systems   36–8
Grand Canyon   17, 33
grass slopes   131–2
guidebooks   23, 33–5, 46, 118–19
gybing problems   161

haemothorax   221
handrails   112–13
harbours   51
harnesses   85–8
hats   57, 62, 94
head injuries   225–8
head torches   67
heart attacks   308–10
heat exhaustion   284–5
heat response   283
heat stroke   152, 285–7
height change calculations   27–8
helicopter rescues   173
helmets   88–90, 94, 98
helping boats in distress   328–9
hi rescue   341–2
high-pressure systems   19
Hinde, John   103, 105, 109
Hong Kong   140
hoop tents   73
horse-flies (clegs)   141
hyperextension   206

hyperthermia   281–2, 282–7
   heat exhaustion   284–5
   heat response   283
   heat stroke   152, 285–7
   sweating   281, 282–3
hyperventilation   223–4
hypothermia   143–4, 201, 281–2,
      287–95
   cold response   288–9
   field rewarming techniques   291
   mild   289–92
   and near-drowning   300
   severe   292–5

ibuprofen   258
ice (cold packs)   257, 258
illnesses   146
increased intracranial pressure
      (ICP)   225–7
index contours   27–8
indigestion   309
infections   263, 267, 312–13, 316
inflammation   262–3
   of eyes   313–14
insect repellents   141, 142
insect toxins   278
insects   140–2, 154
inshore water forecasts   42
insurance   22–3
internal bleeding   205
International Distress Signal   320
International Regulations for the
      Prevention of Collision at Sea
      (IRPCS)   159
International Yacht Racing Rules
      159
ischaemia   192, 237, 238

kayaks see canoeing
Kevlar   169
knee cap dislocations   247–8
knee fractures   258–9
knives   68, 97, 148

lacerations 261
Lairig Ghru 30
Lake District 17, 35
lakes 47
layer clothing system 55–6
leadership 11, 12
lee shores 158
leptospirosis 48
life-jackets 93–4, 97
ligaments 232
lightning strikes 136
line features 103–4
Loch Ossian 134–5
long johns 55, 96
loose rock hazards 139
low-pressure systems 18–19
lumbar spine 251
lung contusion 221
lung injuries 309

MacKenzie, George 210
man overboard recovery 324–5,
    326
maps 23, 26
    distance calculations 27
    glossary of place names 31
    height changes 27–8
    slope calculations 29–30
midges 140–2, 154
Ministry of Defence training areas
    22
misadventures 9, 10
monitoring patients 185
mosquitoes 141
mountains
    altitude sickness 301–4
    causes of injuries 172
    distress signals 117
    weather conditions 20
    see also rock climbing
mouth-to-mouth ventilation 197,
    199–200
muscles 232, 234
mushrooms 276

National Parks and Access to the
    Countryside Act 22
National Rivers Authority 46
nausea 310–11
navigation 14–15
    on land 103–17
        aiming off 112–13
        attack points 113
        in bad weather 115
        bearings from two landmarks
            104–5
        boxing the corrie 107
        check features 113–14
        fixing position on line features
            103–4
        handrails 112–13
        night navigation 115
        reality checks 105–6
        relocation 115–16
        self-deception 116–17
        slope aspect 114–15
    rock climbing 118–19
    route-finding 102, 118
    satellite navigation 26
    on water 119–29
        almanacs 129
        charts 119–25
        difficulties 119
        pilot books 129
        tides 125–8
navigation rights 45–6
neap tides 125, 127
near-drowning 299–301
neck injuries 197, 251
Nepal 21
nervous system 176, 224–30
    abnormal consciousness 207
    acute stress reaction (ASR)
        193–4, 213–15
    compensation mechanism 190
    concussion 227–8
    decompensation 192
    fits 228–9
    increased intracranial pressure
        (ICP) 225–7

peripheral nerve injuries   230
primary surveys   179
and respiratory problems   222–4
spinal injuries   206–7, 229
vital sign changes   193
newspaper weather forecasts   43
night navigation   115
nosebleeds   311–12
Notices for Mariners   44

Oban   126
observation forms for patients   321
open blisters   274
open chest wounds   222
open (compound) fractures   235
oxygenation   189–90

paddle mitts   101
patella (knee cap) dislocations
   247–8
patient assessment   174, 177–88
anticipated problems   185
AVPU scale   182–3, 207
examinations   180–1
medical history assessment   183
monitoring patients   185
observation forms   321
primary surveys   178–80, 186,
   195
response organization   183–5
scene surveys   177–8, 186
secondary surveys   180–3, 186
vital signs   181–2
pelvic fractures   255–6
Pennine Way   22
perfusion   189, 192
peripheral nerve injuries   230
peritoneum   305–6, 307
pilot books   129
Piz Badile   151
plumber's tape   168
pneumonia   220, 313
pneumothorax   221
polyester resin   169
polyethylene canoes   169

pressure bandages   206
primary surveys   178–80, 186, 195
pulmonary fluid   219–20
pulmonary oedema   220
pulse   182, 201–5
puncture wounds   262, 264, 268

rabies immunization   140
radio weather forecasts   42
rafted X-rescue   340–1
rain hazards   135–6, 148–51
Ramblers Association   22
recovery position   204–5
recovery services *see* rescue
'red eye'   313–16
relocation   115–16
repairing canoes   168–70
rescue   23, 116
evacuation   322
helicopter rescues   173
rescue message form   321
see also canoe rescues; emergencies
reservoirs   47
respiratory system   176, 215–24
airway obstructions   196–8,
   218–19
breathing problems   198–200
burned passages   271
chest trauma   221–2
generic treatment   217
hyperventilation   223–4
infections   312–13
mouth-to-mouth ventilation   197,
   199–200
near-drowning   299–301
open chest wounds   222
oxygenation   189–90
primary surveys   179
pulmonary fluid   219–20
respiratory arrest   222–3
respiratory rate   182
resuscitation   195
rewarming techniques   291
ridge tents   71, 73
Ridgeway   22

right of way at sea   160, 161
river crossings   137–9
river grading systems   46–7
rock boots   81–5
rock climbing   31–8
  abandoning the climb   149–50
  boots   81–5
  clothing   90–1
  dangers   31–2, 148–55
    body heat loss   151
    excessive heat   152
    insects   154
    loose rock hazards   139
    rain   148–51
    snow   151–2
    stonefalls   153
  equipment
    boots   81–5
    chalk bags   91
    harnesses   85–8
    helmets   88–90
    sit-harnesses   85–7
  forcing an ascent   150–1
  grading systems   36–8
  guidebooks   33–5, 118–19
  locations   32–3
  navigation   118–19
  route planning   31–8
  runners   150
  safety checklist   154–5
  sea cliffs   153
  topographical diagrams   35–6
  see also mountains
Roman High Street   22
route cards   24–6, 131
route planning   22–38
  access restrictions   22–3
  cross-country routes   29–31
  direct routes   27–9
  escape routes   26
  fitness   24
  flexibility of plans   131
  guidebooks   23, 33–5
  interesting routes   23
  rock climbing   31–8
  route cards   24–6, 131

  see also maps; travel time
route-finding   102, 118
Royalex repairs   169
rucksacks   62–6
  frames   64
  lids   64
  packing   64–6
  pockets   64
  size   62–3
  straps   64
'rule of nines'   269–70
Rum   141
runners   150

sailing   38
  broaching   161–2
  capsizes   157, 162, 322–4
  charts   44–5
  clothing
    drysuits   97
    footwear   92, 96
    gloves   96–7
    hats   94
    inner layers   92
    long johns   96
    mid-layers   92
    waterproofs   92–3, 95
    wetsuits   95–6
  collision avoidance   159–91
  cruising   155
  distress signals   325, 327
  equipment
    buoyancy aids   93–4
    helmets   94
    knives   97
    spares   94
    upgrading   95
  gybing problems   161
  helping boats in distress   328–9
  lee shores   158
  man overboard recovery   324–5, 326
  potential problems   156–8
  racing   155
  right of way   160, 161

safety checklist   156
tides   39, 44
towlines   158–9
weather forecasts   40–3
wind conditions   39, 41
see also canoeing, at sea
salopettes   55, 95
salvage laws   159
satellite navigation   26
scene surveys   177–8, 186
scree slopes   139
sea cliffs   153
seasons   17
second-degree burns   270, 271
secondary surveys   180–3, 186
separation incidents   132–3
shell/core effect   190
shipping forecasts   42
shivering   281, 290
shock   208–13
   assessment   209
   symptoms   209, 210–11
   treatment   211–13
   volume shock   209, 256
shoes   58
shoulder dislocations   244–7
single-skin tents   76
sit-harnesses   85–7
skeleton   233
skin injuries   260–1, 269–74
   blisters   145–6, 273–7
   burns   269–73
   sunburn   147, 274
   see also wounds
Skye   17, 141
sleeping bags   79–80
sleeping mats   80
slope aspect   114–15
slope calculations   29–30
smoke flares   327, 328
snakebites   277–8
snow blindness   15, 147, 314, 316
snow hazards   136–7, 140, 151–2
socks   60, 96, 101
soundings   123
spades   68–9

spinal-cord injuries   251
spine   234
   fractures   250–4
   injuries   206–7, 229
splinting   241–3, 249–50, 255, 265, 266
sprains   232, 256–8
spring tides   125, 127
stable injuries   256–8
Stanage Edge   34
stitches (sutures)   267
stonefalls   153
stoves   21, 66, 70
strains   232, 256–8
strep throat   313
stress *see* acute stress reaction (ASR)
sunburn   147, 274
surfing beaches   50–1
sutures (stitches)   267
sweating   281, 282–3
swellings   190–2, 256
   reducing   258
swimmer-to-kayak rescue   336, 337
swimming   332
Sylglass   168
synoptic charts   18–20

telephone weather forecasts   43
teletext weather forecasts   42
television weather forecasts   42
tendons   232
tents   21, 66, 70–9
   care of   78
   choosing   76, 78
   dome tents   74, 75
   erecting   72–3, 78–9
   fly sheets   70
   geodesic tents   74, 76, 77
   hoop tents   73
   inner tent   70, 72
   ridge tents   71, 73
   single-skin   76
   tunnel tents   73–4, 75
   valances   70
tetanus prophylaxis vaccine   267
third-degree burns   271

thirst 283
throw bags 333–5
tides 39, 44, 125–8
  information on 126–7
  Twelfths Rule 127–8
toe dislocations 248–9
Tophet Wall 35, 37
topographical diagrams 35–6
torches 66–7
tourniquets 206, 265
towing
  boats 158–9
  canoes 331, 336
toxins 275–80
  anaphylaxis 279–80
  basic life support 277
  insect/arachnid 278
  snakebites 277–8
  systemic effects 275
  treatment 276
traction 239–40
transits 124–5
travel time 23, 25–6, 27–31
  cross-country routes 30–1
  direct routes 28–9
  distance calculations 27
  height changes 27–8
  slope calculations 29–30
trivial experiences 9, 10
trousers 55, 57
tunnel tents 73–4, 75
Twelfths Rule 127–8

Uisge Labhar 134–5
Ulysses 34
unstable injuries see dislocations;
  fractures
urine 283

valances 70
vital signs 181–2, 193
volume shock 209, 256
vomiting 310–11

water 142
water bottles 68

waterproof clothing 56, 92–3, 95
waterproof containers 166, 167
weather 17–20, 133–9
  atmospheric pressure 153
  barometric watches 152
  excessive heat 152
  floods 137–9
  forecasts 17–18, 40–3, 152–3
  lightning strikes 136
  in mountainous areas 20
  rain hazards 135–6, 148–51
  and sea canoeing 49–50
  snow hazards 136–7, 151–2
  synoptic charts 18–20
  white-outs 136–7
  wind conditions 20, 26, 39, 41,
    133–5
Weil's Disease 48
wellington boots 60, 96
wetsuits 95–6, 100
whistles 67
white-outs 136–7
wildlife dangers 140
wind conditions 20, 26, 39, 41,
  133–5
Windermere 47
windward capsizes 323–4
wounds 261–8
  abrasions (shallow wounds) 262,
    268–9
  assessment 263
  bite wounds 264
  high-risk 264, 266–8
  infections 263, 267
  natural cleansing 262–3
  puncture wounds 262, 264, 268
  splinting 265, 266
  sutures (stitches) 267
  tetanus prophylaxis vaccine 267
  tourniquets 206, 265
  treatment 263–8
    covering 266
    high-risk wounds 266–8
    irrigating 265–6
    washing 265, 268

X-rescue 338–40